Symbolic Logic

Richmond H. Thomason

Symbolic Logic

An Introduction

The Macmillan Company / Collier-Macmillan Limited, London

First Printing

Library of Congress catalog card number : 72–83069

The Macmillan Company

Collier-Macmillan Canada, Ltd., Toronto, Ontario

Printed in the United States of America

Preface

THIS TEXT is an introduction to modern symbolic logic. It is meant to provide a working understanding of both the mathematical theories used by logicians and their relationship to everyday reasoning. Since the study of logic is sometimes painful for nonmathematicians I have tried to accompany all mathematical material with supplementary discussion and explanation. To make the book self-contained I have included chapters on set theory and mathematical induction. Whatever mathematical techniques are used are explained, so that the book presupposes no specialized training in mathematics.

The book covers what is commonly thought to be the standard material for a beginning course in symbolic logic. It may be used as a textbook for an introductory course at the undergraduate or the graduate level, and will serve for an intensive one-term course or a more leisurely course of two terms. It has been used in a graduate course at Yale and an undergraduate course at

Amherst, and was modified and rewritten subsequent to experience in the classroom.

Plan of the book

The first seven chapters deal with the logic of sentence connectives, or *sentence logic*, and the next five chapters with the logic of quantifiers and identity, or *predicate logic with identity*. These are treated as classical, or two-valued logics; I do not discuss so-called nonclassical logics in this book. The development of both sentence and predicate logic falls into five main areas: informal semantics, proof techniques, syntactic metatheory, semantic metatheory, and semantic completeness.

Informal semantics. This has to do with the relation of the formal languages of symbolic logic to natural language (in this book, to English). Most texts use the notion of *logical form* to account for this relation, although the notion that English sentences come prepackaged in a logical form is now philosophically outmoded. The formal languages of classical logic were devised to account for mathematical reasoning, and serve very well to express mathematical material, but very often it is difficult or impossible to render colloquial English in these languages. Many textbooks avoid this problem by confining their discussions of "formalization" to artificial or concocted examples of English. I think it is more rewarding to face the problem; this is especially important in arriving at an account of the philosophical significance of modern logic.

I therefore treat formalization as a kind of translation; like translation from one natural language to another it is an art to be learned by practice and experience. I try to give examples in which the logical theories do not fit English very well, as well as ones in which there is a good fit. This more open approach gives a flexible and natural view of the interaction between formal and natural language which is more exciting to the student and philosophically satisfying to the teacher.

Proof techniques. An uninterpreted formal system is presented in Chapter I to introduce students to the notion of a system of logic. This seems to me the best way of showing that the grammar and rules of proof of a formal system can be defined without reference to the "meanings" of its symbols. The ideas exemplified in Chapter I will be taken up and explained in later chapters, and it is best not to linger over this material.

All other discussions of proof techniques deal with systems of *natural deduction*. These systems, modeled after F. B. Fitch's, are designed to be as close as possible to patterns of reasoning that are commonly used. The rules of proof are justified and made plausible by referring to examples of valid arguments in English. In order to foster efficient use of these systems I have included sections devoted to the strategy of finding derivations.

Syntactic metatheory. Beginning students often find metatheory a mysterious and difficult topic. I try to make the transition to metatheory as easy as possible by discussing at length the issues and concepts related to it. Distinctions such as the one between object-language and metalanguage are explained at this point, and the metalinguistic notation used in this book is elucidated. Proofs of early metatheorems are presented in great detail, while the metatheorems themselves are carefully motivated and made to seem as natural as possible.

Semantic metatheory. The development of syntactic metatheory prepares the way for a treatment of semantics that is up to current standards of rigor. My discussion of semantic material is influenced by modern mathematical formulations of this subject and emphasizes those concepts that these formulations have shown to be most significant. In the semantics of sentence logic, for instance, I stress the concept of satisfaction rather than truth-tables.

Semantic completeness. The chapters dealing with this topic discuss equivalences between syntactic and semantic concepts and proceed to establish these equivalences as metatheorems. The metatheorems are proved using the techniques developed by L. Henkin; I have made the proofs as streamlined and simple as possible.

Internal organization

For efficient cross-referencing, each chapter is divided into sections, which are numbered with Arabic numerals. 'IX.6' refers to Section 6 of Chapter IX; if this reference were made in Chapter IX, it would simply be referred to as Section 6. Examples are numbered with lower-case Roman numerals, starting with 'i' at the beginning of each chapter. To cite the seventh example of Chapter II, for instance, I would use 'II.vii', or just 'vii' if the citation were made in Chapter II. Metatheorems and definitions are numbered starting with 'M1' and 'D1' at the beginning of each chapter.

At the end of chapters are exercises and problems. The problems are meant to provide breadth and excitement; each of them requires either originality or familiarity with some subject not explained in the book. Some of them are open-ended in that there is no agreement among logicians as to their solution. Not all the exercises are easy or routine, but all of them can be solved on the basis of what is supplied in the text.

There is an index of symbols as well as a general index; symbols are listed in the former index according to their first occurrence in the book. The reference given in this index will enable the reader to find a definition or explanation of the symbol.

Using the Book as a Text

In a two-term course, it is natural to do sentence logic (Chapters I to VII) during the first term and predicate logic (Chapters VIII to XII) during the second. Chapter XIII is best used to provide background for metatheoretic work in earlier chapters. A good plan would be to do XIII.1 to XIII.9 between Chapters IV and V, and XIII.10 to XIII.21 between Chapters X and XI. Sometimes a class will need a lecture or two on mathematical induction before they feel at home with the technique. Chapter XIV can be used in coordination with such lectures, or can be covered separately at any time.

Chapter I is meant to provide students with an idea of what an uninterpreted formal system is like. I have found that, if one begins with natural deduction systems, this point is harder to make. There is no need to spend much time on Chapter I, and certainly no need to frustrate students by requiring them to become adept at manipulating the rules of the system. The purpose of the chapter will have been served as soon as students know what the system is, i.e., as soon as they can recognize formulas and proofs. Some instructors may wish to omit this chapter entirely.

In a one-term course it will be necessary to devote less time to some material. The chapters on translation are particularly flexible in this regard. Depending on how much attention is given to examples, they can be gone through briskly or at a slower pace. The final sections of many chapters can be omitted without sacrificing continuity. This applies particularly to V.16, VI.14, VI.17 to VI.19, VII.9 to VII.10, VIII.18 to VIII.19, X.12 to X.14, and XII.7 to XII.9.

Acknowledgments

This book of mine owes everything to my teachers, Professors Alan Anderson, Nuel Belnap, Jr., and Frederic Fitch. I hope that the excitement and life they give to logic is reflected here and there in what follows. I owe thanks to Professor Robert Meyer for his judgment on many points concerning the manuscript itself. My wife, Sally, has gone over the text carefully and made the prose readable, as well as suggesting many other improvements. Most of what is graceful in the book is her doing.

R. H. T.

Contents

Symbolic Logic

I Uninterpreted Syntax of a Logical System

1. This section has to do with some rules for constructing certain strings of symbols called *formulas*, and for manipulating these formulas to build arrays called *proofs*.

Some of you have studied formulas and proofs of this sort before; for the present, please try to forget what you have learned about them. The idea is to approach this material without any reference to what the "formulas" and "proofs" may mean; the rules for manipulating symbols are enough like the rules of games so that they can be regarded in a gamelike way, without regard to anything external.

Incidentally, this sort of "horseshoe pushing" is one way of caricaturing what logicians do. But despite this, many logicians aren't very interested in this sort of thing; what they do is much more abstract and conceptual. As we go on to more advanced topics you will be able to see the contrast between these two sorts of activities.

2. All our formulas will be strings made up of the following eight symbols.

$$p \qquad q \qquad r \qquad s$$
$$(\qquad) \qquad \supset \qquad \sim$$

For instance, the following are formulas.

$(p \supset q)$ $((p \supset q) \supset (r \supset s))$

$\sim r$ s

$\sim(\sim(r \supset s) \supset \sim\sim p)$ $\sim\sim\sim(q \supset q)$

p $((p \supset q) \supset q)$

But not every string of symbols is a formula; for instance, the following are not formulas.

$\sim(\sim p)$ $)p($

$p \supset (q)$ $((p \supset \sim q) \supset \sim q$

$p \supset q$ $\supset$

These examples should give you an idea of how to recognize and make formulas; the idea is that any of the four letters 'p', 'q', 'r', and 's' is a formula, and that more complicated formulas can be made by applying the symbol '$\sim$' to the left of any formula, or the symbol '$\supset$' between any two formulas. In the latter case, notice that parentheses have to be added in the appropriate places.

Note: Here are some things to think about. How long can formulas get? How many formulas are there? What is the difference between saying there is no bound on the length of formulas and saying that there is no formula of unbounded length? These are questions that will seem familiar to those with some mathematical training, but others may have difficulty with them at first. In the latter case, you should do some thinking about these matters, and may want to read something about elementary set theory. See Chapter XIII of this book, or one of the works listed in the bibliography.

3. *Proofs* are built up from *axioms* using certain *rules of inference*. The directions for generating proofs are quite simple: any axiom may be written down at any time in a proof, and rules may be applied to any formulas already written down in a proof. Often we are interested in finding proofs *of* certain formulas; a proof is said to be a proof of the formula that is its last item.

The system S_0 with which we will be dealing for the time being has just three axioms; these are the formulas

      A1. $(p \supset (q \supset p))$

      A2. $((p \supset (q \supset r)) \supset ((p \supset q) \supset (p \supset r)))$

      A3. $((\sim p \supset \sim q) \supset (q \supset p))$.

The following columns of formulas qualify as proofs in S_0.

(p ⊃ (q ⊃ p))
  (i)

(p ⊃ (q ⊃ p))
(p ⊃ (r ⊃ p))
(r ⊃ (r ⊃ r))
((~p ⊃ ~q) ⊃ (q ⊃ p))
  (ii)

(p ⊃ (q ⊃ p))
(p ⊃ (p ⊃ p))
((p ⊃ (q ⊃ r)) ⊃ ((p ⊃ q) ⊃ (p ⊃ r)))
((p ⊃ (p ⊃ r)) ⊃ ((p ⊃ p) ⊃ (p ⊃ r)))
((p ⊃ (p ⊃ p)) ⊃ ((p ⊃ p) ⊃ (p ⊃ p)))
((p ⊃ p) ⊃ (p ⊃ p))
  (iii)

((~p ⊃ ~q) ⊃ (q ⊃ p))
((~~p ⊃ ~q) ⊃ (q ⊃ ~p))
((~~p ⊃ ~~~p) ⊃ (~~p ⊃ ~p))
  (iv)

((p ⊃ (q ⊃ r)) ⊃ ((p ⊃ q) ⊃ (p ⊃ r)))
(((~p ⊃ ~~p) ⊃ (q ⊃ r)) ⊃ (((~p ⊃ ~~p) ⊃ q) ⊃ ((~p ⊃ ~~p) ⊃ r)))
(((~p ⊃ ~~p) ⊃ (~p ⊃ r))
        ⊃ (((~p ⊃ ~~p) ⊃ ~p) ⊃ ((~p ⊃ ~~p) ⊃ r)))
(((~p ⊃ ~~p) ⊃ (~p ⊃ p))
        ⊃ (((~p ⊃ ~~p) ⊃ ~p) ⊃ ((~p ⊃ ~~p) ⊃ p)))
((~p ⊃ ~q) ⊃ (q ⊃ p))
((~p ⊃ ~~p) ⊃ (~p ⊃ p))
(((~p ⊃ ~~p) ⊃ ~p) ⊃ ((~p ⊃ ~~p) ⊃ p))
  (v)

Before reading the explanation given below of the rules of proof construction, you may wish to work them out for yourself by inspection of the above examples.

4. There are just two rules of inference in the system S_0. The first, *modus ponens,* may be used in case you have already gotten two steps in a proof, one of which is the result of putting the symbol '⊃' after the other, following the '⊃' by a formula, and then enclosing the whole in parentheses. *Modus ponens* then allows you to infer the second of these formulas.

Notice how obscure and complicated the above explanation has become. It is much easier to say things of this sort by making a picture. We can diagram the rule *modus ponens* as follows.

$$\frac{\text{---} \qquad (\text{---} \supset \ldots)}{\ldots}$$

Any result of replacing the dashes in this scheme by a formula, and the dots by a (not necessarily distinct) formula will be a diagram of an instance of *modus ponens*. For example,

$$\frac{(p \supset (q \supset p)) \qquad ((p \supset (q \supset p)) \supset ((p \supset q) \supset (p \supset p)))}{((p \supset q) \supset (p \supset p))}$$

is such an instance: here, we have put in '$(p \supset (q \supset p))$' for the dashes, and '$((p \supset q) \supset (p \supset p))$' for the dots. The formulas '$(p \supset (q \supset p))$' and '$((p \supset (q \supset p)) \supset ((p \supset q) \supset (p \supset p)))$' are the *premisses* of the inference, and '$((p \supset q) \supset (p \supset p))$' is the *conclusion*.

Notice that this particular instance of *modus ponens* is one that might turn up in a proof, since both of its premisses are provable in S_0 (in fact, they are axioms). But even though the inference

$$\frac{p \qquad (p \supset q)}{q}$$

is not one that could occur in a proof (as we will see much later, 'p' is not a provable formula of S_0), it is still an instance of *modus ponens*.

5. You may have observed that a minute ago we ran into trouble when we tried to use plain English to state something general about the system S_0: the rule *modus ponens*. Obviously we cannot state this rule by listing all of its possible instances, since there are infinitely many of these. We have to use our language, to the best of our ability, to express general things of this sort. And in doing this we resorted above to the device of drawing a picture involving dashes and dots.

A plan that proves to be much more flexible and accurate is to use letters in place of the dashes and dots. To avoid confusion, we ought to select for this purpose symbols that don't resemble the 'p', 'q', 'r', and 's' of S_0—let's choose, say, the italic capitals 'A', 'B', 'C', and 'D'. We now can state the rule of *modus ponens* a bit more explicitly.

If in a proof steps A and $(A \supset B)$ have occurred, then the result of writing down B as another step is still a proof.

Later on, we will become more self-conscious about the A's and B's and will want to discuss in a systematic way methodological matters such as syntactic notation. But there is no need for this yet—all we have to remember is that *these letters occur nowhere in the system* S_0. They are letters that we use to say general things about S_0.

6. The second rule of S_0 is a rule of substitution; the rule allows you to replace 'p', 'q', 'r', or 's' *in* any formula *by* any formula. One must replace *all* occurrences of the letter substituted for in the formula on which one is working; the following is not an instance of the substitution rule.

$$\frac{(p \supset (q \supset p))}{(p \supset (q \supset (p \supset p)))}$$

Although '$(p \supset p)$' is substituted for the second occurrence of 'p' in '$(p \supset (q \supset p))$', it is not substituted for the first occurrence of 'p' in that formula.

We might express this aspect of the rule by saying that it is a rule of *simultaneous* substitution. But the substitutions must be done one at a time; the following also is not an instance of the substitution rule.

$$\frac{(p \supset (q \supset p))}{((p \supset p) \supset (r \supset (p \supset p)))}$$

We *can* get from '$(p \supset (q \supset p))$' to '$((p \supset p) \supset (r \supset (p \supset p)))$', but it takes two steps, as in the following proof.

$$(p \supset (q \supset p))$$
$$(p \supset (r \supset p))$$
$$((p \supset p) \supset (r \supset (p \supset p)))$$

Notice that the substitution rule does not allow substitutions for formulas other than 'p', 'q', 'r', and 's', so that inferences like the following one also are not sanctioned by this rule.

$$\frac{(p \supset ((q \supset r) \supset p))}{(p \supset (q \supset p))}$$

The rule of substitution is quite a different thing from *modus ponens*, and cannot be diagrammed in the same way. We could invent special notation for displaying substitutions, but at present would gain nothing by doing so; the rule should now be clear enough so that you can recognize instances of it, and that is enough.

7. We can now characterize explicitly the notion of a proof in the system S_0; a proof is any column of formulas (the *steps* of the proof), such that every step of the column is an axiom, or follows from two previous steps of the column by means of *modus ponens*, or follows from one previous step of the column by means of substitution.

According to this definition a column which consists of just one step, that step being an axiom, is a proof. Thus every axiom of S_0 has a proof in S_0 (or is *provable* in S_0 or a *theorem* of S_0).

To help in recognizing proofs, it is convenient to number steps and to include justifications, as in the following annotated version of example iii.

1	$(p \supset (q \supset p))$	A1
2	$(p \supset (p \supset p))$	1, subst
3	$((p \supset (q \supset r)) \supset ((p \supset q) \supset (p \supset r)))$	A2
4	$((p \supset (p \supset r)) \supset ((p \supset p) \supset (p \supset r)))$	3, subst
5	$((p \supset (p \supset p)) \supset ((p \supset p) \supset (p \supset p)))$	4, subst
6	$((p \supset p) \supset (p \supset p))$	2, 5, m p

(iii′)

Example iii′ is more than a proof; it is a proof together with auxiliary notations that make it easier to perceive as a proof.

Exercises

1. Which of the following are formulas of S_0?

   (a) r
   (b) $\sim\sim(p)$
   (c) $(p \supset (q \supset t))$
   (d) $(q \supset (r \supset)s)$
   (e) $\sim\sim p \supset (q \supset (r \supset p))$
   (f) $(((p \supset \sim\sim q) \supset \sim\sim\sim s) \supset \sim(p \supset p))$
   (g) $((((p \supset p) \supset p) \supset p) \supset p)$
   (h) $(p \supset (p \supset (p \supset p)))$

2. Write down some formulas of S_0.
3. Annotate the proofs given in examples i, ii, iii, iv, and v.
4. Write down some proofs in S_0.
5. Find proofs in S_0 for the following formulas, and annotate these proofs.

   (a) $(p \supset (r \supset (r \supset r)))$
   (b) $(((\sim\sim p \supset \sim q) \supset q) \supset ((\sim\sim p \supset \sim q) \supset \sim p))$
   (c) $(p \supset p)$
   (d) $(\sim q \supset (q \supset p))$
   (e) $((p \supset q) \supset ((r \supset p) \supset (r \supset q)))$

Problems

1. Find a definition of 'formula of S_0'. Make it as rigorous as possible. (*Hint:* Consult the definition given in V.3, if necessary.)
2. Use your definition to show that if a string S of symbols follows from another string T of symbols by the rule of substitution, then S is a formula of S_0 if T is.
3. Try to construct a definition of 'theorem of S_0' like your definition of 'formula of S_0'. This definition should not involve the notion of a proof explicitly.

II Implication and Negation: Informal Semantics

1. Let's begin to make some sense of S_0. At this stage our interpretation of the system will be pretty crude and will not help us much in working with the system; but at least it will begin to give us an inkling of what the system has to do with the language and reasoning we use.

The letters 'p', 'q', 'r', and 's' are to be thought of as playing the grammatical role of declarative sentences, e.g., 'People who live in glass houses ought not to throw stones' or 'Queen Victoria died in 1066'. And when we translate natural languages into formulas of S_0, these letters *stand for* such sentences; for this reason, symbols such as 'p', 'q', 'r', and 's' are often called *sentence variables* or *sentence parameters*.

The symbols '~' and '⊃', on the other hand, play the grammatical role of conjunctions; they do not stand for declarative sentences, but serve to form compound sentences out of simpler sentences. We will reserve the word 'conjunction' for another purpose, and call these symbols *sentence connectives* or just *connectives*.

The connective '∼' is interpreted as negation; so if 'q' stands for 'Queen Victoria died in 1066', then '∼q' stands for 'Queen Victoria did not die in 1066'. The symbol '⊃' is a conditional or implicative connective; if 'r' stands for 'I'll eat my hat' and 'q' is read as before, then 'q ⊃ r' is translated 'If Queen Victoria died in 1066 then I'll eat my hat'. Finally, the parentheses make for unambiguous groupings of symbols in formulas; we wouldn't be able to distinguish '∼(p ⊃ q)' from '∼p ⊃ q' without parentheses.

2. Armed with this interpretation of S_0, we can do several things. First, we can make some sense of formulas, and can begin to see how the axioms and rules of inference of S_0 can be justified as axioms and rules about some subject matter. Maybe we will decide that these are good axioms and rules for negation and implication and maybe that they are bad; but in any case we are no longer looking at S_0 as a game. The system has acquired a purpose and a meaning. It may even be that this new sense of meaningfulness will serve to illuminate the exercises of Chapter I. For instance, our interpretation of the connectives may suggest new formulas that ought to be theorems, and help to devise strategies for finding proofs of them.

Second, we can translate at least some sentences of natural language into S_0. For instance,

(*i*)   If Sam is not sick, then if he is not at school he is playing hooky

might be translated

(*ii*) $(\sim p \supset (\sim q \supset r))$.

As with more familiar cases of translation, there is no unique way of rendering such English sentences in S_0; but we can say in certain cases that one translation is better than another. There isn't much difference between 'Can you speak German?' and 'Do you speak German?' as a translation of 'Sprechen Sie Deutsch?' But there is no doubt that both of these are better than 'Can she speak German?' It is the same way with S_0. The formula

(*ii'*) $(\sim q \supset (\sim p \supset s))$

is as good a translation as ii of i, and both translations are better than

(*iii*) $(q \supset (\sim p \supset s))$

because they capture more of the structure of the English sentence. Although iii is a *sound* translation into S_0 of i, it isn't a *complete* translation, since it neglects the fact that 'Sam is not sick' is expressed negatively in i. On the other hand, iii would be a good translation of 'If Sam is well, then if he is not at school he is playing hooky'.

Let's look at some more examples. Other sound translations of i—none of them as good as ii—are

(*iv*) $(q \supset (p \supset s))$

(*v*) $(\sim q \supset r)$

and

(*vi*) $(p \supset q)$.

Even the formula

(*vii*) p

is a sound translation of i into S_0, although a very uninformative one. It tells us absolutely nothing about the structure of the English sentence i, since formulas such as 'p' can stand for *any* indicative sentence.

One mark, then, of a good translation into S_0 is that only those English sentences that cannot be analyzed as negations and implications are translated into the atomic formulas 'p', 'q', 'r', and 's'. Notice that this is true of translation ii, where 'p' stands for 'Sam is sick', 'q' for 'Sam is at school', and 'r' for 'Sam is playing hooky'.

(We have put 'Sam' for 'he' here, ignoring the difference between a proper name and a relative pronoun. But for the time being, let's not worry about this. We'll be able to say something about this difference later, when we get to predicate logic.)

Finally, there are many unsound or incorrect ways of translating i into S_0. For example,

(*viii*) $\sim p$

and

(*ix*) $((q \supset q) \supset (q \supset q))$

would simply be mistaken as renderings of i; they differ from translations like iv in the way a falsehood differs from an understatement. Rather than failing to represent structure that *is* in i, they represent structure that *is not* in that sentence.

In short, one can err in translating into S_0 by saying too little, or by saying too much. The idea is to get it just right.

3. Up to this point we have managed to keep a major complication at arm's length: in practice it isn't as easy to spot negations and implications in

English as we have made out. Let's start out with some simple examples, which show that implication is not always expressed in English by the locution 'if . . . then –––'.

(x) White will win if Black isn't careful.

(xi) White will win only if Black isn't careful.

If we let 'p' stand for 'White will win' and 'q' for 'Black is careful', x would be translated '$(\sim q \supset p)$' and xi '$(p \supset \sim q)$'; yet neither x nor xi uses the 'if . . . then –––' construction. And there are many other forms of English that ought also to be translated by means of the connective '$\supset$'; subjunctive constructions such as

(xii) We will stop by to see you, should we be in New York this summer

are sometimes used in this way. You may find it interesting to try to find other English phrases that serve this purpose.

Much the same thing happens with negation. Here we have forms such as

(xiii) John doesn't drink.

(xiv) Alice is no slouch.

(xv) It is by no means the case that familiarity breeds contempt.

It also seems reasonable to translate

(xvi) Sally is atypical

as '$\sim p$', letting 'p' stand for 'Sally is typical'. But in many such cases we must watch our step: 'Bill is unhappy' doesn't seem to mean quite the same thing as 'Bill is not happy'. (Bill could fail to be happy, and yet not be unhappy, either.)

Now, let's take stock. In Section 2 we talked about the soundness and completeness of translations of English sentences into S_0. In this discussion, translation seemed a pretty cut-and-dried affair; it was as if the English sentence came neatly packaged in some logical form or other, and good translation was just a matter of fitting this form. Now it appears that it isn't always so simple; at least, there are no unique English constructions that correspond to the connectives '$\supset$' and '$\sim$' of S_0.

But things are more complicated even than this; not only are there many ways of expressing implication in English, but often English constructions which seem to express implication do not in fact do so. A simple example is

(xvii) You can have some cake if you like

or, even better,

(*xviii*)   You will fasten your safety belts, if you please.

In xviii the 'if' functions as part of a polite formula which has little or no connection with the implication of S_0. One way of seeing this is to consider the sheer inanity of the following argument.

(*xix*)   You will fasten your safety belts, if you please.
                 You please.
                 Therefore you will fasten your safety belts.

Examples of another sort are

(*xx*)   If butter is warmed, it melts

and

(*xxi*)   If anyone is sick, he should report to the doctor.

You should feel that something is a bit odd about both of the following arguments—particularly, the second.

(*xxii*)   If butter is warmed, it melts.
                     Butter is warmed.
                     Therefore butter melts.

(*xxiii*)   If anyone is sick, he should report to the doctor.
                     Anyone is sick.
                     Therefore he should report to the doctor.

(We will not really be able to sort these two examples out until we get to Chapter VIII. But one way of preparing xx for translation into logical notation is to render it as 'Whenever any piece of butter is warmed, it melts'. This can then be treated as a statement of universality—a universally quantified sentence—rather than as one of implication. Example xxi would similarly be treated as a statement of universality.)

   Finally, there are a number of difficulties concerning the logical translation of subjunctive and so-called "contrary-to-fact" conditionals. Again, we can use the *modus ponens* test to indicate that something is fishy about examples such as

(*xxiv*)   If Cromwell had not been born, Charles I would not have been
             executed.

We don't use xxiv to infer 'Charles I would not have been executed' from 'Cromwell had not been born'; this isn't even grammatical English. Even tinkering with the verbs doesn't help much; 'If Cromwell was not born then Charles I was not executed' seems very different from xxiv. Still another difficulty is that A3 of S_0 does not seem to apply to this example. The sentence 'If Charles I had been executed, then Cromwell would have been born' is not exactly a welcome consequence of xxiv, as it should be if this example involved the sort of implication at stake in S_0.

Probably this subject has now been belabored enough. The point is, there are no simple recipes for translating natural language into logical systems. As in more familiar cases of translation one has gradually to become bilingual—to get one's ear in—and to acquire the knack of good translating through diligent practice. (Incidentally, this makes the exercises on translation in this and later chapters rather important.)

4. Systems such as S_0 are often called *formal* systems and the process of translating natural languages into them is often called *formalization*. The idea behind this is that there are certain forms which sort out what is relevant to valid or logically correct inference. These logical types are captured by the grammar of the formal system.

For instance, take the following two inferences.

If Jones is an honest man, he will not be arrested by the police.
Jones will be arrested by the police.
Therefore Jones is not an honest man.

If space is four-dimensional, it is not three-dimensional.
Space is three-dimensional.
Therefore space is not four-dimensional.

Inspection of these inferences *with regard only to* correctness of the reasoning involved gives a very forcible impression that the one inference is logically correct if and only if the other is. And this can be confirmed and explained by using the formal system S_0; we can say that these arguments share the logical form

$$\frac{(p \supset \sim q)}{\sim p}.$$

Notice that in placing these arguments in the same category we are ignoring many features such as the truth or falsity of their component sentences or their moral and emotional overtones that people usually find more interesting than logical form. Sometimes people find it difficult to carry out the feat of abstraction needed to view texts from the standpoint of logic; it is for this reason that E. Beth has said that "undue moral rectitude" is a handicap in the study of logic. One of the things a course in logic can do for people is to develop an ability to look at specimens of reasoning in this disinterested way; this can be a handy thing if your line of work involves the generation or evaluation of good arguments. Fortunately, this ability does not seem to detract from the appreciation of other things in language and life.

Exercises

1. Translate the following into S_0.
   (a) We'll go to the beach today, provided it doesn't rain.
   (b) If you do what you're told you won't get along badly here.
   (c) The dog was not treated unkindly.
   (d) If he castles if I move my pawn, then if I don't lose my queen I should be able to beat him.
   (e) All mice are mortal.
   (f) If I miss my train I can arrive only five minutes late, assuming the next train is on time.
   (g) Sam isn't over five feet tall, unless he has grown.

2. Translate the following inferences into S_0. Which of them strike you as logically valid?
   (a) If today is Monday then tomorrow isn't Wednesday.
       Therefore if tomorrow is Wednesday then today is not Monday.
   (b) It is not the case that man does not live by bread alone.
       Therefore man lives by bread alone.
   (c) If murder is wrong, then attempted murder is wrong.
       If attempted murder is wrong, then the very thought of murder is wrong.
       Therefore if murder is wrong, then the very thought of murder is wrong.
   (d) If God is dead then everything is permitted.
       God is not dead.
       Therefore it is not the case that everything is permitted.
   (e) It is not the case that if God is dead then everything is permitted.
       Therefore God is dead.
   (f) If roses are red if violets are blue, then violets are blue.
       Therefore violets are blue.

III Implication Logic:

Natural Deduction

Techniques

1. You couldn't have helped noticing that it was not an easy matter to find proofs in S_0. The source of this trouble with S_0 is that the system does not reproduce very accurately the way in which people in fact argue.

The aim of this chapter is to remedy this by formulating a system of logic which is more easy to work with. This system, $S_{\supset}$, is one of a family of systems of so-called *natural deduction* which have been designed with an eye to the "nature" of ordinary reasoning.

2. Let's begin by considering some specimen arguments which people use. Since we want these arguments to be as good and rigorous as possible, our examples are drawn from mathematics.

Problem: to show that if triangle ABC has side AC equal to side BC, then angles CBA and CAB are equal.

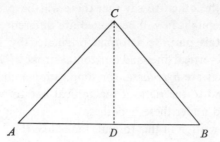

PROOF

1. Suppose that triangle ABC has side AC equal to side BC.
2. Let D be the midpoint of AB, and draw the line CD.
3. Since AC equals BC, DA equals DB, and CD equals CD, triangles ACD and BCD are congruent.
4. Corresponding angles of congruent triangles are equal.
5. Angles CBA and CAB are equal.   Q.E.D.

(i)

If we consider only the features of this argument that have to do with implication, our attention is directed to the statement of the problem and to steps 1 and 5 of the proof. Translating these into S_0, we find that in argument i a sentence (namely, 'If triangle ABC has side AC equal to side BC, then angles CBA and CAB are equal') having the form '$(p \supset q)$' is proved by *supposing* 'p' and then *deducing* 'q'.

There is no doubt that we have discovered here a very important characteristic of the way we argue. A glance at any systematic body of reasoning in disciplines such as mathematics, the natural sciences, or philosophy will reveal a high density of words such as 'suppose', 'let', and 'assume' which signal that a hypothesis has been made.

We also reason hypothetically in more everyday situations. For instance, if we are considering which of two jobs to accept, we imagine that we have taken the one job and try to infer what will happen, and do likewise with the other job. Then we try to compare the consequences.

3. Our first task, then, is to devise a way in which supposition can be handled within some formal system. Clearly we want some notation that will distinguish *supposition* from *assertion* since, for instance, to *assert* that there will be war with China and to *suppose* that there will be war with China are entirely different things. Also we will want to be able to keep track of which sentences are inferred from which suppositions, since, on the one hand, to say that there will be prosperity under the hypothesis that a Democrat will be elected and, on the other, to say that there will be prosperity under the hypothesis that a Republican will be elected are different things.

We will use for this purpose a format originated by Frederic B. Fitch, which uses arrays of vertical lines and horizontal strokes. The sentences above the horizontal strokes are *hypotheses* (or suppositions), and those below the horizontal stroke and to the right of the vertical line to which the stroke is attached are inferred under these hypotheses.

Example i, when written in this format, looks like this.

> Triangle ABC has side AC equal to side BC.
> Let D be the midpoint of AB, and draw the line CD.
> Since AC equals BC, DA equals DB, and CD equals CD, triangles ACD and BCD are congruent.
> Corresponding angles of congruent triangles are equal.
> Angles CBA and CAB are equal.

(ii)

The first step, being above the stroke, is a hypothesis; the succeeding steps are made under this hypothesis.

Since example i was a proof of the implication 'If triangle ABC has side AB equal to side BC, then angles CBA and CAB are equal', we want this implication to follow from the argument ii as a whole. Note, however, that this implicative conclusion is *not* subject to the hypothesis 'Triangle ABC has side AB equal to side AC'. It is *categorical*; i.e., it is subject to *no* hypotheses. We can represent this by placing it outside the vertical line, as follows.

> Triangle ABC has side AC equal to side BC.
>
> Angles CBA and CAB are equal.
> If triangle ABC has side AC equal to side BC, then angles CBA and CAB are equal.

(iii)

4. We can't at present do much more with example i, since the inner steps of the argument have to do with principles of geometry rather than with principles valid in logic. So instead of pursuing this matter further, let's discuss the notion of a hypothetical derivation using other examples.

You might think that all of the entries in such a derivation would be sentences, as in example i, but a little reflection shows that this is not general enough. We may want to have derivations *within* derivations.

Suppose, for instance, that we want to prove something like 'If n is a prime number, then if $n \neq 2$ then n is odd'. We would begin by assuming that n is a prime number (i.e., a number like 7, which is evenly divisible only by 1 and itself). Our next step, however, would not be an inference from this hypothesis, but would be a new hypothesis. We will then have to separate these hypotheses by drawing another vertical line, thus.

n is a prime number.

$n \neq 2.$

(*iv*)

It will be instructive to complete this argument; the reasoning is as follows.

1	n is a prime number
2	$n \neq 2$
3	All prime numbers are evenly divisible only by 1 and themselves.
4	n is a prime number.
5	So n is evenly divisible only by 1 and itself.
6	Therefore n is evenly divisible by 2 only if $n = 2$.
7	But $n \neq 2$.
8	So n is not evenly divisible by 2.
9	All numbers are odd if and only if they are not evenly divisible by 2.
10	n is odd if and only if n is not evenly divisible by 2.
11	n is odd.

(*v*)

The steps in this example are numbered for the sake of convenience in referring to them.

No mathematician would dream of writing this argument out in such tedious detail, but example v, by virtue of its very tediousness, illustrates some points that will prove useful. It is very nearly a logically complete argument, although it will be a while until we have enough formal horsepower available to deal with all of the inferences used in it.

Example v divides naturally into two units, as follows.

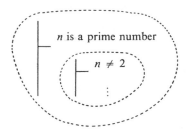

These units will be called *derivations*. (Fitch calls them "subproofs", but I will try to reserve the term 'proof' for proofs such as those in S_0.) As the diagram shows, one of these derivations is a subunit of the other (in fact, the outermost derivation consists of two items, its hypothesis and the second derivation). We will express this by saying that the second derivation is *subordinate* to the first.

Having allowed this much subordination, we have no reason to stop anywhere, and no amount of complexity of subordination can be excluded. For instance, we must be prepared to accept derivations organized like the following one.

(*vi*)

Here (for the first and only time), the numbers serve to label derivations. We will understand 'subordination' in a cumulative sense, so that in example vi derivations 2, 3, 4, 5, and 6 are subordinate to derivation 1, derivations 3 and 4 are subordinate to derivation 2, derivation 4 is subordinate to derivation 3, and derivation 6 is subordinate to derivation 5. Derivation 5, however, is *not* subordinate to derivation 2.

We have still another thing to learn from example v. Notice that at step 4, we repeated the hypothesis of the first derivation. We did this because it was required at this point for the argument; we would not have been able to get the desired conclusion, that *n* is odd, without using somewhere the assumption that *n* is prime.

Our restating at step 4 of the hypothesis that *n* is prime may have seemed gratuitous. But it was more than just a matter of stuttering since, after all, at this stage we are working in a different derivation which does *not* have this hypothesis. We will say that moves of this sort are justified by a rule of *reiteration*, which enables us to make use of hypotheses that are in force through subordinations.

In general, the rule even allows the reiteration of steps that are not hypotheses: stated accurately, the rule is as follows.

If one derivation D_1 is subordinate to another, D_2, then any step in D_2 which appears above the hypothesis of D_1 can be reiterated into D_1.

In other words, anything above and to the left can be reiterated. Many uses of this rule will be found below in this chapter.

Having dragged so much information out of example v, it is only fair to complete this argument. Where we left it, we had gotten to 'n is odd' from the hypothesis '$n \neq 2$'; this entitles us to conclude that if $n \neq 2$, then n is odd.

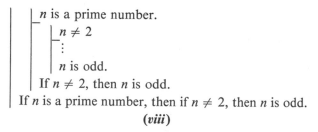

$$n \text{ is a prime number.}$$
$$n \neq 2.$$
$$\vdots$$
$$n \text{ is odd.}$$
$$\text{If } n \neq 2, \text{ then } n \text{ is odd.}$$

(*vii*)

Again, our conclusion does not depend on the second hypothesis, that $n \neq 2$. We have *discharged* this hypothesis in inferring the implication, and represent this by placing this step to the left of the derivation which proceeds from that hypothesis. At this point, the derivation has terminated.

But our conclusion is still subject to a hypothesis: the one of the outermost derivation. We can go on to discharge this hypothesis as well, if we wish.

$$n \text{ is a prime number.}$$
$$n \neq 2$$
$$\vdots$$
$$n \text{ is odd.}$$
$$\text{If } n \neq 2, \text{ then } n \text{ is odd.}$$
$$\text{If } n \text{ is a prime number, then if } n \neq 2, \text{ then } n \text{ is odd.}$$

(*viii*)

This last conclusion is dependent on no hypotheses at all; it is *categorical*. (In such cases try to be careful to draw a line to the left of the whole derivation, with no hypotheses-strokes. This makes the whole thing look a bit neater.)

5. Up to this point our discussion of things like hypotheses, derivations, subordination, reiteration, and categoricity has provided a general structural framework on which arguments can be hung. We have also suggested a rule for deriving implications.

It is high time now to put these ideas to work within the context of some formal system. For this purpose we'll work at first with a class of formulas that in a way is more general, and in a way more restricted than the class of formulas of S_0. We will allow more (infinitely more!) sentence parameters than the four of S_0 but will not, for the time being, allow the use of negation.

The formulas of $S_\supset$, then, are defined as follows.

1. Any of the sentence parameters

$$
\begin{array}{cccc}
p & q & r & s & \ldots \\
p_1 & q_1 & r_1 & s_1 & \ldots \\
p_2 & q_2 & r_2 & s_2 & \ldots \\
& & \vdots & &
\end{array}
$$

is a formula of $S_\supset$;

2. If A and B are formulas of $S_\supset$, then so is $(A \supset B)$.

A string of symbols qualifies as a formula of $S_\supset$ only if it can be shown to be a formula by repeated applications of 1 and 2.

Derivations in $S_\supset$ will use the format we developed in the previous section, the steps in these derivations being formulas rather than English sentences. Knowing only this much, we can form the following derivations in $S_\supset$.

(*ix*) (*x*)

But we aren't going to get very far this way, just making hypotheses and using the reiteration rule. We need additional rules in order to really do something with the system. We don't have to look very far for such rules; we already used one likely candidate in examples iii and viii. This rule, you remember, allowed us to infer an implication (like '(p ⊃ q)') from a derivation of its consequent ('q', in this case) from its antecedent ('p'). Schematically, we can picture the rule as follows.

This diagram means that whenever in a derivation we have completed a pattern looking like

$$
\left|\ \right\lvert\!\!\begin{array}{l} A \\ \vdots \\ B \end{array}
$$

(so that 'A' and 'B' will be replaced by particular formulas, and the dots by an argument using rules of $\mathbf{S}_{\supset}$), we can go on to infer $(A \supset B)$ as shown.

We will call this rule the rule of *implication introduction*, since it allows us to infer *to* an implication; it shows us how to introduce implications in an argument by means of reasoning.

The rule of implication introduction can be combined with the reiteration rule to produce more complicated and interesting derivations, such as these.

$$
\begin{array}{l} \lvert\,(p \supset q) \\ \quad \lvert\,p \\ \quad \lvert\,(p \supset q) \\ \quad (p \supset (p \supset q)) \\ \qquad (\textit{xi}) \end{array}
\qquad
\begin{array}{l} \lvert\,p \\ \quad \lvert\,q \\ \quad \lvert\,p \\ \quad (q \supset p) \\ (p \supset (q \supset p)) \\ \qquad (\textit{xii}) \end{array}
$$

We can also use the rule of implication introduction to derive formulas such as '$(p \supset p)$' categorically; this can be done in the following way.

$$
\begin{array}{l} \quad \lvert\,p \\ (p \supset p) \\ \quad (\textit{xiii}) \end{array}
$$

In a way, this is a lazy application of implication introduction, since nothing at all is derived from the hypothesis 'p' before it is discharged; but nevertheless, we will regard examples such as this as correct uses of implication introduction.

6. There is just one more thing that needs to be added in order to complete the system $\mathbf{S}_{\supset}$. There are various ways to see what is needed; one way is to try to see what would be required to derive '$((p \supset (q \supset r)) \supset ((p \supset q) \supset (p \supset r)))$' categorically.

But general considerations of symmetry also suggest that $\mathbf{S}_{\supset}$ should have a rule of *implication elimination* to complement its rule of implication introduction. After all, we need to argue *from* implications as well as *to* them.

Again there is little doubt about what this rule ought to be; the rule of *modus ponens* is the most plausible candidate. Putting this suggestion into practice, let's agree that applications of the rule of implication elimination (or *modus ponens*) are permitted in the system $S_{\supset \sim}$ as follows.

$$
\begin{array}{l|l}
A & A \supset B \\
\vdots & \vdots \\
A \supset B & A \\
\vdots & \vdots \\
B & B
\end{array}
$$

That is, any time when we have both formulas A and $A \supset B$ in a derivation, we may infer B by the rule of implication elimination.

In the following examples all the rules of $S_{\supset}$ are employed.

$$
\begin{aligned}
&(p \supset (q \supset r)) \\
&\quad (p \supset q) \\
&\qquad p \\
&\qquad (p \supset q) \\
&\qquad q \\
&\qquad (p \supset (q \supset r)) \\
&\qquad (q \supset r) \\
&\qquad r \\
&\quad (p \supset r) \\
&\ ((p \supset q) \supset (p \supset r)) \\
&((p \supset (q \supset r)) \supset ((p \supset q) \supset (p \supset r)))
\end{aligned}
$$

(xiv)

$$
\begin{aligned}
&((p \supset q) \supset r) \\
&\quad q \\
&\qquad p \\
&\qquad q \\
&\quad (p \supset q) \\
&\quad ((p \supset q) \supset r) \\
&\quad r \\
&(q \supset r)
\end{aligned}
$$

(xv)

As in the case of S_0, it often is helpful to annotate derivations, showing the reasons for steps. This will become particularly useful later on when we will be working with more rules. Example xv, if annotated in this way, looks like this.

1	$((p \supset q) \supset r)$	hyp
2	q	hyp
3	p	hyp
4	q	2, reit
5	$(p \supset q)$	3–4, imp int
6	$((p \supset q) \supset r)$	1, reit
7	r	5, 6, m p
8	$(q \supset r)$	2–7, imp int

(*xv'*)

7. For some purposes it is convenient to have derivations with multiple hypotheses. (One reason for this is that in everyday cases we frequently want to argue from many hypotheses—in no particular order of subordination—down to a conclusion.) It is easy to allow such derivations in $S_\supset$. Here is an example, closely related to example xiv above.

1	$(p \supset (q \supset r))$	hyp
2	$(p \supset q)$	hyp
3	p	hyp
4	$(p \supset q)$	2, reit
5	q	3, 4, m p
6	$(p \supset (q \supset r))$	1, reit
7	$(q \supset r)$	3, 6, m p
8	r	5, 7, m p
9	$(p \supset r)$	3–8, imp int

(*xvi*)

8. There are several mistakes that beginners often make in trying to find derivations in systems such as $S_\supset$. One of the most common misunderstandings leading to mistakes of this kind has to do with subordination.

For instance, suppose we are set the task of deriving 'r' from 'q' and '$((p \supset q) \supset r)$'. In the course of solving this problem we may be forced to make hypotheses; and since we can make any hypothesis we like, why not assume '$(p \supset q)$'? This will enable us to get to 'r' as follows.

1	q	hyp
2	$((p \supset q) \supset r)$	hyp
3	$(p \supset q)$	hyp
4	$((p \supset q) \supset r)$	2, reit
5	r	3, 4, m p

(*xvii*)

The trouble with xvii is that it isn't a solution to the problem. Its last step, 'r', is indeed the conclusion we wanted; but in this step 'r' has not been obtained as an item of the main derivation; it is an item of a subordinate derivation in which a further hypothesis is made. In step 5, 'r' is subject not only to the hypotheses 'q' and '$((p \supset q) \supset r)$', but also to the hypothesis '$(p \supset q)$'.

To see just how mistaken this technique is, it's only necessary to consider an extreme example of it like the following "derivation" of 'q' from 'p'.

$$\vdash \begin{array}{l} p \\ \vdash \begin{array}{l} q \\ \vdash \end{array} \end{array}$$

(xviii)

This example is the most blatant possible case of the fallacy known as *petitio principii*: assuming what was to be proved. Example xvii is a more disguised version of the same fallacy. Using this method, it would be easy to "derive" anything from anything.

What is asked, then, by a request to derive B from hypotheses $A_1, \ldots, A_n$ is that B should be obtained as an item in a derivation headed by the hypotheses $A_1, \ldots, A_n$—not as an item in a derivation in which other hypotheses are in force as well. To derive B from $A_1, \ldots, A_n$ means to derive B from $A_1, \ldots, A_n$ *only*.

On the other hand, this doesn't mean that other hypotheses can't be made in carrying out a derivation. It means only that these hypotheses must be *discharged* in the course of the argument.

Consider, for instance, our original problem: to derive 'r' from 'q' and '$((p \supset q) \supset r)$'. The insight needed here is that we could obtain 'r' by *modus ponens* if we could get '$(p \supset q)$'. We are then led to attempt a derivation along the following lines.

$$\begin{array}{|l} q \\ ((p \supset q) \supset r) \\ \hline ? \\ (p \supset q) \\ r \end{array}$$

(xix)

In a situation like this, when you're trying to argue to an implication, it is never a bad idea to try to get it by implication introduction. So we set up a subordinate derivation with 'p' as hypothesis, and try to obtain 'q' in this new derivation.

$$q$$
$$((p \supset q) \supset r)$$
$$\begin{array}{l} p \\ ? \\ q \end{array}$$
$$(p \supset q)$$
$$r$$

(xx)

The last step of this subordinate derivation isn't an implication, so we can't get it by implication introduction. Therefore we look up at the formulas that can be reiterated into the derivation, to see whether we can use them to get 'q'. In this case, it's easy; 'q' *is* one of these formulas, and we can end the derivation as it stands. The end product looks like this.

1	q	hyp
2	((p ⊃ q) ⊃ r)	hyp
3	p	hyp
4	q	1, reit
5	(p ⊃ q)	3–4, imp int
6	r	2, 5, m p

(xxi)

Notice that although another hypothesis has been made in xxi, it has been discharged by step 6. In this step 'r' is subject to only the hypotheses 'q' and '((p ⊃ q) ⊃ r)', as is shown by its not being separated by any lines from the outermost line of the derivation.

Another misapprehension that sometimes causes trouble is that hypotheses made in a derivation must be *used* in getting to the conclusion. So far is this from being true that very often we have to make hypotheses that are quite irrelevant to the conclusion. This occurs, for instance, in trying to find a categorical derivation of '(p ⊃ (q ⊃ q))'.

In solving this problem, we should follow the policy of getting implications by implication introduction and begin as follows.

$$\begin{array}{l} p \\ ? \\ (q \supset q) \end{array}$$
$$(p \supset (q \supset q))$$

(xxii)

The danger here is to assume that '(q ⊃ q)' must come by somehow using the hypothesis 'p'. If you try to do this you'll get stuck.

The right way to proceed in cases such as this is to rely mechanically on the advice that implications should be obtained by implication introduction; we then form a subordinate derivation with 'q' as hypothesis.

$$
\begin{array}{l}
\lfloor p \\
\quad \lceil q \\
\quad \quad ? \\
\quad (q \supset q) \\
(p \supset (q \supset q)) \\
\quad \textit{(xxiii)}
\end{array}
$$

Since, as we explained in Section 5, we regard steps such as

$$
\begin{array}{l}
\lceil q \\
\\
(q \supset q)
\end{array}
$$

as instances of implication introduction, we need proceed no further; to finish the problem it's only necessary to fill in reasons.

1	⌊p	hyp
2	⌈q	hyp
3	(q ⊃ q)	2, imp int
4	(p ⊃ (q ⊃ q))	1–3, imp int
	(xxiv)	

This is a perfectly correct derivation, even though no use whatsoever was made of the hypothesis 'p' in deriving '(q ⊃ q)'.

Exercises

1. Find derivations of the following in $S_\supset$.

  (a) (p ⊃ q) from (r ⊃ q) and (p ⊃ r)
  (b) (r ⊃ (p ⊃ (q ⊃ r))) from (p ⊃ (r ⊃ (q ⊃ r)))
  (c) (p ⊃ (p ⊃ p)) from q
  (d) (p ⊃ p) from (q ⊃ r)
  (e) r from ((p ⊃ (q ⊃ p)) ⊃ r)
  (f) ((r ⊃ q) ⊃ q) from ((p ⊃ q) ⊃ q) and (p ⊃ r)
  (g) ((p ⊃ r) ⊃ r) from ((p ⊃ q) ⊃ q), (q ⊃ r), and (r ⊃ q)
  (h) r from p and (((q ⊃ q) ⊃ p) ⊃ r)

  (i) $((p \supset q) \supset (r \supset r))$ from $((p \supset q) \supset (r \supset q))$

  (j) p from $((p \supset q) \supset p)$, $(p \supset (r \supset q))$, and r

  (k) $(r \supset p)$ from $((p \supset r) \supset ((q \supset r) \supset (r \supset p)))$

  (l) $(p \supset q)$ from $(((r \supset q) \supset (q \supset p)) \supset (p \supset q))$

2. Find categorical derivations of the following in $\mathbf{S}_\supset$.

  (a) $((p \supset q) \supset ((q \supset r) \supset (p \supset r)))$

  (b) $(r \supset ((p \supset q) \supset (s \supset (p \supset q))))$

  (c) $(((p \supset p) \supset p) \supset p)$

  (d) $((p \supset (p \supset q)) \supset (p \supset q))$

  (e) $(((p \supset (q \supset r)) \supset s) \supset (r \supset s))$

  (f) $(((p \supset p) \supset q) \supset q)$

  (g) $((p \supset q) \supset (((r \supset q) \supset s) \supset ((r \supset p) \supset s)))$

Problems

1. Show that if there is a categorical derivation of a formula A in $\mathbf{S}_\supset$ then there is a categorical derivation of $(B \supset A)$ in $\mathbf{S}_\supset$, where B is any formula of $\mathbf{S}_\supset$.

2. Show that, if there is a categorical derivation of a formula A in $\mathbf{S}_\supset$, then there is a categorical derivation of any substitution instance of A.

3. Is there a categorical derivation in $\mathbf{S}_\supset$ of '$(((p \supset q) \supset p) \supset p)$'? If you claim there is none, can you devise any clearcut way of demonstrating that your claim is true?

4. In the next chapter, we are going to add rules for negation ('$\sim$'), conjunction ('$\wedge$'), disjunction ('$\vee$'), and equivalence ('$\equiv$'). Figure out what these rules must be.

IV Sentence Logic:

Informal Semantics

and Natural Deduction

Techniques

1. In the last chapter we constructed a framework, consisting of the apparatus of subordination and reiteration, in which hypothetical reasoning could be displayed. Then we devised a formal system accounting for implication by adding rules to this underlying framework. Just two rules were added, one for introducing the connective '⊃' and one for eliminating it.

One nice thing about natural deduction is that these features recur in very tidy and systematic fashion as we expand our logical horizons. If we wish to add more connectives we only have to find out the right pair of rules for the connective; this is almost always an easy thing to do, requiring only a little sensitivity to the way we reason. Once we have got the right pair of rules, we know at once how to incorporate the connective into the logical system.

In this chapter we will be able to dispose quickly of negation and a number of other connectives as well: conjunction, disjunction, and equivalence. By the time we are through, we will have a system of logic that can handle many new sorts of reasoning.

2. Of course, besides adding new rules, we will have to add new formulas as well. A rule for '$\sim$' wouldn't be of much use in a system unless the system allowed formulas involving the connective '$\sim$'. So in all, we will be adding four connectives to the system $S_\supset$ of the last chapter: '$\wedge$', '$\vee$', '$\sim$', and '$\equiv$'. Each time we add one of these connectives we will extend the class of formulas with which we are working, and in fact, by the time we finish this chapter, we will have discussed a number of logical systems: $S_{\supset\wedge}$, $S_{\supset\wedge\vee}$, $S_{\supset\wedge\vee\sim}$, and $S_{\supset\wedge\vee\sim\equiv}$.

But it would just be too fussy to have to keep track of things in this way. Rather than discussing at each stage the additions we are making to the set of formulas and giving each of these a name, we will simply regard them as part of a big system. Then we can describe the formulas of that system and be done with it.

The formulas of this inclusive system, S_s, are built up according to the following rules.

1. Any of the sentence parameters of $S_\supset$ (see III.5) is a formula of S_s;
2. If A and B are formulas of S_s, then so is $(A \supset B)$;
3. If A is a formula of S_s, then so is $\sim A$;
4. If A and B are formulas of S_s, then so is $(A \wedge B)$;
5. If A and B are formulas of S_s, then so is $(A \vee B)$;
6. If A and B are formulas of S_s, then so is $(A \equiv B)$.

Again, a string of symbols qualifies as a formula of S_s only if it can be shown to be a formula by repeated applications of rules 1 to 6.

Mixing up all these rules at once can lead to the construction of some pretty complicated formulas. The following are examples of formulas of S_s.

$$((p \supset ((q \wedge r) \equiv \sim(s \vee (p \wedge q)))) \vee (r_5 \supset (s \wedge p)))$$
$$(((((q \wedge q) \wedge q) \wedge q) \vee p)$$
$$((\sim\sim p_2 \vee \sim\sim q_1) \equiv (p \wedge q_5))$$
$$(\sim p \supset ((q \wedge q) \vee \sim(r \wedge s)))$$

In the sections below we will deal in turn with each of these new connectives. The plan will be (1) to discuss briefly the translation of sentences of natural language into formulas involving the connective, (2) to discuss specimen arguments using English equivalents of the connective, and (3) to use these arguments in figuring out introduction and elimination rules for the connective.

3. In this section we will consider conjunction, which means that on the formal side of things we will be dealing with the connective '∧', and on the informal side with the word 'and'. The sentence 'Brasidas was a great general, and Thucydides was a great historian' would be translated into S_s as 'p ∧ q', letting 'p' and 'q' stand for the conjuncts of the English sentence. Similarly, 'Chicago and New York are large cities' would appear as a formula like 'p ∧ q'; but here one must be sensitive to nuances. 'Jack and Jill went up the hill', or better, 'Jack and Jill got married' conveys something more than the conjunction in which we are interested for logical purposes; there is the suggestion that the acts are done together in the first case, and reciprocally in the second. 'Jack counted three and pulled the ripcord', on the other hand, suggests that the actions were performed in a certain order; this also is a feature not taken into consideration in logical conjunction.

In working out logical rules for conjunction, our problem is to decide how we reason to conjunctions in arguments, and how we reason from them. As it turns out, this is a very simple matter; if you think about it a minute you should be able to work out the answer.

Suppose, for instance, that we want to show that the square root of 5 is less than 3 and greater than 2. Well, we would have to show two things: that $\sqrt{5}$ is less than 3 and that $\sqrt{5}$ is greater than 2. (It doesn't matter in which order we do this, as long as we get them both.)

So, we might argue as follows. (To keep from digressing too far, we'll suppose that for all real numbers x and y, x < y if and only if $x^2 < y^2$—a real number is less than another just in case its square is less than the other's square.)

1. $3^2 = 9$.
2. $(\sqrt{5})^2 = 5$.
3. $5 < 9$.
4. So $(\sqrt{5})^2 < 3^2$, in view of 1, 2, and 3.
5. But then $\sqrt{5} < 3$.
6. $2^2 = 4$.
7. $4 < 5$.
8. So $2^2 < (\sqrt{5})^2$, in view of 2, 6, and 7.
9. But then $2 < \sqrt{5}$.
10. Therefore, in view of 5 and 9, $\sqrt{5} < 3$ and $2 < \sqrt{5}$.

(i)

The step in which we are interested here is the last, number 10. If we translate the inference used in passing from 6 and 9 to 10 into the notation of S_s, we get something like this.

$$
\begin{array}{|l}
\vdots \\
p \\
\vdots \\
q \\
\vdots \\
(p \wedge q)
\end{array}
$$

(ii)

And now it's easy to state in general the introduction rule for '$\wedge$' in S_s; we have to be careful to remember, though, that the order in which we got the premisses in i didn't matter; we could as well have proved that $2 < \sqrt{5}$ before proving that $\sqrt{5} < 3$. Now for the rule; applications of the rule of *conjunction introduction* (*conj int*) are permitted in the system S_s, as follows.

$$
\begin{array}{|l}
\vdots \\
A \\
\vdots \\
B \\
\vdots \\
(A \wedge B)
\end{array}
\qquad
\begin{array}{|l}
\vdots \\
B \\
\vdots \\
A \\
\vdots \\
(A \wedge B)
\end{array}
$$

That is, whenever we have written down two formulas A and B (in any order) in a derivation in S_0, we may then write down in that derivation the result $(A \wedge B)$ of conjoining A with B.

4. If anything, it's easier to grasp the rule of conjunction elimination, and to avoid being long-winded we may as well state it without any fanfare. This rule is applied as follows.

$$
\begin{array}{|l}
\vdots \\
(A \wedge B) \\
\vdots \\
A
\end{array}
\qquad
\begin{array}{|l}
\vdots \\
(A \wedge B) \\
\vdots \\
B
\end{array}
$$

Whenever we have written a conjunction $(A \wedge B)$ in a derivation, we may thereafter write down either of its conjuncts, A and B.

So far then, we have discussed two pairs of rules for logical connectives of the system S_s: the connectives '$\supset$' and '$\wedge$'. Here are some specimen derivations making use of these rules.

1	$\vert\underline{\ }p$	hyp
2	$\vert\ \ \ \vert\underline{\ }q$	hyp
3	$\vert\ \ \ \vert\ p$	1, reit
4	$\vert\ \ \ \vert\ (p \wedge q)$	2, 3, conj int
5	$\vert\ \ (q \supset (p \wedge q))$	2–4, imp int
6	$\vert\ (p \supset (q \supset (p \wedge q)))$	1–5, imp int

(*iii*)

1	$\vert\underline{\ }(p \wedge (q \wedge r))$	hyp
2	$\vert\ p$	1, conj elim
3	$\vert\ (q \wedge r)$	1, conj elim
4	$\vert\ q$	3, conj elim
5	$\vert\ (p \wedge q)$	2, 4, conj int
6	$\vert\ r$	3, conj elim
7	$\vert\ ((p \wedge q) \wedge r)$	5, 6, conj int

(*iv*)

5. Now for disjunction, expressed often by the English 'or'. The connective '$\vee$' of S_s corresponds to the inclusive sense of 'or', in which the alternative in which both disjuncts hold true is not meant to be excluded.

For instance, if Smith maintains that Jones is a miser or a vindictive troublemaker, we would not say that Smith was wrong in case both turn out to be true. Smith may not have supposed that both in fact were true, or he would not have made his point so guardedly; he would have said that Jones was a miser *and* a vindictive troublemaker. But still, the disjunctive claim is true under these circumstances. This inclusive sense of 'or' is sometimes expressed by 'and/or' in circumstances (for instance those in which one is formulating rules of some sort) where the speaker feels it is important to make his meaning very precise.

The English 'unless' also has an inclusive sense which would be properly translated in S_0 by uses of '$\vee$'. For instance 'Unless my memory is bad the sun is 93 million miles from the earth' could be translated by '$(p \vee q)$', where 'p' stands for 'My memory is bad' and 'q' for 'The sun is 93 million miles from the earth'. In this example, the first claim would still hold good in case 'My memory is bad' and 'The sun is 93 million miles from the earth' are both true; I may have made a lucky guess.

There are difficulties with 'unless' which make it risky to translate English sentences involving this word into S_s using '$\vee$'. Briefly, the trouble is that

S_s will sanction the inference of '$(q \lor p)$' from '$(p \lor q)$'. But this inference is not valid for 'unless'; for instance, it would be nonsense to claim that 'Unless you will see the stars tonight, it is cloudy' is true if 'Unless it will be cloudy, you will see the stars tonight' is. I would say that this problem indicates a limitation of S_s, that cannot be cleared up without constructing a formal theory of subjunctive conditionals (see II.3, example xxiv). But that's another story.

Bearing in mind the point that disjunction in S_s is inclusive, let's consider a few more examples. Sentences such as 'Alaska or Texas is the largest state in the union' and 'It will rain tonight or I'm a monkey's uncle' would be translated in S_s by sentences of the form '$(p \lor q)$'. But we ought to be a bit hesitant about translating something like 'My son will mow the lawn or I'll take away his teddy bear' in this way, since it connotes that it will not be the case that both disjuncts hold true.

There are many examples in which the joint case simply does not come up: for instance, 'He is in Boston or Zagreb', or 'Either he beats his wife or he doesn't'. In both of these, the situation in which both disjuncts are true is excluded out of hand, and it doesn't seem a matter of great importance whether or not we say these sentences are true in case both of their disjuncts are. For this reason, there seems to be no harm in translating these into S_s by formulas of the sort '$p \lor q$'.

6. Let's turn now to the question of logical rules for disjunction. In this case, it's more convenient to take up the elimination rule first. The rule of disjunction elimination is more complicated than the rules we have discussed up to now; but it corresponds closely to the way we actually reason from disjunctions, and again is made to seem natural by considering examples of this sort of reasoning. Let's consider a case in which we must argue from a disjunction to some conclusion; for instance, suppose we want to show that if a number n is greater than 20 or less than 10, then $(n - 15)^2$ is greater than 25. The thing to do is to reason as follows.

1. Assume that $n > 20$ or $n < 10$.
2. Suppose that $n > 20$.
3. Then $(n - 15) > 5$, so $(n - 15)^2 > 25$.
4. On the other hand, suppose that $n < 10$.
5. Then $(n - 15) < -5$.
6. So in this case also, $(n - 15)^2 > 25$.
7. Therefore, $(n - 15)^2 > 25$.
8. Hence, if $n > 20$ or $n < 10$, then $(n - 15)^2 > 25$.

$$(v)$$

Translating the key steps of this argument into S_s and putting the argument into the format of subordinated derivations, we get something like this.

$$
\begin{array}{l}
(p \lor q) \\
\quad p \\
\quad \vdots \\
\quad r \\
\\
\quad q \\
\quad \vdots \\
\quad r \\
r \\
((p \lor q) \supset r) \\
\textit{(vi)}
\end{array}
$$

Here, 'p' stands for '$n > 20$', 'q' for '$n < 10$', and 'r' for '$(n - 15)^2 > 25$'. Example vi gives us a pretty good picture of how to get a conclusion from a disjunction '$(p \lor q)$'. Besides '$(p \lor q)$' we need two other premisses in order to extract a conclusion 'r': a derivation of 'r' from 'p' and one of 'r' from 'q'.

In general, the rule of *disjunction elimination* (*dis elim*) looks like this.

$$
\begin{array}{lll}
\vdots & \vdots & \vdots \\
(A \lor B) & (A \lor B) & \quad B \\
\vdots & \vdots & \quad \vdots \\
\quad A & \quad B & \quad C \\
\quad \vdots & \quad \vdots & \vdots \qquad \text{etc.} \\
\quad C & \quad C & (A \lor B) \\
\vdots & \vdots & \vdots \\
\quad B & \quad A & \quad A \\
\quad \vdots & \quad \vdots & \quad \vdots \\
\quad C & \quad C & \quad C \\
\vdots & \vdots & \vdots \\
C & C & C
\end{array}
$$

That is, whenever we have obtained as items in a derivation a formula $(A \lor B)$ and derivations of C from A and of C from B (in any order), we may then write down C. Above, all the different possible arrangements aren't displayed; there are six in all.

Notice, by the way, that the rule of dis elim makes good sense from the standpoint of truth. If $(A \lor B)$ is true, then A is true or B is true, and so if C follows from A and follows from B, then C is true if A is, and also true if B is.

So C is true in either case. We will develop this idea in great detail below in Chapter VI, where we discuss the semantic interpretation of S_s.

The rule of disjunction elimination, by the way, corresponds to one of the favorite devices of classical orators. This is to discuss a question by beginning with two alternatives, and then giving a pair of speeches designed to show that in either case the desired conclusion follows. Socrates' speech about death in the *Apology* is an example: he asserts that death is either a form of unconsciousness or of consciousness and then argues that in either case it is a good.

7. It isn't easy to motivate the rule of disjunction introduction in the same way we have developed previous rules by referring to samples of reasoning. This is because we hardly ever use this rule in actual argumentation; after we have worked out the rule you will see why this is so.

However, we can get at the rule in a slightly different way by talking about the *justification* of a disjunctive claim. If Peterson asserts that Scrags' car has a short in the generator or a broken fanbelt, how would we go about justifying this assertion? Well, we will have determined that Peterson is right as soon as we have verified that the car has a short in the generator, or verified that it has a broken fanbelt. We know that a disjunctive claim is true as soon as we know that either of its disjuncts is true.

Surely, the rule sanctioning this sort of justification is one which permits the inference of a disjunction from either of its disjuncts: for instance, 'Scrags' car has a short in the generator or a broken fanbelt' from 'Scrags' car has a short in the generator', and 'Scrags' car has a short in the generator or a broken fanbelt' from 'Scrags' car has a broken fanbelt'.

The formal counterpart in S_s of this rule will permit us to argue to disjunctions $(A \lor B)$; this rule of *disjunction introduction* (*dis int*) takes the following form.

$$
\begin{array}{ll}
\left|\begin{array}{l} \vdots \\ A \\ \vdots \\ (A \lor B) \end{array}\right. & \qquad \left|\begin{array}{l} \vdots \\ B \\ \vdots \\ (A \lor B) \end{array}\right.
\end{array}
$$

Whenever in a derivation we have written either A or B, we may thereafter write the disjunction $(A \lor B)$.

Now that we have the rule, we can go back to the point with which we began this section and explain why the rule is not often used explicitly in argumentation. The reason is that if we already *know* a thing—say, that the car has a broken fanbelt—we wouldn't bother to reason from this to a disjunction—say, that the car has a short in the generator or a broken fanbelt. We would only lose information in doing this; it is silly, unless one is dissimulating, to assert a disjunction when one knows which of the two disjuncts is true.

Nevertheless, we have shown that dis int is important in the justification of disjunctive statements, and it turns out to be just the right rule for formal purposes. As we will see later, it generates, together with the other rules, a theory of disjunction which is *semantically complete*.

8. At this point we have, besides reit, six rules with which to build derivations. (Two rules apiece for each of the connectives '⊃', '∧', and '∨'; remember that 'implication elimination' is just another name for *modus ponens*.) Here are some examples.

1	(p ∨ (p ∧ r))	hyp
2	p	hyp
3	(p ∧ r)	hyp
4	p	3, conj elim
5	p	1, 2, 3–4, dis elim

(vii)

1	((p ∨ q) ⊃ r)	hyp
2	p	hyp
3	(p ∨ q)	2, dis int
4	((p ∨ q) ⊃ r)	1, reit
5	r	3, 4, m p
6	(p ⊃ r)	2–5, imp int

(viii)

1	(p ∨ (q ∧ r))	hyp
2	p	hyp
3	(p ∨ q)	2, dis int
4	(p ∨ r)	2, dis int
5	((p ∨ q) ∧ (p ∨ r))	3, 4, conj int
6	(q ∧ r)	hyp
7	q	6, conj elim
8	(p ∨ q)	7, dis int
9	r	6, conj elim
10	(p ∨ r)	9, dis int
11	((p ∨ q) ∧ (p ∨ r))	8, 10, conj int
12	((p ∨ q) ∧ (p ∨ r))	1, 2–5, 6–11, dis elim

(ix)

1	$((p \lor q) \land (q \supset r))$	hyp
2	$(q \supset r)$	1, conj elim
3	$(p \lor q)$	1, conj elim
4	p	hyp
5	$(p \lor r)$	4, dis int
6	q	hyp
7	$(q \supset r)$	2, reit
8	r	6, 7, m p
9	$(p \lor r)$	8, dis int
10	$(p \lor r)$	3, 4–5, 6–9, dis elim

$$(x)$$

1	$(p \land ((p \supset q) \lor r))$	hyp
2	p	1, conj elim
3	$((p \supset q) \lor r)$	1, conj elim
4	$(p \supset q)$	hyp
5	p	2, reit
6	q	4, 5, m p
7	$(q \lor r)$	6, dis int
8	r	hyp
9	$(q \lor r)$	8, dis int
10	$(q \lor r)$	3, 4–7, 8–9, dis elim

$$(xi)$$

9. Now we come to negation. We have, of course, already dealt with proofs involving '$\sim$' in the system S_0 of Chapter I, and have discussed in Chapter II the translation of negative English sentences into formal notation. Let's turn at once, then, to the problem of reproducing in S_s the way in which negation figures in correct reasoning.

The rule of negation introduction is fairly straightforward. Suppose that we want to prove something negative: say, that the square root of 2 is irrational. This means that there are no whole numbers n and m such that $\sqrt{2} = n/m$. This is to say, $\sqrt{2}$ is not a fraction, or *ratio*.

The following proof of the irrationality of $\sqrt{2}$ was known in antiquity.

1. Suppose that $\sqrt{2}$ is rational.
2. Then for some whole numbers n and m, $\sqrt{2} = n/m$.

3. By factoring out all the common divisors of n and m, we obtain whole numbers j and k having no common divisors but 1, such that $j/k = {}^n/m$.
4. In view of step 3, j/k is in lowest terms.
5. Since $\sqrt{2} = j/k$, $2 = j^2/k^2$.
6. Therefore $2 \cdot k = j^2$, so that j^2 is divisible by 2.
7. But if 2 divides j^2 (i.e., divides $j \cdot j$), then 2 is a factor of j, and so j is even.
8. Since j is even, 4 is a factor of j^2.
9. But then, since $2 \cdot k^2 = j^2$, 2 is a factor of k.
10. Therefore k and j are both divisible by 2.
11. So j/k is not in lowest terms, which contradicts step 4.
12. Therefore $\sqrt{2}$ is not rational.

$$(\textbf{\textit{xii}})$$

In the last step of xii, a negative conclusion has been inferred from steps 1 to 11. For our purposes, the crucial features of the reasoning are steps 1, 4, and 11; the remaining steps are mathematical stages in the extraction of a contradiction from the assumption that $\sqrt{2}$ is rational.

Translating these main steps into S_s and casting the argument into subordinated form we obtain the following pattern.

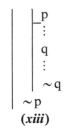

$$(\textbf{\textit{xiii}})$$

This rendering of xii displays the rule of neg int perspicuously enough so that it is a simple matter to extract the general rule. Again, however, we have to remember that in xiii we could as well have gotten '$\sim q$' before 'q'.

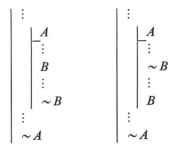

Whenever we obtain as an item in a derivation a subordinated derivation of two contradictory formulas B and $\sim B$ (in either order) from a hypothesis A, we may conclude $\sim A$ in the original derivation.

You may already know the traditional name of this rule: *reductio ad absurdum*. Certainly, you have used arguments which are instances of this rule. Neg int is one of the most frequently used argument patterns in everyday reasoning; in any situation in which the object is to show that something is not the case, the natural thing to do is to assume it and attempt to derive an absurdity. In ordinary cases, this absurdity is not a flat contradiction, as we have required in S_s; it often is a conclusion contrary to popular opinion, or perhaps to the accepted tenets of some profession. We can handle arguments of this sort in S_s by treating these opinions, tenets, or whatever as hypotheses of the whole argument. They would then be reiterated to produce an out-and-out contradiction: that is, a formula together with its negation.

10. The rule of negation elimination raises questions which are more ticklish than any we have encountered so far in this section. It is possible to disagree radically concerning this rule, and the decision made at this juncture can lead to various different logics. Nor are all of these options—in particular, the so-called intuitionistic and classical logics—mere formal games. Both have their appropriate philosophical justification, and both are founded in patterns of reasoning that actually are employed.

An examination of these issues thorough enough to give satisfaction would carry us far astray from the task of presenting the fundamental techniques of modern logic. So we will ride roughshod over the subtleties, and just present the classical approach. Once the techniques are out in the open, they can be applied as readily to intuitionistic as to classical systems of logic, and it will be more easy to appreciate subtleties. For the time being, though, keep in mind that there are legitimate alternatives to the course we will take.

11. To isolate a rule of negation elimination that will generate the classical logic, let's go back to *reductio ad absurdum* arguments. There is a frequently used type of argument which uses the device of reduction to absurdity and yet does not fit the pattern of negation elimination.

I am thinking here of cases in which the conclusion of the argument is not a negative statement. Consider, for instance, the following proof by *reductio* that every real number is equal to, greater than, or less than zero.

1. Suppose that it is not the case that for every real number x, x = 0 or x > 0 or x < 0.

2. Then for some real number, say r, it is not the case that r = 0 or r > 0 or r < 0.
3. Therefore not r = 0 and not r > 0 and not r < 0.
4. But since not r = 0 and not r > 0, then r < 0.
5. And in view of step 3, not r < 0; which contradicts step 4.
6. Therefore for every real number x, x = 0 or x > 0 or x < 0.

(*xiv*)

From the mathematical standpoint this argument is superficial, but it illustrates our point. Rendering the most important parts of xiv (namely, steps 1, 4, 5, and 6) in S_s, we get something looking like this.

$$
\begin{array}{l}
\quad \begin{array}{|l} \underline{} \sim p \\ \quad \vdots \\ \quad q \\ \quad \sim q \end{array} \\
p
\end{array}
$$

(*xv*)

Example xv is certainly reminiscent of the rule of negation introduction, but if you look back at this rule you will see that xv is *not* an instance of neg int. Now, can we *derive* the inference xv using neg int and the other rules of S_s? That is, can we use the rules we have discussed so far to get to 'p' from a derivation of 'q' and of '~q' from '~p'? You may want to try before reading on.

If you did, I hope you didn't succeed! Example xv cannot be derived from our present stock of rules. (I say this, though it isn't as easy as you might think to find a convincing proof that this is so.) The closest we can come is this.

$$
\begin{array}{l}
\quad \begin{array}{|l} \underline{} \sim p \\ \quad \vdots \\ \quad q \\ \quad \sim q \end{array} \\
\sim \sim p
\end{array}
$$

(*xvi*)

In xvi, '~~p' is justified by the rule of neg int. But there is no way to get from '~~p' to 'p', our desired conclusion.

By now, you must have guessed what the rule of neg elim will be: it is precisely what we need in this situation, and can be pictured as follows.

$$
\begin{array}{|l}
\vdots \\
\sim\sim A \\
\vdots \\
A
\end{array}
$$

The rule of neg elim permits one to write down A in any derivation in which a step $\sim\sim A$ has appeared.

12. Using the rules of neg int and neg elim in connection with the other rules discussed above, we can build derivations of considerable complexity. Adding rules for negation, in fact, makes things much less straightforward than they were before; it often is necessary to be devious and indirect in finding derivations, as in the categorical derivation (example xviii) of '(p ∨ ∼p)' below.

For this reason we will provide in this section a number of examples of derivations of various kinds. In all but two of these examples the reasons are omitted; filling the rest in is left as an exercise.

1	p	hyp
2	∼p	hyp
3	∼q	hyp
4	p	1, reit
5	∼p	2, reit
6	∼∼q	3–5, neg int
7	q	6, neg elim

(xvii)

The next derivation shows that our system conforms to the law of excluded middle: '(p ∨ ∼p)' can be derived categorically in S_s. The laws of excluded middle and noncontradiction are among the first principles of logic to have been formulated. According to the principle of excluded middle any sentence such as 'It is raining this afternoon or it isn't' which corresponds to the formula '(p ∨ ∼p)' must be true. According to the principle of non-contradiction any sentence such as 'It is raining this afternoon and it isn't' which corresponds to the formula '(p ∧ ∼p)' must be false.

Like many derivations in S_s with disjunctive conclusions, the argument is indirect. It would be impossible to obtain '(p ∨ ∼p)' in a categorical derivation by the rule dis int, since neither 'p' or '∼p' can be derived categorically in S_s. (We can't prove this yet, but it's so anyway.) The only way to carry out the derivation is to obtain '~~(p ∨ ~p)' using neg int and the rules for disjunction; then '(p ∨ ~p)' can be obtained by neg elim.

1	~(p ∨ ~p)	hyp
2	p	hyp
3	(p ∨ ~p)	2, dis int
4	~(p ∨ ~p)	1, reit
5	~p	2–4, neg int
6	(p ∨ ~p)	5, dis int
7	~~(p ∨ ~p)	1–6, neg int
8	(p ∨ ~p)	7, neg elim

(xviii)

The derivations below use the rules of S₈ (except for the rules for '≡', which we've not yet discussed) in various combinations.

```
  ~(p ∨ q)                    (~p ∨ q)
    p                           p
    (p ∨ q)                     (~p ∨ q)
    ~(p ∨ q)                    ~p
  ~p                            ~q
    q                           p
    (p ∨ q)                     ~p
    ~(p ∨ q)                  ~~q
  ~q                         q
  (~p ∧ ~q)
    (xix)                     q

                            q
                          (p ⊃ q)
                            (xx)
```

```
  ~~(p ∧ ~p)                  p
  (p ∧ ~p)                    ~q
  p                           (p ⊃ q)
  ~p                          p
  ~~~(p ∧ ~p)                 q
    (xxi)                     ~q
                            ~(p ⊃ q)
                              (xxii)
```

$(p \supset \sim q)$
q
p
$(p \supset \sim q)$
$\sim q$
q
$\sim p$
$(q \supset \sim p)$
$((p \supset \sim q) \supset (q \supset \sim p))$
(*xxiii*)

$\sim(p \supset q)$
q
p
q
$(p \supset q)$
$\sim(p \supset q)$
$\sim q$
(*xxiv*)

13. The only connective of S_s which we've not yet discussed is equivalence or, as it is sometimes called, the biconditional. This is often expressed in English by 'if and only if', or by locutions using phrases such as 'necessary and sufficient condition'. For instance, 'The senate will pass the bill if and only if the house of representatives does', and 'This polygon has three sides if and only if it has three angles' would both be rendered in S_s by formulas of the sort '$(p \equiv q)$'.

At this point there probably is no need to produce examples of arguments to and from biconditional statements. All that is needed to work out the rules for '$\equiv$' is the thought that statements such as 'Harrison is the mayor if and only if he has been duly elected' amount to conjunctions of implicative statements—in this case, to the conjunction 'Harrison is the mayor if he has been duly elected, and Harrison is the mayor only if he has been duly elected'; i.e., to the conjunction 'If he has been duly elected then Harrison is the mayor, and if Harrison is the mayor then he has been duly elected'.

The rules for '$\equiv$', then, will be doubled versions of the rules for '$\supset$'. Thus the rule of equivalence introduction takes the following form.

A
$\vdots$
B

B
$\vdots$
A
$(A \equiv B)$

B
$\vdots$
A

A
$\vdots$
B
$(A \equiv B)$

Whenever we have obtained derivations of A from B and of B from A (in

either order) as items in another derivation, we may thereafter write down
$(A \equiv B)$.

And the rule of equivalence elimination is like *modus ponens*, although it is
symmetrical.

$$
\begin{array}{llll}
\vdots & \vdots & \vdots & \vdots \\
(A \equiv B) & (A \equiv B) & A & B \\
\vdots & \vdots & \vdots & \vdots \\
A & B & (A \equiv B) & (A \equiv B) \\
\vdots & \vdots & \vdots & \vdots \\
B & A & B & A
\end{array}
$$

Whenever we have obtained both $(A \equiv B)$ and A (in any order) in a derivation,
we may conclude B; and whenever we have obtained both $(A \equiv B)$ and B
(in any order) in a derivation, we may conclude A.

14. Below are some examples of derivations using the rules of eqv int and
eqv elim, together with the other rules of S_s.

1	$(p \supset q)$	hyp
2	$\sim q$	hyp
3	p	hyp
4	$(p \supset q)$	1, reit
5	q	3, 4, m p
6	$\sim q$	2, reit
7	$\sim p$	3–6, neg int
8	$(\sim q \supset \sim p)$	2–7, imp int
9	$(\sim q \supset \sim p)$	hyp
10	p	hyp
11	$\sim q$	hyp
12	$(\sim q \supset \sim p)$	9, reit
13	$\sim p$	11, 12, m p
14	p	10, reit
15	$\sim \sim q$	11–14, neg int
16	q	15, neg elim
17	$(p \supset q)$	10–16, imp int
18	$((p \supset q) \equiv (\sim q \supset \sim p))$	1–8, 9–17, eqv int

$$(xxv)$$

```
1    │ (p ≡ (q ≡ q))              hyp
2    │  │ q                       hyp
     │  ├─
3    │ (q ≡ q)                    2, eqv int
4    │ p                          1, 3, eqv elim
```

(*xxvi*)

In this last example, step 3 suffices to introduce '(q ≡ q)' by eqv int, because it is not required by this rule that the derivations of *B* from *A* and of *A* from *B* needed to introduce (*A* ≡ *B*) must be distinct. In this particular case *A* is the same formula as *B* and there is just one derivation, consisting only of step 2, but this is enough to justify step 3.

```
│ (p ≡ q)                        │ (p ≡ q)
│ (r ≡ s)                        │  │ (p ∧ ~q)
│  │ (p ⊃ r)                     │  │ p
│  │  │ q                        │  │ ~q
│  │  │ (p ≡ q)                  │  │ (p ≡ q)
│  │  │ p                        │  │ q
│  │  │ (p ⊃ r)                  │ ~(p ∧ ~q)
│  │  │ r                        │  │ (~p ∧ q)
│  │  │ (r ≡ s)                  │  │ ~p
│  │  │ s                        │  │ q
│  │ (q ⊃ s)                     │  │ (p ≡ q)
│  │                             │  │ p
│  │ (q ⊃ s)                     │ ~(~p ∧ q)
│  │  │ p                        │ (~(p ∧ ~q) ∧ ~(~p ∧ q))
│  │  │ (p ≡ q)                         (xxviii)
│  │  │ q
│  │  │ (q ⊃ s)
│  │  │ s
│  │  │ (r ≡ s)
│  │  │ r
│  │ (p ⊃ r)
│ ((p ⊃ r) ≡ (q ⊃ s))
        (xxvii)
```

15. Before turning to other matters, let's think a moment about how to find derivations in S_s. In this area nothing can substitute for practice, and in working on the exercises you may already have discovered for yourself some of the tricks discussed below. But maybe it will be helpful to make them explicit here.

First, there are some rules that can be very useful in keeping on the right track when trying to construct a derivation. They can never get you into trouble and often will keep you out of blind alleys.

1. When trying to derive a formula of the sort $(A \supset B)$, always set up a subordinate derivation with hypothesis A and try to get B.
2. Similarly, when trying to derive $\sim A$, set up a subordinate derivation with hypotheses A, and try to get a contradiction.
3. Do the same with formulas of the sort $(A \land B)$ and $(A \equiv B)$; that is, try to get them by the appropriate introduction rules.
4. Be careful about getting formulas of the sort $(A \lor B)$ directly, by dis int. Often you have to get it from $\sim\sim(A \lor B)$ by neg elim, or by dis elim or some other elimination rule. See, for instance, example xviii and the paragraphs preceding it.
5. Whenever you have a premiss of the sort $(A \lor B)$, use dis elim unless there is some obvious other way of getting the desired conclusion.
6. Whenever there is an obvious application of an elimination rule—for instance, if you have two formulas A and $(A \supset B)$, or a formula $(A \land B)$ —use the elimination rule unless you see some obvious other way to get the desired conclusion.
7. In general, work from the top and bottom of an incomplete derivation in towards the middle, using rules 1 to 6 wherever applicable. This means, roughly, using elimination rules to argue from the formulas given at the top and introduction rules to get the formulas desired at the bottom. If the problem is solvable, you often will see at once how to fill in the middle to obtain the desired derivation. But sometimes ingenuity is required, even after using rules 1 to 6 as much as they can be used. Practice is the only thing that can develop real skill in such situations.

We've called the above admonitions "rules", but you must realize that they aren't *rules of* the system S_s. The latter sort of rules, if you like, are rules for *recognizing* (or *characterizing*) derivations; the former are rules of thumb for *finding* derivations. It is like the difference between rules of chess like 'Try not to lose your queen' and 'The king may move one square in any direction, unless the square is threatened by an opposing piece'. The latter is one of the rules constituting the game of chess; the former is a piece of advice intended to help a player do well.

At the risk of making this analogy tedious, let's consider one more point.

To play chess at all well, you have to think ahead—and this requires the assimilation of certain recurring patterns. You learn that if you take a piece that is defended, the attacking piece will usually be taken; for instance, if you take a defended knight with a bishop, the bishop will ordinarily be taken itself. Stringing together such patterns, one is able to extrapolate a position into the future and weigh possible alternatives with more skill. Very good chess players learn by rote large numbers of classical openings, many of them quite long and complicated.

Actually, this sort of thing is not peculiar to games—it takes place in learning any skill. Basic steps cluster into patterns, and these in turn form into larger groups. And in learning to find derivations in S_s, the sort of patterns one has to learn are *argument forms*. For instance, example xvii establishes an important such pattern: whenever you have contradictory formulas A and $\sim A$ in a derivation you can use the rules of proof of S_s to obtain any formula B whatsoever. The strategy is this.

$$
\begin{array}{ll}
\begin{array}{l}
\vdots \\
A \\
\vdots \\
\sim A \\
\vdots \\
\quad \begin{array}{l} \sim B \\ A \\ \sim A \end{array} \\
\sim\sim B \\
B
\end{array}
&
\begin{array}{l}
\vdots \\
\sim A \\
\vdots \\
A \\
\vdots \\
\quad \begin{array}{l} \sim B \\ A \\ \sim A \end{array} \\
\sim\sim B \\
B
\end{array}
\end{array}
$$

(*xxix*)

The above display shows in general how to go about getting *any* formula B, once one has obtained *any* contradiction. In a way, xxix establishes a rule of *contradiction elimination*: from A and $\sim A$ to infer B. But this is not a rule of S_s in the sense that, say, neg elim is a rule of that system. If, for instance, we were simply to proceed as follows,

$$
\begin{array}{l}
p \\
\quad \begin{array}{l} \sim p \\ p \\ q \end{array}
\end{array}
$$

(*xxx*)

this would *not* be a derivation in S_s. But xxix shows us how to fill in steps in xxx to make a derivation in S_s out of it.

Rules such as neg elim are often called *primitive*, and rules such as contradiction elimination *derived*. The former rule is a primitive rule of S_s, in that it is a basic or unanalyzable principle of proof in the system. The latter rule is derivable in S_s, because the primitive rules of S_s may be manipulated in such a way as to justify any instance of contradiction elimination, as is shown by the scheme xxix. Derived rules, then, are justified by argument patterns which are complexes of primitive rules.

Notice, by the way, that the notions of *primitive* and *derived rule* are relative to the system under consideration. Contradiction elimination might well be a primitive rule of some other system.

Here are two more argument patterns, which often are useful in finding derivations.

(xxxi)

(xxxii)

Notice that contradiction elimination is used in constructing example xxxii.

Below are listed some other argument patterns that are especially useful. Rather than filling in the steps of these patterns, however, we will simply list their premises and conclusions. Their completion is left to you.

$$\begin{array}{l} \underline{\mid} \sim(A \lor B) \\ \vdots \\ \mid (\sim A \land \sim B) \end{array} \qquad \begin{array}{l} \underline{\mid} (\sim A \land \sim B) \\ \vdots \\ \mid \sim(A \lor B) \end{array} \qquad \begin{array}{l} \underline{\mid} \sim(A \land B) \\ \vdots \\ \mid (\sim A \lor \sim B) \end{array} \qquad \begin{array}{l} \underline{\mid} (\sim A \lor \sim B) \\ \vdots \\ \mid \sim(A \land B) \end{array}$$

$$\begin{array}{l} \underline{\mid} (\sim A \lor B) \\ \vdots \\ \mid (A \supset B) \end{array} \qquad \begin{array}{l} \underline{\mid} (A \supset B) \\ \vdots \\ \mid (\sim A \lor B) \end{array} \qquad \begin{array}{l} \underline{\mid} \sim(A \supset B) \\ \vdots \\ \mid (A \land \sim B) \end{array} \qquad \begin{array}{l} \underline{\mid} (A \land \sim B) \\ \vdots \\ \mid \sim(A \supset B) \end{array}$$

A final warning. The instructions above will usually result in successful discovery of a derivation, if there is one to be found. Practice in using them is all that is required. But if for some reason you set out to derive something that is underivable in S_s, they of course will not generate an answer; these are instructions for finding a derivation in case one exists, not for showing that there is no derivation in case none exists. One way students sometimes get into trouble is by setting out to derive something that is underivable; then, in order to get an answer, they misapply the rules of S_s. (Deriving '$\sim p$' from '$\sim(p \land q)$' by "conj elim" is a typical mistake of this sort.) So, if you find yourself unable to find a correct derivation of one of the exercises, always check to see whether you have copied or translated the exercise properly.

Exercises

1. Whenever possible, translate the following English sentences into S_s. If you feel that a successful translation is not possible, explain why. In giving a translation, be sure to specify which English sentence each of the sentence parameters in the translation stands for.

   (a) He'll come tomorrow if his car doesn't break down on the way.
   (b) Both Baltimore and Hagerstown are in Maryland.
   (c) I never learned to speak German well, but I can understand you if you speak slowly.
   (d) Where is the nearest post office?
   (e) The accused is guilty if and only if he was not at home on the night of July 15; but his wife will not testify against him and there are no other witnesses.
   (f) I've only been in town a week, and already I've been to three parties and a concert.
   (g) Everyone in this room is unable to read music.
   (h) You are allowed to walk your dog only if you have him on a leash, and the dog must have a license.
   (i) $2^{10} + 1$ is a prime number just in case it is not divisible by 17 or by 21.
   (j) If the boss is neither at home nor at work, then he is at the golf course or something extraordinary has happened and he has been detained; but if he has been detained we'll know about it soon.

(k) New York is nearer to Cleveland than to Kingston.

(l) If we're only two days behind schedule, we may be able to catch up if we get some luck.

(m) Go five miles down the road and turn left at the fire station.

(n) The best way to get there is to go five miles down the road and turn left at the fire station.

(o) He didn't know that Mozart and his father were musicians.

(p) If the train isn't late, I'll stop at a bar and get a drink; and that's for sure.

2. Translate the following into S_s, again specifying which English sentence each of the sentence variables signifies. Then find a derivation in S_s of the conclusion from the hypotheses.

(a) If 2 < 3 then not 3 < 2.
Therefore if 3 < 2 then not 2 < 3.

(b) Oscar is at home, or, if not, he left a message.
Therefore if he didn't leave a message, Oscar is at home.

(c) Albert is either a fool or a liar.
If he is a liar, then what he told me about his sister is false, and I'll look like a fool.
Therefore Albert is a fool or I'll look like a fool.

(d) Fort Wayne is neither in Ohio nor in Illinois.
If Fort Wayne is in Cook County, it is in Illinois.
Therefore it is not the case that Fort Wayne is in Cook County and in Indiana.

(e) If John is arrested he will plead guilty and have to pay a large fine, or plead not guilty and go to a lot of trouble.
If he has to pay a large fine, John will go to a lot of trouble.
Therefore John will go to a lot of trouble if he is arrested.

(f) It is not the case that if God exists, there is unnecessary evil in the world.
Therefore God exists and there is not unnecessary evil in the world.

3. Give derivations in S_s of the following, supplying reasons for all steps.

(a) $(q \lor p)$ from $(p \lor q)$

(b) $(q \land p)$ from $(p \land q)$

(c) $((p \land r) \lor q)$ from $((p \lor q) \land r)$

(d) $((p \land q) \supset r)$ from $(p \supset (q \supset r))$

(e) $(p \supset (q \supset r))$ from $((p \land q) \supset r)$

(f) $\sim\sim r$ from r

(g) $(p \supset (q \lor r))$ from $\sim p$

(h) $((p \lor q) \land (p \lor \sim q))$ from p

(i) $\sim p$ from $(p \supset \sim p)$

(j) p from $(\sim p \supset p)$

(k) $((p \land \sim\sim q) \supset r)$ from $((p \land q) \supset r)$

(l) $((p \lor q) \supset r)$ from $((p \lor \sim\sim q) \supset r)$

(m) $(\sim s \supset (r \lor p))$ from $((p \supset q) \supset (r \lor s))$
(n) p from $((p \supset q) \supset q)$ and $(q \supset \sim q)$
(o) $(((q \supset p) \supset p) \supset p)$ from $((p \supset q) \supset p)$
(p) $(r \supset p)$ from $((p \supset q) \supset (r \supset q))$ and $(q \supset p)$
(q) $((p \supset r) \supset r)$ from $((p \supset q) \supset q)$ and $(q \supset r)$
(r) $(((r \supset q) \supset s) \supset ((r \supset p) \supset s))$ from $(p \supset q)$
(s) $(p \lor r)$ from $(p \lor (q \equiv r))$ and $(p \lor q)$
(t) $((p \land q) \lor (\sim p \land \sim q))$ from $(p \equiv q)$
(u) $(p \lor q)$ from $\sim (p \equiv q)$
(v) $((p \equiv q) \equiv r)$ from $(p \equiv (q \equiv r))$

4. Find categorical derivations in $\mathbf{S_s}$ of the following, supplying a reason for each step.

(a) $(p \lor (p \supset q))$ (b) $((p \supset q) \equiv (\sim p \lor q))$
(c) $((p \lor q) \equiv \sim (\sim p \land \sim q))$ (d) $((p \land q) \equiv \sim (\sim p \lor \sim q))$
(e) $((((p \land q) \lor (\sim p \land q))$ (f) $(((p \supset q) \supset p) \supset p)$
         $\lor (p \land \sim q)) \lor (\sim p \land \sim q))$ (g) $((p \equiv q) \equiv (\sim p \equiv \sim q))$
(h) $(((p \supset q) \supset q) \equiv (p \lor q))$ (i) $((p \lor p) \supset p)$

Problems

1. Devise introduction and elimination rules for the exclusive sense of disjunction, in which the case in which both disjuncts are true is ruled out.
2. Equivalence might have been *defined* in $\mathbf{S_s}$; i.e., formulas such as '$((p \supset q) \land (q \supset p))$' might have been used in place of formulas such as '$(p \equiv q)$'. Are there other connectives of $\mathbf{S_s}$ that can be defined in terms of the remaining connectives? How many connectives of $\mathbf{S_s}$ can be eliminated in this way? What are the criteria that allow us to say that a connective may be defined in terms of others?
3. Let the system $\mathbf{S_s}'$ be like $\mathbf{S_s}$ except that the rules of neg int and neg elim are replaced by the following rule, discussed in Section 11.

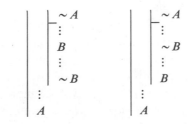

Show that $\mathbf{S_s}$ and $\mathbf{S_s}'$ are equivalent systems. (Clearly, $\mathbf{S_s}$ and $\mathbf{S_s}'$ are not *identical* systems, since they have different rules of inference, so different arrays of formulas will count as proofs in them. Part of the problem is to figure out an appropriate sense of "equivalence" in which the two systems *are* equivalent.)

V Sentence Logic:

Syntax

1. Students sometimes find it difficult to adjust to the sort of thing we will begin to do in this chapter. The purpose of this section and the next is to explain, in a rough and preliminary way, what we will be doing and why it is worthwhile at all.

The subject of our investigation will be a system H_s very like the one presented back in Chapter I. ('H' is for David Hilbert, a mathematician whose name is associated with axiomatic systems of this kind.) But now that we know a bit more about logic, we will be able to develop this material in more generality and depth. Not only will the new system be more powerful and interesting than S_0, but our account of it will be more sophisticated.

Let's discuss the latter, methodological question in more detail. In Chapters I, III, and IV we were concerned primarily with producing proofs and derivations according to the rules of the systems under consideration; in Chapters II and III, we also occupied ourselves with relationships between these formulas and derivations, on the one hand, and sentences and arguments of

English on the other. Now, however, that we've done enough theorem-proving and derivation-finding to get a feel for the relationship of these systems to actual reasoning, we can turn to other matters. We will now begin to concentrate on a more general and theoretical treatment of logical systems.

Some analogies may help to clarify what is going on here. Most people know that there is quite a difference between being a musician and being a musicologist. It's no accident that many people are both, but nevertheless, some very good musicians know almost nothing about harmonic theory and the like, or even about the theory of how to play their instruments. (Such persons are usually bad teachers; they can *use* musical technique, but not communicate about it.) On the other hand, there is no reason why a musicologist has to be a good musician; he may have a ready grasp of the theory of music and be apt at analyzing musical works without being able to compose or even play well.

One of the most spectacular examples of this sort of thing is language. A person may be able to speak a language fluently—to produce and recognize grammatical discourse with ease—without knowing a thing about the grammar of the language. He knows the language, in being able to use it, without knowing about the language in the way that a linguist would be expected to know about it.

To a considerable extent the situation as regards formal languages is parallel to this. Up to this point we've concentrated on learning to *use* these languages—to find proofs in them and so forth. Logicians, however, are more like linguists than native speakers of natural languages; they are interested more in obtaining general and discursive knowledge of logical systems than in being "fluent" users of them.

All of these paragraphs have been devoted to saying in various ways that we are now going to talk *about* formal systems rather than *in* them. We have emphasized this because the distinction often troubles students. One reason for this is that the objects studied in logic are themselves linguistic. There is no danger of confusing bugs and theories about bugs, and so entomologists don't have to worry about distinguishing the two. But logicians must be more careful about such matters, and so distinguish what they call the *object-language* of an investigation from the *metalanguage*. The former is the language under investigation—for instance, S_s in Chapter IV— and the latter is the language used to discuss the object-language. In Chapter IV, then, the metalanguage was English, which is not a formal language.

This distinction is not meant to set a gulf between two kinds of languages, object-languages and metalanguages. The distinction between object-language and metalanguage is not absolute, but is always made with respect to a specific logical investigation, in which a language is used to study a formalized language. This, however, doesn't mean that the metalanguage may not itself be formalized and thus become the object-language for another metalanguage. For instance, logical studies have been carried out in English of two formal languages at once, one of them a metalanguage for the other. In such a case we would have a formalized object-language and a formalized meta-language; the English of the study would be a metametalanguage of the former.

2. We've now agreed to concentrate on talking about logical systems, but haven't said much about how we intend to do this. What tools will we use in developing an account of such systems? Here, the fact that these systems are *formalized* languages is crucial. The precision and definiteness with which such languages are formulated allows logicians to develop their treatments of them *deductively*, with postulates, definitions, and theorems; thus, the more advanced portions of a well-made logical theory will be developed from earlier portions by means of rigorous arguments. In a word, logicians use the methods of mathematics.

To a considerable extent this is like a methodological device used by theoreticians in the natural and social sciences. The technique is this: in studying a subject-matter, first idealize it in mathematical terms, and then direct theoretical attention to this idealization. Sometimes—especially in the social sciences—this sort of enterprise is called building a mathematical *model*. Though this terminology is a bit deprecatory when used of very successful theories, it would not be inaccurate to regard logical systems as mathematical models of certain areas of reasoning.

Do not be surprised later, then, when we begin to state definitions and to prove propositions, as mathematicians do; this is simply the method we'll use in developing our account of formal systems. For purposes of clarity, it is good to distinguish theorems *of* the formal system under consideration (i.e., formulas that can be proved by means of the rules of these systems) from theorems proved *about* these systems in some metalanguage. The latter are usually called *metatheorems*.

3. Proceeding now to the system H_s, we first want to characterize its formulas. Like S_0, H_s will possess only connectives for negation and implication but, like S_s, infinitely many sentence parameters. (It may seem that H_s is impoverished in comparison to S_s as regards connectives; H_s has just two, whereas S_s has five. But this isn't really so; we will show below, in

Section 11, that it's possible to *define* these other connectives in terms of negation and implication.)

1. Any of the sentence parameters $P_1, P_2, P_3, \ldots$ is a formula of $\mathbf{H_s}$.
2. If A is a formula of $\mathbf{H_s}$, then so is $\sim A$.
3. If A and B are formulas of $\mathbf{H_s}$, then so is $(A \supset B)$.

The symbols of $\mathbf{H_s}$ are the connectives $\sim$ and $\supset$, the parentheses) and (, and the sentence parameters $P_1, P_2, \ldots$. A string of symbols of $\mathbf{H_s}$ qualifies as a formula of $\mathbf{H_s}$ only if it can be shown to be a formula by repeated applications of 1, 2, and 3.

The above definition allows formulas to be generated by procedures that resemble proofs. The strings of symbols corresponding to axioms are the sentence parameters; just as axioms are the simplest possible theorems, sentence parameters are the simplest possible formulas. Formulas other than sentence parameters are complexes built up from sentence parameters by means of rules 2 and 3. Thus, if P, Q, and R are sentence parameters of $\mathbf{H_s}$, the following column would show how the formula $\sim\sim(\sim P \supset \sim((Q \supset Q) \supset (\sim R \supset P)))$ is generated.

1	R
2	$\sim R$
3	P
4	$(\sim R \supset P)$
5	Q
6	$(Q \supset Q)$
7	$((Q \supset Q) \supset (\sim R \supset P))$
8	$\sim((Q \supset Q) \supset (\sim R \supset P))$
9	$\sim P$
10	$(\sim P \supset \sim((Q \supset Q) \supset (\sim R \supset P)))$
11	$\sim(\sim P \supset \sim((Q \supset Q) \supset (\sim R \supset P)))$
12	$\sim\sim(\sim P \supset \sim((Q \supset Q) \supset (\sim R \supset P)))$

This column not only shows that $\sim\sim(\sim P \supset \sim((Q \supset Q) \supset (\sim R \supset P)))$ is a formula of $\mathbf{H_s}$, but it also displays the syntactic structure of that formula in showing how it can be produced by the rules that characterize the formulas of $\mathbf{H_s}$.

We have not paid much attention to "proofs" of this kind, because it's easy enough to recognize formulas without their aid. Since, however, we have found as yet no way of recognizing *theorems* without actually producing proofs of them, we have spent (and will spend) a good deal of time discussing proofs and derivations. But it's interesting to observe that with formulas as well as with theorems the same generative sort of characterization may be used.

4. This section is a digression, but has now become unavoidable. Some of you may have noticed that our notation for talking about logical systems was different in the above section; for instance, we made no use at all of quotation marks. Another thing that may have caught your eye and puzzled you is our talking of P, Q, and R as sentence parameters of H_s, although the letters 'P', 'Q', and 'R' do not appear among the symbols 'P_1', 'P_2', and so on. How then can P be a sentence parameter of H_s?

To straighten out these matters we will have to make explicit the conventions used by logicians in talking about formal languages. And this necessitates a full-scale discussion of the use-mention distinction.

In saying that the founder of the Lycaeum was a tutor of Alexander the Great, you *use* a rather roundabout phrase to *mention* Aristotle. A more direct way to do it would be to use the name 'Aristotle', and say that Aristotle was a tutor of Alexander the Great. Whenever we mention a thing we have to use something—usually a phrase or a word, written or spoken—as a name of the other. Now, when we're talking about nonlinguistic things, there is little danger of mixing these things up; we wouldn't be likely to confuse a person John with his name 'John'. But when we do logic, we find ourselves continually talking about expressions, and the danger of confusion is greater. For example, in the sentence

(*i*) John is a word with four letters

the word 'John' is clearly used as a name of itself rather than of a person John; the word is used *autonymously* ("selfnamingly") in this sentence. But the sentence

(*ii*) The first sentence in this chapter contains exactly six words

is *ambiguous*. It's not clear whether the phrase 'The first sentence in this chapter' is used autonymously here (in which case ii would be true) or as a name of the first sentence in this chapter (in which case ii would be false). Now, unless one is careful to distinguish use and mention, object-language and metalanguage, ambiguities of this sort can easily arise in doing logic. For this reason, logicians are often very attentive to policies designed to avoid confusion of use and mention.

It happens that there exists a convention ready-made for this purpose: quotation marks. Thus, example i and the true sense of example ii would more properly be written like this.

(*i'*)   'John' is a word with four letters.

(*ii'*)   'The first sentence in this chapter' contains exactly six words.

Compare also the use of quotation marks in the following pair of sentences.

(*iii*)   Chicago is a city by Lake Michigan.

(*iv*)   'Chicago' is a seven-letter word.

In iii, one speaks of a city by way of its name. Similarly, in iv one speaks of
the name of that city by way of an expression formed with quotation marks.
Thus, in iii, 'Chicago' is used to name the city Chicago, and in iv ' 'Chicago' '
is used to name the word 'Chicago'.

We have already used this device in speaking about S_0 and other formalized
languages; e.g., when we mentioned formulas such as '$(p \supset q)$'. But in one
respect—and in this we follow ordinary practice—we have allowed excep-
tions to this rule. When an expression is *displayed*, rather than appearing in
the text, it is not quoted; thus, above, the sentence iv is mentioned, not used.
We have followed this use of quotation marks carefully, and will continue to
follow it below, even though there isn't much likelihood of confusion arising
from omitting quotes in discussing formalized languages. Often, the formulas
of these languages have no customary use, and it would be clear from context
that they are being mentioned, not used. For instance, expressions such as
'$(p \supset q)$', unlike 'The first sentence in this chapter', have no customary
English use. For this reason, no confusion would have been likely to arise
even if we had neglected to use quotes entirely in Chapters I to IV.

Besides quotation marks, there is another way of talking about expressions
that's especially important for logical purposes. In Section 1, above, we said
that logicians are interested in *general* characteristics of formal systems. Just
as we use quotes to form names of particular expressions (e.g., 'p' and
'$(p \supset q)$') so we need an efficient way of talking about these general characteristics. A long time ago, in I.4, we discovered that plain English isn't very
good for saying general things about the system S_0, and introduced letters
such as 'A' to improve this situation. These variables enable us to express
such things in a more elegant and perspicuous way.

As before, we will use the letters 'A', 'B', 'C', and 'D' to stand for formulas;
in this chapter, for formulas of H_s. Letters such as these are often called
metavariables; in particular, 'A', 'B', and so on are metavariables taking
formulas of H_s as values. Now a variable, roughly speaking, is any symbol
that functions grammatically like a name, but which is allowed to assume
various values for the sake of expressing general propositions. Using numeri-

cal variables 'm' and 'n', for instance, we might say that for all whole numbers m there is a whole number n such that $n = m + 1$. This expresses something general about numbers.

Our use of metavariables should produce no difficulty; everyone who has studied high-school algebra is familiar with variables and can handle them easily. And metavariables are used just like other variables; the only difference is that they occur in some metalanguage and usually take linguistic things as values.

Still another device that we have employed to refer to expressions is the use of names not involving quotation marks. For example, in this chapter 'iii' is a name of the sentence 'Chicago is a city by Lake Michigan'. In other words, iii *is* the sentence 'Chicago is a city by Lake Michigan'. Don't be deceived by this last way of putting it; it's perfectly correct. The only thing that may make it look a bit odd at first is that people aren't very used to names of expressions. Thus, it's easy to feel that 'iii' is used autonymously here, as a name of itself. But this is a mistake; 'iii' is not iii, any more than 'Chicago' is Chicago; iii is a sentence containing seven words, whereas 'iii' is a Roman numeral.

5. Now let's apply these ideas to our metalanguage for H_s. The letters 'P_1', 'P_2', and so on are *names* of the sentence parameters of H_s; they are *used*, not *mentioned*, in characterizing the formulas of this system. Thus, like the numeral 'iii' in the last example, 'P_1' is a name of an expression. Although it's perfectly proper to say that P_1 is a sentence parameter of H_s, this by no means guarantees that 'P_1' is to be found among the sentence parameters of H_s.

Like the metavariable 'A', the name 'P_1' is metalinguistic; this is the reason it is italicized, like 'A'. Unlike 'A', however, 'P_1' is always used to refer to a fixed expression, the first sentence parameter of H_s; 'P_1' is a metalinguistic *constant*. This explains why 'P_1', 'P_2', and 'P_3' weren't quoted in Section 3, above; they were used, not mentioned.

Besides constants such as 'P_1' which name sentence parameters, it's convenient also to have *metavariables* that take sentence parameters of H_s as values; we will use 'P', 'Q', 'R', and 'S' for this purpose. Thus, 'P' may stand for any of the sentence parameters P_1, P_2, and so on. It should now be clear why it is legitimate to say, for instance, 'Let P be a sentence parameter of H_s'; this is exactly like saying 'Let A be a formula of H_s'. Both are proper and correct, though 'P' is not a sentence parameter and 'A' not a formula of H_s.

There is one more point to be settled: what of symbols such as '$\supset$'?

According to the treatment of Chapters I to IV, '$\supset$' is a symbol of the object-language. This means that expressions such as '$A \supset B$' are hybrids, constituted of metalinguistic as well as object-linguistic symbols. Thus, in using '$A \supset B$' to speak of a formula $A \supset B$, 'A' and 'B' are used and '$\supset$' is mentioned. To be systematic in our policies concerning use and mention we must work out an account of these mixed expressions.

Various logicians have solved this problem differently. In his *Mathematical Logic*, W. V. Quine handles it by introducing special quotation marks '$\ulcorner$' and '$\urcorner$'. These *quasi-quotes* are used to indicate that object-linguistic signs such as '$\sim$', '$\supset$', ')', and '(' are mentioned, while metalinguistic signs are used. Thus $\ulcorner \sim A \urcorner$ is an abbreviated way of referring to the formula resulting from placing '$\sim$' before the formula A. According to Quine, then, it would be correct to say that if A is a formula of $\mathbf{H_s}$, then $\ulcorner \sim A \urcorner$ is a formula of $\mathbf{H_s}$.

Alonzo Church, in his *Introduction to Mathematical Logic*, formulates a policy that makes it unnecessary to use special quotation marks. His idea is to make symbols such as '$\sim$' part of the metalanguage as well as the object-language, and to use them autonymously as names of themselves. Thus, for Church, '$\sim$' is *used* as well as mentioned when one speaks of a formula of the sort $\sim A$, and there is no need for quotes. The expression '$\sim A$' is no longer so much of a cross-breed, since both '$\sim$' and 'A' are used in it; but '$\sim$' is used as a name of itself. Church's convention is a very natural and simple one to use and our practice in previous chapters could be justified as a variant of this policy.

But in fact, we will adopt neither Quine's nor Church's approach. Instead, we will go one step further than Church, and follow the more radical usage of H. B. Curry's *Foundations of Mathematical Logic*. In practice, Curry's policy does not differ greatly from Church's, but in theory it is more abstract.

Consider as an example the metalinguistic assertion

(*v*)   If A and B are formulas of $\mathbf{H_s}$, then so is $(A \supset B)$.

Quine would say that '$\supset$' is used, not mentioned in v; Church would say that '$\supset$' is used *and* mentioned. According to Curry, on the other hand, '$\supset$' is used, but need not be mentioned at all in v. Like the symbol 'P_1', '$\supset$' is part of the metalanguage for $\mathbf{H_s}$, and is a *name* of some symbol—not necessarily the symbol '$\supset$'—of the object-language. Curry's idea is to absorb the business of logic into the metalanguage: to make the treatment of logical systems entirely a matter of use. To some extent, this cuts us adrift from the object-language, although we still know everything about it that matters for logical purposes. For instance, we have no notion any more of what '$\supset$' names; its denotation may be 'b' or 'Δ', or perhaps '$\supset$'. It may even be a sound, or the moon. The question "What *are* the formulas and symbols of H_s?" is left completely unanswered.

But really, there isn't any reason why we should expect to be presented with the symbols of H_s. It's possible to learn a great deal about a subject without being handed the objects it studies; what we find, for instance, in a book on Roman history is not Julius Caesar or Augustus in person, but their names and a lot of talk about them. But a closer analogy is found in modern mathematical theories; in the study of whole numbers, the question "What *is* the number two?" is somehow inappropriate. The theory of whole numbers has many realizations and to fasten on only one of them as correct would detract from the generality of the theory. The same applies to logic; in an abstract treatment of logical systems, it's unnecessary to seize on a particular symbolic structure as *the* one that is intended. It is even unnecessarily restrictive to insist that only structures made up of written symbols be realizations of H_s; for instance, H_s might be a sign language or spoken code of some sort.

6. This abstract approach enables us to simplify a number of matters. As an illustration, we will develop in this section a number of conventions regarding the elimination of parentheses.

The definition give in Section 3 of the formulas of H_s has fixed once and for all the number of parentheses which occur in any given formula of that system. But we are free to *talk about* formulas in any way that we find convenient. And since too many parentheses can be awkward and hard to read in names of formulas, it's convenient to have conventions for eliminating them. We must of course be careful that these conventions don't lead to any ambiguity or confusion in our metalanguage.

Our first convention is that outermost parentheses can always be dropped in referring to formulas. Thus, '$P_1 \supset P_1$' and '$A \supset (B \supset A)$' abbreviate '$(P_1 \supset P_1)$' and '$(A \supset (B \supset A))$' and so refer to the formulas $(P_1 \supset P_1)$ and $(A \supset (B \supset A))$, respectively.

A second convention allows us to eliminate parentheses by using dots after the symbol '$\supset$'. A metalinguistic expression containing '$\supset.$' is an abbreviation that is expanded by replacing '$\supset.$' by '$\supset($' and matching the left parenthesis with a right parenthesis placed as far as possible to the right without going through a right parenthesis mated with a left parenthesis to the left of the occurrence of '$\supset.$'. Thus, if there is no ')' to the right of the occurrence of '$\supset.$' mated with a '(' to the left of the occurrence of '$\supset.$', the left parenthesis is matched by a right parenthesis placed to the right of the entire expression. Otherwise, the left parenthesis is matched by a right parenthesis

placed next to the first appearance of ')' to the right of the occurrence of
'⊃.' which is mated with a '(' to the left of the occurrence of '⊃.'.

This is something that gets fussy and complicated when stated generally,
but isn't very difficult to pick up from examples. According to this convention,

$$A \supset . B \supset C$$

abbreviates

$$A \supset (B \supset C),$$

and

$$P \supset . (Q \supset (R \supset P)) \supset \; \sim Q$$

abbreviates

$$P \supset ((Q \supset (R \supset P)) \supset \; \sim Q).$$

In '$(A \supset . B \supset C) \supset D$', however, there are mated parentheses spanning the
occurrence of '⊃.', so this abbreviates '$(A \supset (B \supset C)) \supset D$'. Likewise,

$$((P \supset Q) \supset . \sim Q \supset R) \supset S$$

abbreviates

$$((P \supset Q) \supset (\sim Q \supset R)) \supset S.$$

If there are several occurrences of '⊃.' in a name of a formula, the abbreviation can still be eliminated without ambiguity; it makes no difference in which
order parentheses are restored. For instance,

$$B \supset . C \supset . D \supset B$$

abbreviates

$$B \supset (C \supset (D \supset B))$$

and

$$(A \supset . B \supset C) \supset . A \supset . (B \supset C) \supset \; \sim (A \supset B)$$

abbreviates

$$(A \supset (B \supset C)) \supset (A \supset ((B \supset C) \supset \; \sim (A \supset B))).$$

With a little practice, this dot notation becomes very convenient and easy to
read.

A final convention that we will sometimes employ is that, where use of the
above conventions does not result in an unambiguous name of a formula of

$\mathbf{H_s}$, the missing parentheses are to be restored by grouping at the left. A simple case of this is '$A \supset B \supset C$', which according to this convention abbreviates '$(A \supset B) \supset C$'. Other examples are

$$P \supset Q \supset P \supset P$$

which abbreviates

$$((P \supset Q) \supset P) \supset P$$

and

$$A \supset B \supset B \supset . C \supset A$$

which abbreviates

$$A \supset B \supset B \supset (C \supset A)$$

according to our second convention, and so in turn abbreviates

$$((A \supset B) \supset B) \supset (C \supset A).$$

Also

$$(P \supset (Q \supset R)) \supset ((P \supset Q) \supset (P \supset R))$$

can be written in abbreviated form as

$$(P \supset . Q \supset R) \supset . P \supset Q \supset . P \supset R.$$

Notice that in restoring parentheses to abbreviated names of formulas, '$\sim$' is always taken to apply to the smallest possible grouping: '$\sim A \supset B \supset B$' refers to $(\sim A \supset B) \supset B$, not to $\sim (A \supset B) \supset B$ or to $\sim ((A \supset B) \supset B)$. Thus, our conventions do not allow us to abbreviate a name of a formula by dropping parentheses after a '$\sim$'.

7. As in $\mathbf{S_0}$, proofs in $\mathbf{H_s}$ are generated from axioms by means of rules of inference. Our formulation of these axioms and rules, however, will be simpler than was the case with $\mathbf{S_0}$ in that we will be able to get along without any rule of substitution. This gain in simplicity is offset by the fact that we must then allow *infinitely* many axioms, rather than only three. But in practice this turns out to be no drawback, since the axioms of $\mathbf{H_s}$ fall into three easily recognizable kinds. In fact, these kinds correspond to the axioms of $\mathbf{S_0}$. Any formula of $\mathbf{H_s}$ having one of the following three forms qualifies as an axiom of $\mathbf{H_s}$.

> AS1.　$A \supset . B \supset A$
> AS2.　$(A \supset . B \supset C) \supset . A \supset B \supset . A \supset C$
> AS3.　$\sim A \supset \sim B \supset . B \supset A$

The metalinguistic expressions '$A \supset . B \supset A$', and so forth are called *axiom-schemes* (above, 'AS' stands for 'axiom-scheme'). Each of them determines infinitely many axioms of $\mathbf{H_s}$. For instance, $P_1 \supset . P_2 \supset P_1$, $P_1 \supset . P_1 \supset P_1$, and $\sim P_1 \supset . \sim (P_2 \supset P_3) \supset \sim P_1$ are all formulas of $\mathbf{H_s}$ which have the form $A \supset . B \supset A$, and so each of them is an instance of AS1 and hence an axiom of $\mathbf{H_s}$. And clearly, there is no limit to the number of axioms of this sort.

The only primitive rule of inference of $\mathbf{H_s}$ is *modus ponens*:

$$\frac{A \qquad A \supset B}{B}.$$

Below we will furnish a metalinguistic proof that the rule of substitution is unnecessary. (See M31—i.e., metatheorem 31—in Section 13.) More precisely, what we will show is that the addition of substitution to $\mathbf{H_s}$ as a primitive rule of inference would not yield any new theorems.

The notion of a *proof* in $\mathbf{H_s}$ is sufficiently important to call for a full-scale definition. (Below, 'D1' stands for 'definition 1'.)

D1. A proof in $\mathbf{H_s}$ is an array $A_1, \ldots, A_n$ of formulas of $\mathbf{H_s}$ such that every entry of the array is an axiom of $\mathbf{H_s}$ or follows from previous entries by modus ponens. In other words, for all numbers i such that $1 \leq i \leq n$, A_i is an axiom of $\mathbf{H_s}$, or there exist numbers $j, k < i$ such that A_j is $A_k \supset A_i$. An array $A_1, \ldots, A_n$ which is a proof is said to be a proof of its last entry A_n.

If it isn't at once clear to you that the second sentence of D1 is a reformulation of the condition given in the first sentence, you should pause to verify that this is so. Formulations of this kind are usually convenient when one wants to use a definition in proving some metatheorem, and we will make use of them below.

The following is an example of a proof in $\mathbf{H_s}$ of $P_1 \supset P_1$. Notice, by the way, that our abundance of axioms enables us to do this proof much more economically than, say, the proof of '$p \supset p$' in $\mathbf{S_0}$.

$$(P_1 \supset . P_1 \supset P_1 \supset P_1) \supset . P_1 \supset (P_1 \supset P_1) \supset . P_1 \supset P_1$$
$$P_1 \supset . P_1 \supset P_1 \supset P_1$$
$$(P_1 \supset . P_1 \supset P_1) \supset . P_1 \supset P_1$$
$$P_1 \supset . P_1 \supset P_1$$
$$P_1 \supset P_1$$

(vi)

Notice that AS3 is not used in this proof.

D2. A formula A is provable in $\mathbf{H_s}$ *(or, equivalently, is a theorem of* $\mathbf{H_s}$*) in case there exists a proof of A in* $\mathbf{H_s}$*. It will be convenient to express this symbolically with the aid of a metalinguistic sign* '⊢': *thus* '⊢$_{\mathbf{H_s}}$ A' *means that A is a theorem of* $\mathbf{H_s}$*. In this and the next two chapters, we need not write the subscript* '$\mathbf{H_s}$' *time after time, and will simply omit it.*

In view of vi, we know that $P_1 \supset P_1$ is a theorem of $\mathbf{H_s}$, i.e., that ⊢$P_1 \supset P_1$. We could dignify this fact with the name of *metatheorem* (or theorem of the metalanguage). But this would be foolishly specific, since any substitution instance of $P_1 \supset P_1$ can be proved by the same method as the one used in vi. This can be indicated directly, by means of a so-called *proof-scheme.*

$$(A \supset . A \supset A \supset A) \supset . A \supset (A \supset A) \supset . A \supset A$$
$$A \supset . A \supset A \supset A$$
$$(A \supset . A \supset A) \supset . A \supset A$$
$$A \supset . A \supset A$$
$$A \supset A$$

(vii)

Since the metavariable 'A' can stand for any formula of $\mathbf{H_s}$ whatsoever, the scheme vii shows that any formula of the sort $A \supset A$ is provable in $\mathbf{H_s}$, and so we have a general metatheorem.

M1. ⊢ $A \supset A$.

8. In III.2, we introduced the notion of *hypothetical* reasoning, which proved to be a key idea in formulating $\mathbf{S_\supset}$ and other systems of natural deduction. This idea is also useful in developing the system $\mathbf{H_s}$. We can put it to work by speaking of *deductions* in $\mathbf{H_s}$—arrays like proofs except that hypotheses are allowed in them as well as axioms. To keep track of the hypotheses used in deductions, we will always speak of deductions *from sets of formulas*; in a deduction from a particular set of formulas, only members of that set can be used as hypotheses.

Since in discussing deductions we will be referring frequently to sets of formulas, we'll need some notation or other for talking about such sets. To a large extent, we can use the standard set-theoretic notation discussed in Chapter XIII, Sections 1 to 9. Thus, $\{P, P \supset Q\}$ is the set containing just the formulas P and $P \supset Q$, and $\{A \supset B \mid A$ and B are formulas of $\mathbf{H_s}\}$ is the set of formulas of $\mathbf{H_s}$ having the form $A \supset B$. But it's also convenient to have special metavariables taking sets of formulas as values; for this purpose, we'll use the capital Greek letters 'Γ', 'Δ', 'Θ', and 'Ξ'.

D3. Let Γ be a set of formulas of $\mathbf{H}_s$. An array $A_1, \ldots, A_n$ of formulas of $\mathbf{H}_s$ is a deduction of A_n from hypotheses Γ in case for all i such that $1 \leq i \leq n$, (1) A_i is an axiom of $\mathbf{H}_s$, or (2) A_i is a member of Γ, or (3) for some j, k < i, A_j is $A_k \supset A_i$.

As a simple example, consider the following deduction of P_1 from the set $\{\sim P_1 \supset \sim P_2, P_2\}$.

$$\sim P_1 \supset \sim P_2$$
$$\sim P_1 \supset \sim P_2 \supset . P_2 \supset P_1$$
$$P_2 \supset P_1$$
$$P_2$$
$$P_1$$

(viii)

Example viii shows that P_1 is *deducible* from the set $\{\sim P_1 \supset \sim P_2, P_2\}$ of formulas. Unlike provability, deducibility isn't a property of formulas; it's a relation that holds between sets of formulas and formulas. We will employ the same symbol '$\vdash$' that we used to stand for provability to express the relation of deducibility; '$\Gamma \vdash A$' will mean that A is deducible from the set Γ of formulas. It may seem awkward to give '$\vdash$' these two meanings, but we will show in M2 that provability can be regarded as a special case of deducibility.

D4. A formula A is deducible in $\mathbf{H}_s$ from a set Γ of formulas of $\mathbf{H}_s$ in case there exists a deduction in $\mathbf{H}_s$ of A from Γ. We write '$\Gamma \vdash_{\mathbf{H}_s} A$' to indicate that A is deducible in $\mathbf{H}_s$ from Γ, and as in the case of provability we will omit the subscript in this and the next two chapters.

The proof of M1 consisted in displaying a proof-scheme that was a generalization of the proof given vi. Here, as well, we can generalize the deduction viii to obtain the following *deduction-scheme*.

$$\sim A \supset \sim B$$
$$\sim A \supset \sim B \supset . B \supset A$$
$$B \supset A$$
$$B$$
$$A$$

(ix)

Example ix shows that for all formulas A and B of $\mathbf{H}_s$, $\sim A \supset \sim B, B \vdash A$. (We will often omit curly brackets in our notation for deducibility. There is no danger of ambiguity arising from this practice.)

We now state and prove a metatheorem that shows that deducibility is a generalization of provability; i.e., provability amounts to deducibility from *no* hypotheses. This is so straightforward it hardly requires proof at all, but since it's one of our first metatheorems we will give it special treatment.

M2. ⊢ A if and only if ∅ ⊢ A.

PROOF. As is explained in XIII.7, ∅ is the empty set: the set that contains no members. Suppose first that ⊢ A; this means that there exists a proof $B_1, \ldots, B_n$ of A. But since this array is a proof, no hypotheses are used in it and hence by D3 it is a deduction of A from ∅. But then there is such a deduction, and so ∅ ⊢ A. Conversely, suppose that ∅ ⊢ A; this means there is a deduction $B_1, \ldots, B_n$ of A from ∅. But since ∅ has no members, no hypotheses can be used in this deduction and hence it is a proof of A. Since there is such a proof, A is provable; i.e., ⊢ A.

This metatheorem justifies a certain laxity of notation; below, we will use '⊢ A' interchangeably with '∅ ⊢ A'.

Our next metatheorem expresses an important property of deducibility; the proof of this metatheorem depends on the fact that all deductions in $\mathbf{H_s}$ are finite arrays of formulas. This follows from D1, which says that every proof in $\mathbf{H_s}$ is an array $A_1, \ldots, A_n$ of formulas. Thus every proof will only have some number *n* of steps and so will be finite.

M3. Γ ⊢ A if and only if for some finite subset Δ of Γ, Δ ⊢ A.

PROOF. Suppose first that Γ ⊢ A; then there is a deduction $B_1, \ldots, B_n$ of A from Γ. Now, only finitely many members of Γ can be used in this deduction. In fact, let Γ' be Γ ∩ {$B_1, \ldots, B_n$}; the array $B_1, \ldots, B_n$ is a deduction of A from Γ', and so Γ' ⊢ A. But Γ' is finite; hence, for some finite subset Δ of Γ, Δ ⊢ A. Conversely, suppose that A is deducible from some finite subset Δ of Γ; then there is a deduction $B_1, \ldots, B_n$ of A from Δ. But since every member of Δ is also a member of Γ, $B_1, \ldots, B_n$ is also a deduction of A from Γ, and so Γ ⊢ A.

It may help to clarify the point of M3 if we remark that this metatheorem is trivial if Γ is finite. In that case, if Γ ⊢ A then Γ itself would be a finite subset of Γ such that Γ ⊢ A. The case in which M3 tells us something is the one in which Γ is an *infinite* set of formulas, such as {$P_1, P_2, P_3, \ldots$}. Here, M3 ensures that anything deducible from Γ must be deducible from a finite part of Γ. For instance, it is true that {$P_1, P_2, P_3, \ldots$} ⊢ $\sim P_1 \supset P_2$, and so M3 guarantees that there must be a finite subset Γ of $\{P_1, P_2, P_3, \ldots\}$ such that $\Gamma \vdash \sim P_1 \supset P_2$. And indeed, $\{P_2\}$ is just such a set.

We will now list a number of further important properties of the deducibility relation $\vdash$; their proofs are not difficult, and are left as exercises. You may wish to try them before reading on.

M4. *If* $A \in \Gamma$, *then* $\Gamma \vdash A$.
M5. *If* $\Gamma \vdash A$, *then* $\Gamma \cup \Delta \vdash A$.
M6. *If* $\Gamma \vdash A$ *and* $\Delta \cup \{A\} \vdash B$, *then* $\Gamma \cup \Delta \vdash B$.
M7. *If* $\Gamma \vdash A \supset B$, *then* $\Gamma \cup \{A\} \vdash B$.

When $\vdash$ is thought of as deducibility with regard to informal reasoning, all of these four characteristics make sense. We have in mind situations where we single out a given set of sentences (e.g., the set of sentences believed by a person at a given time, or the set of sentences in *Paradise Lost*), and are interested in those sentences that can be deduced from the sentences of this set, taken together. The analogue of this for a set Γ of formulas of $\mathbf{H}_s$ would be those formulas A such that $\Gamma \vdash A$.

Now, it is reasonable to suppose that (M4) every sentence is deducible from any set of sentences of which it is a member, and that (M5) if every sentence in some set is contained in some larger set, then every sentence deducible from the smaller set is deducible from the larger one. Also (M6) if from one set we can deduce a sentence that together with another set yields a second sentence, then the two sets together should yield both sentences— and, in particular, the second. This is actually a general form of *modus ponens*. Finally (M7), if an implication is deducible from a set, then that set together with the antecedent of the implication should yield the consequent of the implication.

If nothing else, the above paragraph is a material lesson in the usefulness of specialized metalinguistic notation, as opposed to plain prose. Hardly more is said in the above paragraph than in the four lines constituting the statement of M4 to M7, and yet this paragraph is not wordy. There is just no clear way of saying this more briefly, without resorting to some notation or other.

9. This section is devoted to the explanation, proof, and application of a metatheorem about deductions, known as the *deduction theorem*. It will be our first metatheorem calling for a full-scale proof.

In the systems of Chapters III and IV, a deduction of a conclusion from some hypothesis is used to establish the corresponding implication; the hypothesis is discharged, and the implication asserted categorically. We discussed this in detail back in Chapter III. Now, if H_s is to be at all adequate as a characterization of such reasoning, it should have some property corresponding to the rule of implication introduction. We might formulate this property by saying that if $A \vdash B$, then $\vdash A \supset B$: if there is a deduction of B from A, then there is a proof of $A \supset B$. But a more general formulation would allow for other hypotheses besides A—say, a set Γ of them. We arrive in this way at the conjecture that if there is a deduction of B from the set consisting of A together with all the members of Γ, then there is a deduction of $A \supset B$ from Γ. We will state this conjecture as a metatheorem, and then proceed to prove it. A careful analysis of the proof, by the way, would show that all that is needed for this result is the presence of axiom-schemes 1 and 2, and the rule of *modus ponens*.

M8. (*Deduction theorem for* H_s). *If* $\Gamma \cup \{A\} \vdash B$, *then* $\Gamma \vdash A \supset B$.

PROOF. We must show that if there is a deduction of B from $\Gamma \cup \{A\}$, then there is a deduction of $A \supset B$ from Γ. To accomplish this, we will present general instructions for transforming a deduction $C_1, \ldots, C_n$ of B from $\Gamma \cup \{A\}$ into a deduction of $A \supset B$ from Γ.

Let $C_1, \ldots, C_n$ be a deduction of B from $\Gamma \cup \{A\}$. (Note that under these circumstances C_n is the same formula as B.) In the first step of our transformation of $C_1, \ldots, C_n$ into a deduction of $A \supset B$ from Γ, we replace every entry C_i of the array by $A \supset C_i$, thus obtaining the array $A \supset C_1, \ldots, A \supset C_n$. This second array is no longer a deduction, but we now proceed systematically through it, inserting steps according to the set of instructions given below. The resulting array will be a deduction.

Since $C_1, \ldots, C_n$ is a deduction from $\Gamma \cup \{A\}$, we know that for every entry C_i, either (1) C_i is an axiom of H_s; or (2) C_i is a member of $\Gamma \cup \{A\}$; or (3) for some $j, k < i$, C_j is $C_k \supset C_i$. Our instructions for inserting steps in the array $A \supset C_1, \ldots, A \supset C_n$ are divided into parts according to these three cases, as follows.

1. If C_i is an axiom of H_s, insert the following steps before $A \supset C_i$.

$$C_i$$
$$C_i \supset . A \supset C_i$$

2. If C_i is a member of $\Gamma \cup \{A\}$, there are two subcases.
2.1. If C_i is a member of Γ, insert the following steps before $A \supset C_i$.

$$C_i$$
$$C_i \supset . A \supset C_i$$

2.2. If C_i is A, insert the following steps before $A \supset C_i$ (i.e., before $A \supset A$).

$$(A \supset. A \supset A \supset A) \supset. (A \supset. A \supset A) \supset. A \supset A$$
$$A \supset. A \supset A \supset A$$
$$(A \supset. A \supset A) \supset. A \supset A$$
$$A \supset. A \supset A$$

(Notice that in this case we are merely building a copy of example vii.)

3. If for some $j, k < i$, C_j is $C_k \supset C_i$, insert the following steps before $A \supset C_i$.

$$(A \supset. C_k \supset C_i) \supset. A \supset C_k \supset. A \supset C_i$$
$$A \supset C_k \supset. A \supset C_i$$

When we have finished going through $A \supset C_1, \ldots, A \supset C_n$ inserting steps according to the above rules we will obtain a longer array, say $D_1, \ldots, D_m$. Now, we claim that $D_1, \ldots, D_m$ is a deduction of $A \supset B$ from Γ. First, note that D_m is the same formula as $A \supset B$, since D_m is $A \supset C_n$ and C_n is B. Thus, to verify that $D_1, \ldots, D_m$ is a deduction of $A \supset B$ from Γ, we must go back and check that the conditions of D3 are met for each entry D_h of this array; this is accomplished by systematic inspection of cases 1 to 3 above. First, it is clear that if D_h is one of the entries inserted in applying the rules, then D_h is either an axiom of $\mathbf{H_s}$, or a member of Γ, or a consequence by *modus ponens* of previous entries in the array $D_1, \ldots, D_m$. For example, if D_h is inserted according to the instructions given in case 1, then D_h is either an axiom C_i, or else an instance $C_i \supset. A \supset C_i$ of AS1. And similarly in the remaining cases.

This leaves the entries D_h which were not inserted; here, D_h is $A \supset C_i$. Under these circumstances, we know that C_i is an axiom of $\mathbf{H_s}$ (case 1), or a member of $\Gamma \cup \{A\}$ (cases 2.1 and 2.2), or a consequence by *modus ponens* of two previous formulas, $C_k \supset C_i$ and C_k (case 3).

In cases 1 and 2.1, D_h (i.e., $A \supset C_i$) will follow by *modus ponens* from the two preceding steps inserted. In case 2.2, D_h will be $A \supset A$, which again follows by *modus ponens* from the two preceding steps. (Notice that since no hypotheses are inserted here, this case is engineered in such a way that A is discharged as a hypothesis.) And in case 3, D_h will be $A \supset C_i$, where $A \supset. C_k \supset C_i$ and $A \supset C_k$ occur previously in the array $D_1, \ldots, D_m$. But in this case D_h is a consequence by *modus ponens* of the entries $A \supset C_k$ and $A \supset C_k \supset. A \supset C_i$, both of which occur previously.

Thus, the array $D_1, \ldots, D_m$ meets the conditions of D3, and *is* in fact a deduction of D_m from Γ; but D_m is the desired formula, $A \supset B$. Thus, our proof of the metatheorem is complete.

If we are interested in what sorts of things are provable in H_s, M8 is a very useful piece of information. Obviously, it's one thing to assure oneself that a certain action (like driving from Philadelphia to St. Louis in a day) can be done, and another thing to actually do it. Similarly, it's one thing to show that a formula is provable and another to actually produce a proof of the formula. Up to this point, the only way we had of telling that a theorem of H_s is provable was by actually producing a proof (or rather, a metalinguistic scheme standing for a proof), but M8 can assure us of the existence of such proofs without our having to go to this sort of trouble.

As an example, consider any formula of the sort $A \supset B \supset . B \supset C \supset . A \supset C$. M8 tells us that if $A \supset B \vdash B \supset C \supset . A \supset C$, then $\vdash A \supset B \supset . B \supset C \supset . A \supset C$. We are thus led to ask whether in fact $A \supset B \vdash B \supset C \supset . A \supset C$ and successive steps of this sort lead eventually to the question, whether $A \supset B, B \supset C, A \vdash C$.

But it's easy to see how the formula C can be obtained from hypotheses $A \supset B, B \supset C$, and A by means of the rules of H_s. Such a deduction as the following does the job. For convenience, reasons are supplied in this example.

1	$A \supset B$	hyp
2	A	hyp
3	B	1, 2, m p
4	$B \supset C$	hyp
5	C	3, 4, m p

$$(x)$$

This shows that $A \supset B, B \supset C, A \vdash C$, and successive applications of M8 yield the result that $\vdash A \supset B \supset . B \supset C \supset . A \supset C$, as desired. So without ever having seen a proof of $A \supset B \supset . B \supset C \supset . A \supset C$, we have proved the following metatheorem.

$M9.$ $\vdash A \supset B \supset . B \supset C \supset . A \supset C$.

Returning now to M8, it's important to observe that the argument given in the proof of this metatheorem yields a uniform method or recipe for constructing a deduction of B from $\Gamma \cup \{A\}$. If we wished, for instance, we could systematically transform any deduction of the sort given in example x into a proof of $A \supset B \supset . B \supset C \supset . A \supset C$ by means of this method, although, of course, the details of this transformation would be very tedious. But as an illustration of the general strategy, here is a deduction of $A \supset C$ from $\{A \supset B, B \supset C\}$, obtained from example x according to the instructions we gave in proving M8.

	1	$A \supset B$	hyp
	2	$A \supset B \supset . A \supset . A \supset B$	AS1
$A \supset . A \supset B$	3	$A \supset . A \supset B$	1, 2, m p
	4	$(A \supset . A \supset A \supset A) \supset .$	
		$\qquad\qquad (A \supset . A \supset A) \supset . A \supset A)$	AS2
	5	$A \supset . A \supset A \supset A$	AS1
	6	$(A \supset . A \supset A) \supset . A \supset A$	4, 5, m p
	7	$A \supset . A \supset A$	AS1
$A \supset A$	8	$A \supset A$	6, 7, m p
	9	$(A \supset . A \supset B) \supset . A \supset A \supset . A \supset B$	AS2
	10	$A \supset A \supset . A \supset B$	3, 9, m p
$A \supset B$	11	$A \supset B$	8, 10, m p
	12	$B \supset C$	hyp
	13	$B \supset C \supset . A \supset . B \supset C$	AS1
$A \supset . B \supset C$	14	$A \supset . B \supset C$	12, 13, m p
	15	$(A \supset . B \supset C) \supset . A \supset B \supset . A \supset C$	AS2
	16	$A \supset B \supset . A \supset C$	14, 15, m p
$A \supset C$	17	$A \supset C$	11, 16, m p
(xi)		**(xii)**	

The column to the left, xi, is obtained from x by prefixing A as in the proof of M8, and xii is obtained from xi by inserting steps according to the instructions given in that proof. Clearly, xii is not the most economical deduction of $A \supset C$ from $\{A \supset B, B \supset C\}$. Step 11, for instance, is already a hypothesis, but it is obtained in xii by *modus ponens*. But what matters is that it *is* a deduction, and the mechanical method of M8 will always produce such a deduction.

If, by the way, you had any difficulty in following the proof of M8, examples xi and xii may help to make the argument clearer.

Before going on to other matters, we will record a useful corollary of M8, leaving its proof to you.

M10. If $A_1, \ldots, A_n \vdash B$, then $\vdash A_1 \supset . \cdots \supset . A_n \supset B$.

10. This section is devoted to extending our knowledge of the deductions that can be made in $\mathbf{H_s}$. We will have to wade through some tedious detail in obtaining the results of this section, but the metatheorems we have established above will be a great help to us.

M11. If $\Gamma \vdash A \supset B$ and $\Delta \vdash A$, then $\Gamma \cup \Delta \vdash B$.
   PROOF. If there is a deduction of $A \supset B$ from Γ and one of A from Δ, the

result of putting these two deductions together and following them by B will be a deduction of B from $\Gamma \cup \Delta$. (*Note:* there is another proof of this metatheorem, using M6 and M7.)

M12. If $\Gamma \cup \{\sim A\} \vdash \sim B$, *then* $\Gamma \cup \{B\} \vdash A$.

    PROOF. If $\Gamma \cup \{\sim A\} \vdash \sim B$, then by M8 $\Gamma \vdash \sim A \supset \sim B$. But in view of AS3, $\vdash \sim A \supset \sim B \supset. B \supset A$; hence, by M11, $\Gamma \vdash B \supset A$. Thus, by M7, $\Gamma \cup \{B\} \vdash A$.

In proving the following metatheorems we will use a more tabular presentation that should help to make the proofs easier to follow.

M13. $\sim A, A \vdash B$.
    PROOF. 1. $\sim A, \sim B \vdash \sim A$ M4
            2. $\sim A, A \vdash B$ 1, M12

M14. $\sim\sim A \vdash A$.
    PROOF. 1. $\sim\sim A, \sim A \vdash \sim\sim\sim A$ M13
            2. $\sim\sim A \vdash A$ 1, M12

In this last demonstration, step 2 may require some explanation. Written out in full, step 1 is '$\{\sim\sim A, \sim A\} \vdash \sim\sim\sim A$'; using M12, we then see from step 1 that $\{\sim\sim A, \sim\sim A\} \vdash A$. But $\{\sim\sim A, \sim\sim A\}$ (i.e., the set containing just $\sim\sim A$ and $\sim\sim A$) is simply the set $\{\sim\sim A\}$. Thus, we have step 2.

M15. $\sim\sim A, \sim\sim(A \supset \sim A) \vdash \sim\sim\sim A$.
    PROOF. 1. $\sim\sim A \vdash A$ M14
            2. $\sim\sim(A \supset \sim A) \vdash A \supset \sim A$ M14
            3. $\sim\sim A, \sim\sim(A \supset \sim A) \vdash \sim A$ 1, 2, M11
            4. $\sim A, A \vdash \sim\sim\sim A$ M13
             5. $\sim\sim A, \sim A \vdash \sim\sim\sim A$ 1, 4, M6
            6. $\sim\sim A, \sim\sim(A \supset \sim A) \vdash \sim\sim\sim A$ 3, 5, M6

M16. $A \supset B, A \supset \sim B \vdash A \supset \sim A$.
    PROOF. 1. $A \supset B, A \vdash B$ *modus ponens*
            2. $A \supset \sim B, A \vdash \sim B$ *modus ponens*
            3. $\sim B, B \vdash \sim A$ M13
            4. $A \supset B, A, \sim B \vdash \sim A$ 1, 3, M6
            5. $A \supset B, A \supset \sim B, A \vdash \sim A$ 2, 4, M6
            6. $A \supset B, A \supset \sim B \vdash A \supset \sim A$ 5, M8

M17. $A \supset \sim A \vdash \sim A$.

   PROOF. 1. $\sim\sim A, \sim\sim(A \supset \sim A) \vdash \sim\sim\sim A$ M15
            2. $\sim\sim A \vdash \sim(A \supset \sim A)$ 1, M12
            3. $A \supset \sim A \vdash \sim A$ 2, M12

M18. $A \supset B, A \supset \sim B \vdash \sim A$.

   PROOF. 1. $A \supset B, A \supset \sim B \vdash A \supset \sim A$ M16
            2. $A \supset \sim A \vdash \sim A$ M17
            3. $A \supset B, A \supset \sim B \vdash \sim A$ 1, 2, M6

M19. If $\Gamma \vdash \sim\sim A$, then $\Gamma \vdash A$.

   PROOF. 1. $\Gamma \vdash \sim\sim A$ assumption
            2. $\sim\sim A \vdash A$ M14
            3. $\Gamma \vdash A$ 1, 2, M6

M20. If $\Gamma \cup \{A\} \vdash B$ and $\Gamma \cup \{A\} \vdash \sim B$, then $\Gamma \vdash \sim A$.

   PROOF. 1. $\Gamma \cup \{A\} \vdash B$ assumption
            2. $\Gamma \vdash A \supset B$ 1, M8
            3. $A \supset B, A \supset \sim B \vdash \sim A$ M18
            4. $\Gamma \cup \{A \supset \sim B\} \vdash \sim A$ 2, 3, M6
            5. $\Gamma \cup \{A\} \vdash \sim B$ assumption
            6. $\Gamma \vdash A \supset \sim B$ 5, M8
            7. $\Gamma \vdash \sim A$ 4, 6, M6

11. Back in Section 2 when we defined the formulas of H_s, it may have seemed to you that our definition narrowed somewhat the logical horizons that had opened in Chapter IV. The system H_s has only two connectives— negation and implication—as compared with the five of S_s. But as it turns out, the poverty of H_s is only apparent. In fact, we will show in this section that all the connectives that figure in S_s can be obtained in H_s by means of *definitions*.

Logicians differ in their policies concerning definition; the one to which we will subscribe in defining new connectives of H_s is perhaps the simplest of these. Rather than regarding defined connectives as new symbols introduced in the object-language by rules of definition, we regard them as abbreviative conventions made in our metalanguage. From our point of view, then, definitions make no change in the formulas of H_s, only in our way of talking about them. In this regard they are just like the abbreviations for eliminating parentheses which we discussed in Section 6, above. What we will do in defining, say, the connective $\vee$ is to find a complex formula $f(A, B)$ of H_s depending on A and B, which will serve as a good definition of $\vee$. (Here, 'f' stands for an unspecified way of constructing a complex formula out of A and B; for instance, $A \supset. B \supset \sim A$ or $\sim(A \supset B)$.) Until we get to Chapter VI, we will not be able to give a really satisfactory account of what a good definition is. But we at least do know how disjunction behaves in S_s, and the definition chosen below of $\vee$ does in fact behave in H_s just as disjunction behaves in S_s.

In D5 and later definitions, '$=_{df}$' stands for 'is by definition'.

D5. '$A \vee B$' $=_{df}$ '$A \supset B \supset B$'.

According to D5, whenever an expression of our metalanguage contains a part such as '$A \vee B$', this part will be replaceable without change of meaning by '$A \supset B \supset B$'. Thus, $(A \vee B) \supset B \supset C$ is the formula $A \supset B \supset B \supset B \supset C$, and $(\sim A \vee B) \supset (A \vee (B \vee A))$ is the formula $\sim A \supset B \supset B \supset. A \supset (B \vee A) \supset (B \vee A)$, which in turn is $\sim A \supset B \supset B \supset. A \supset (B \supset A \supset A) \supset (B \supset A \supset A)$. By the same token, when we say that $\vdash A \vee \sim A$, we mean that $\vdash A \supset \sim A \supset \sim A$, which can be shown using M17 and M8; this, then, shows that $\vdash A \vee \sim A$.

We want to define conjunction and equivalence as well; this is done in the following two definitions.

D6. '$A \wedge B$' $=_{df}$ '$\sim(A \supset \sim B)$'.
D7. '$A \equiv B$' $=_{df}$ '$(A \supset B) \wedge (B \supset A)$'.

In order to see what a formula such as $(A \equiv B) \equiv C$ amounts to in terms of implication and negation, we must use both D7 and D6. D7 tells us that

$$(A \equiv B) \equiv C$$

is

$$((A \supset B) \wedge (B \supset A)) \equiv C$$

which is

$$(((A \supset B) \wedge (B \supset A)) \supset C) \wedge (C \supset ((A \supset B) \wedge (B \supset A))).$$

D6 now tells us that this in turn is

$$(\sim(A \supset B \supset \sim(B \supset A)) \supset C) \wedge (C \supset \sim(A \supset B \supset \sim(B \supset A))).$$

Finally, another application of D6 yields

$$\sim(\sim(A \supset B \supset \sim(B \supset A)) \supset C \supset \sim(C \supset \sim(A \supset B \supset \sim(B \supset A)))).$$

As this example shows, D5 to D7 allow us to talk about some rather complex formulas much more briefly, inasmuch as '$(A \equiv B) \equiv C$' is much shorter than its unabbreviated equivalent.

12. To a certain extent our choice of the above definitions was arbitrary, but we could not have chosen just any definitions. For instance, '$B \supset B \supset \sim A$' would be wholly inappropriate as a definition of '$A \lor B$'. (We take it for granted here that the symbol '$\lor$' is to have something to do with disjunction as it is ordinarily understood.) This means that our task isn't ended once we have laid down definitions D5 to D7. We must go on to show somehow that they are appropriate. In order to accomplish this we will prove in this section some metatheorems which show in effect that the connectives $\lor$, $\land$, and $\equiv$, as defined above, satisfy analogues in $\mathbf{H_s}$ of the introduction and elimination rules of $\mathbf{S_s}$. For instance, we will show that if $\Gamma \vdash A$ and $\Gamma \vdash B$, then $\Gamma \vdash A \land B$, and that if $\Gamma \vdash A \land B$, then $\Gamma \vdash A$ and $\Gamma \vdash B$. These correspond to the rules of conjunction introduction and conjunction elimination of $\mathbf{S_s}$. Our first metatheorems accomplish this for disjunction.

M21. If $\Gamma \vdash A$ then $\Gamma \vdash A \lor B$; and if $\Gamma \vdash B$ then $\Gamma \vdash A \lor B$.
   PROOF. 1. $\Gamma \vdash A$ assumption

2. $A, A \supset B \vdash B$	*modus ponens*
3. $\Gamma \cup \{A \supset B\} \vdash B$	1, 2, M6
4. $\Gamma \vdash A \supset B \supset B$	3, M8
5. $\Gamma \vdash A \lor B$	4, D5

1. $\Gamma \vdash B$	assumption
2. $\Gamma \cup \{A \supset B\} \vdash B$	1, M5
3. $\Gamma \vdash A \supset B \supset B$	2, M8
4. $\Gamma \vdash A \lor B$	3, D5

M22. If $\Gamma \vdash A \lor B$ and $\Gamma \cup \{A\} \vdash C$ and $\Gamma \cup \{B\} \vdash C$, then $\Gamma \vdash C$.

	PROOF.	
	1. $\Gamma \cup \{A\} \vdash C$	assumption
	2. $\Gamma \cup \{\sim C, A\} \vdash C$	1, M5
	3. $\Gamma \cup \{\sim C, A\} \vdash \sim C$	M4
	4. $\Gamma \cup \{\sim C\} \vdash \sim A$	2, 3, M20
	5. $\sim A, A \vdash B$	M13
	6. $\sim A \vdash A \supset B$	5, M8
	7. $\Gamma \vdash A \lor B$	assumption
	8. $\Gamma \vdash A \supset B \supset B$	7, D5
	9. $\Gamma \cup \{\sim A\} \vdash B$	6, 8, M11
	10. $\Gamma \cup \{\sim C\} \vdash B$	4, 9, M6
	11. $\Gamma \cup \{B\} \vdash C$	assumption
	12. $\Gamma \cup \{\sim C\} \vdash C$	10, 11, M6
	13. $\Gamma \cup \{\sim C\} \vdash \sim C$	M4
	14. $\Gamma \vdash \sim\sim C$	12, 13, M20
	15. $\Gamma \vdash C$	14, M19

M23. If $\Gamma \vdash A$ and $\Gamma \vdash B$, then $\Gamma \vdash A \wedge B$.
   PROOF. 1. $\Gamma \vdash A$
        2. $A, A \supset \sim B \vdash \sim B$
        3. $\Gamma \cup \{A \supset \sim B\} \vdash \sim B$
        4. $\Gamma \vdash B$
        5. $\Gamma \cup \{A \supset \sim B\} \vdash B$
        6. $\Gamma \vdash \sim(A \supset \sim B)$
        7. $\Gamma \vdash A \wedge B$

Filling in reasons in the above proof is left as an exercise, as are the entire proofs of M24 to M26, below.

M24. If $\Gamma \vdash A \wedge B$, then $\Gamma \vdash A$ and $\Gamma \vdash B$.
M25. If $\Gamma \cup \{A\} \vdash B$ and $\Gamma \cup \{B\} \vdash A$, then $\Gamma \vdash A \equiv B$.
M26. If $\Gamma \vdash A \equiv B$ and $\Gamma \vdash A$, then $\Gamma \vdash B$; and if $\Gamma \vdash A \equiv B$ and $\Gamma \vdash B$, then $\Gamma \vdash A$.

13. Among the more important characteristics of $\mathbf{H_s}$ which have not yet been established are admissible rules of *replacement of equals by equals* and of *substitution*. It is the business of this section to demonstrate that $\mathbf{H_s}$ has these characteristics.

An error that beginners sometimes make in working with the system $\mathbf{S_s}$ illustrates what we mean by 'replacement by equals'. Given a step in a derivation—say, $B \vee \sim\sim A$—containing a part $\sim\sim A$, they will proceed to infer $B \vee A$, giving in justification of this step the rule of negation elimination. This is a mistake, because the rule of negation elimination applies only when the *entire premiss* has the form $\sim\sim C$; but in this case, the premiss is a disjunction. The correct way to obtain $B \vee A$ from $B \vee \sim\sim A$ in $\mathbf{S_s}$ is by disjunction elimination, as follows.

1	$B \vee \sim\sim A$	hyp
2	B	hyp
3	$B \vee A$	2, dis int
4	$\sim\sim A$	hyp
5	A	4, neg elim
6	$B \vee A$	5, dis int
7	$B \vee A$	1, 2–3, 4–6, dis elim

Now, perhaps the reason why inferring $B \lor A$ directly from $B \lor \sim\sim A$ is an attractive mistake is that we know A and $\sim\sim A$ to be provably equivalent in S_s: $A \equiv \sim\sim A$ is categorically derivable in that system. And under these circumstances it's natural to feel that the formulas A and $\sim\sim A$ should be interchangeable without affecting derivability. The mistake comes only when one supposes that this is a *primitive* rather than a *derived* rule of S_s, passing directly to the conclusion $B \lor A$ without filling in the intervening steps.

Applying these ideas to H_s, we arrive at the thought that if $\vdash A \equiv B$ and $\vdash C$, then any formula gotten by replacing A by B in C should also be provable in H_s. For instance, if $\vdash A \equiv \sim\sim A$ and $\vdash D \supset A$, then $\vdash D \supset \sim\sim A$.

Before trying to show that this is so, it would be a good idea to obtain a clearer formulation of what is meant by 'a result of replacing A by B in C'. Now, when we say that A is in C, we mean that the formula A is a constituent or *subformula* of C, as, for instance, A is a subformula of $B \supset \sim A$. One way of defining this notion is to say that A is a subformula of C if A is a formula and is to be found among those consecutive strings of symbols which are parts of C. But a more useful characterization is one that employs the inductive technique that was used in the first place to define the formulas of H_s.

D8. 1. *A is a subformula of A.*
     2. *If $B \supset C$ is a subformula of A, then both B and C are subformulas of A.*
     3. *If $\sim B$ is a subformula of A, then B is a subformula of A.*

A string of symbols of H_s qualifies as a subformula of A only if it can be shown to be a subformula of A by repeated applications of 1, 2, and 3. Note, by the way, that according to D8 every formula is a subformula of itself.

Let's take an example to illustrate how D8 works. Referring back to the column of formulas on p. 55, above, we'll use D8 to show that $(Q \supset Q)$ is a subformula of $\sim\sim(\sim P \supset \sim((Q \supset Q) \supset (\sim R \supset P)))$. First, clause 1 of D8 tells us that $\sim\sim(\sim P \supset \sim((Q \supset Q) \supset (\sim R \supset P)))$ (i.e., step 12) is a subformula of itself. Clause 3 then shows that step 11 is a subformula of step 12, and again that step 10 is a subformula of step 12. Clause 2 shows that step 8 is a subformula of step 12, and clause 3 shows that step 7 is a subformula of step 12. Finally, clause 2 shows that step 6 (i.e., $(Q \supset Q)$) is a subformula of step 12.

This example should make it clear that D8 works just like the inductive definition of the formulas of H_s, only backwards.

Similarly, we can give an inductive definition of the notion of a result of replacing A in C by B. Here, it's important to realize that there can be many such results, since A can occur as a subformula at more than one place in C.

Thus, all three of the formulas $\sim(B \supset A \supset D)$, $\sim(A \supset B \supset D)$, and $\sim(B \supset B \supset D)$ are results of replacing A in $\sim(A \supset A \supset D)$ by B. A result of replacing A by B in C is accordingly a result of replacing any number of occurrences of A in C by B. We will understand this in such a way that zero is allowed as such a number. Since the result of replacing no occurrences of A in C by B is just C, C itself is always a result of replacing A in C by B. This allows for *vacuous* replacements, and these permit us to speak meaningfully of the result (namely, C) of replacing A in C by B even when A is not a subformula of C. The definition is as follows.

D9. 1. *If A is (the same formula as) C, then both C and B are results of replacing A by B in C.*
2. *If A is not (the same formula as) $C \supset D$, then if C' is a result of replacing A by B in C, and D' a result of replacing A by B in D, then $C' \supset D'$ is a result of replacing A by B in $C \supset D$.*
3. *If A is not (the same formula as) $\sim C$, then if C' is a result of replacing A by B in C, then $\sim C'$ is a result of replacing A by B in $\sim C$.*
4. *If A is not (the same formula as) P, then P is a result of replacing A by B in P.*

A string of symbols of $\mathbf{H_s}$ qualifies as a result of replacing A by B in C only if it can be shown to be such a result by repeated applications of clauses 1, 2, 3, and 4 of D9.

Armed with D9, we can return to the problem of showing that if $\vdash A \equiv B$ and $\vdash C$ and C' is a result of replacing A by B in C, then $\vdash C'$. It frequently happens that when one wishes to show something, the easiest and most straightforward way to do it is to prove something stronger and then obtain the desired result as a corollary. In the present case, what we will first show is M29. M27 and M28 are two minor metatheorems required in the demonstration of M29; their proofs are left as exercises.

M27. $A \equiv B, C \equiv D \vdash (A \supset C) \equiv (B \supset D)$.
M28. $A \equiv B \vdash \sim A \equiv \sim B$.

M29. *For all formulas C of $\mathbf{H_s}$, if C' is any result of replacing A by B in C, then $A \equiv B \vdash C \equiv C'$.*

proof. Our proof proceeds by induction on the complexity of C. This means that we will first establish that if C is a sentence parameter, then $A \equiv B \vdash C \equiv C'$ for all results C' of replacing A by B in C. Then we will let C be an arbitrary complex formula and assume, for all formulas D shorter than C, that $A \equiv B \vdash D \equiv D'$ for any result D' of replacing A by B in D; we will then show under this assumption that $A \equiv B \vdash C \equiv C'$ for any result C' of replacing A by B in C. The theorem will then follow by the principle of induction. (For discussion of this principle, see Chapter XIV.)

First, suppose that C is a sentence parameter P. Then by D9, either (1) C' is P or (2) A is P and C' is B. In case 1, since by M4 $P \vdash P$, we have $\vdash P \equiv P$ by M25. Hence, by M5, $A \equiv B \vdash P \equiv P$; i.e., $A \equiv B \vdash C \equiv C'$. In case 2, by M4, $P \equiv B \vdash P \equiv B$; i.e., $A \equiv B \vdash C \equiv C'$. This completes the *basis step* of the induction.

Now, for the *inductive step*, assume that C is not a sentence parameter and make the following hypothesis of induction: for all D shorter than C, $A \equiv B \vdash D \equiv D'$ for any result D' of replacing A by B in D. We know that either (1) C is an implication $C_1 \supset C_2$ or (2) C is a negation $\sim D$. In case 1, D9 guarantees that either (1.1) C' is C; or (1.2) A is C and C' is B; or (1.3) C' is $C_1' \supset C_2'$, where C_1' is a result of replacing A by B in C_1 and C_2' a result of replacing A by B in C_2. Cases 1.1 and 1.2 are just like cases 1 and 2 of the basis step. In case 1.3, we know that C_1 and C_2 are both shorter than C; hence, the hypothesis of induction ensures that $A \equiv B \vdash C_1 \equiv C_1'$ and $A \equiv B \vdash C_2 \equiv C_2'$. Now, by M27, $C_1' \equiv C_1'$, $C_2 \equiv C_2' \vdash (C_1 \supset C_2) \equiv (C_1' \supset C_2')$; i.e., $C_1 \equiv C_1'$, $C_2 \equiv C_2'$, $\vdash C \equiv C'$. Using M6, then, we first obtain $A \equiv B$, $C_2 \equiv C_2' \vdash C \equiv C'$ and then $A \equiv B \vdash C \equiv C'$, as desired.

In case 2, D9 guarantees that either (2.1) C' is C; or (2.2) A is C and C' is B; or (2.3) C' is $\sim D'$, where D' is a result of replacing A by B in D. Again, cases 2.1 and 2.2 are like cases 1 and 2 of the basis step. In case 2.3, we know that D is shorter than C; hence, the hypothesis of induction ensures that $A \equiv B \vdash D \equiv D'$. Now, by M28, $D \equiv D' \vdash \sim D \equiv \sim D'$; i.e., $D \equiv D' \vdash C \equiv C'$. Using M6, we then have $A \equiv B \vdash C \equiv C'$, as desired.

This completes the inductive step, and so M29 is proved.

M30. *If* $\Gamma \vdash C$ *and* $\Gamma \vdash A \equiv B$, *and* C' *is a result of replacing* A *by* B *in* C, *then* $\Gamma \vdash C'$.

Given M29, the proof of M30 is straightforward; it is left as an exercise.

Although we've been acquainted with the notion of substitution ever since Chapter I, we will now have to demonstrate a metatheorem that involves this concept. For this reason it is necessary to write down a rigorous definition of the result of substituting A for P in B. Again, the definition is inductive with respect to the complexity of B.

D10. 1. *If B is a sentence parameter, the result of substituting A for P in B is A in case P is the same sentence parameter as B, and is B otherwise.*
   2. *If B is C ⊃ D, the result of substituting A for P in B is C' ⊃ D', where C' is the result of substituting A for P in C and D' the result of substituting A for P in D.*
   3. *If B is ~C, the result of substituting A for P in B is ~C' where C' is the result of substituting A for P in C.*

A string of symbols of H_s qualifies as the result of substituting A for P in B only if it can be shown to be so by applications of rules 1 to 3.

You will recall that the rule of substitution permits one to infer A' from A, where for some sentence parameter P, A' is the result of substituting B for P in A. We will now show that this rule, when applied to theorems of H_s, yields only theorems of H_s.

M31. If ⊢ A, and A' is the result of substituting B for P in A, then ⊢ A'.

PROOF. Suppose that ⊢ A; then there is a proof of A. We will use induction on the number of steps in a proof of A with minimal length.

First, if this length is 1, A is an axiom of H_s. But in that case, clearly A' is also an axiom of the same sort. For example, if A has the form $C ⊃. D ⊃ C$, then A' has the form $C' ⊃. D' ⊃ C'$. This completes the basis step.

Assume the following hypothesis of induction: for all formulas C, if C has a proof with fewer than n steps, and C' is the result of substituting B for P in C, then ⊢ C'. Let A have a proof of length n, and let A' be the result of substituting B for P in A. If A is an axiom of H_s, then by the argument of the basis case, ⊢ A'. If A follows by *modus ponens* from two previous steps D and $D ⊃ A$, then both these steps have proofs of length less than n, and so by the hypothesis of induction ⊢ D' and ⊢ $(D ⊃ A)'$, where D' and $(D ⊃ A)'$ are the results, respectively, of substituting B for P in D and in $D ⊃ A$. But by clause 2 of D10, $(D ⊃ A)'$ is $D' ⊃ A'$. Hence, by *modus ponens*, ⊢ A', as desired.

We have presented this proof in such detail here because it's our first example of an induction on length of proof. This is a commonly used technique, and a working acquaintance with it is desirable. In practice, there is no reason to go to the trouble of mentioning explicitly the length of proofs. One can look instead at such inductions as resting on the following principle: if all the axioms of a system have a certain property, and if whenever the premisses of a primitive rule of inference of the system have the property then the conclusion does, then every theorem of the system has the property. In the above argument, then, all we really needed to show was that all substitution instances of axioms $\mathbf{H_s}$ are theorems of $\mathbf{H_s}$, and that if all substitution instances of D and of $D \supset A$ are theorems of $\mathbf{H_s}$, then all substitution instances of A are theorems of $\mathbf{H_s}$.

Finally there is still another, more pictorial way to prove M31. This is to notice that any result of substituting B for P throughout a proof in $\mathbf{H_s}$ is still a proof in $\mathbf{H_s}$.

14. M31 shows that the addition of substitution to $\mathbf{H_s}$ as a primitive rule would not increase the theorems of the system. This feature of substitution is sometimes expressed by saying that it is an *admissible* rule of $\mathbf{H_s}$. (See E14, below.)

It is important to bear in mind, however, that substitution does *not* correspond to deductions which can be carried out in $\mathbf{H_s}$. This is shown by the fact that, whereas the inference

$$\frac{P}{\sim P}$$

is an instance of substitution, we certainly do not want $\sim P$ to be *deducible* from P; we want to reject the claim that $P \vdash \sim P$.

One reason for hoping that $\sim P$ isn't deducible from $\{P\}$ in $\mathbf{H_s}$ is that $\sim P$ is clearly not a logical consequence of P, and $\mathbf{H_s}$ is supposed to be a system of logic. We have to take it on faith that it isn't the case that $P \vdash \sim P$, since we don't yet have a way of proving that this is so. But at least we can use meta-theorems we have already proved to show that if $\sim P$ is derivable in $\mathbf{H_s}$ from $\{P\}$, then any formula whatsoever is provable in $\mathbf{H_s}$. For, suppose that $P \vdash \sim P$. By M8 we would have $\vdash P \supset \sim P$, and so by M31, $\vdash P \supset P \supset \sim (P \supset P)$. Since $\vdash P \supset P$, we would have both $\vdash P \supset P$ and $\vdash \sim (P \supset P)$. But in view of M13, $P \supset P$, $\sim (P \supset P) \vdash A$ for all formulas A of $\mathbf{H_s}$. So it follows by M6 that $\vdash A$ for all formulas A of $\mathbf{H_s}$. On the basis of this argument, we know at least that something would be very wrong indeed with $\mathbf{H_s}$ if it were the case that $P \vdash \sim P$.

Contrast this situation with the rule of replacement: from $A \equiv B$ and C to infer C', where C' is any result of replacing A by B in C. M30 shows that the rule of replacement is admissible in $\mathbf{H_s}$; the rule does not lead us out of the theorems of $\mathbf{H_s}$. But we also showed something more than this: M29 guarantees that $A \equiv B$, $C \vdash C'$, where C' is any result of replacing A by B in C. (See E14(d).)

In contrast with the rule of substitution, then, replacement turns out to be sanctioned by deductions of H_s as a correct form of inference. That is, the conclusion of any instance of the rule of replacement is deducible in H_s from the premisses of that instance. Rules of this sort are said to be *derived rules* of H_s; substitution is an admissible but not a derived rule of H_s, whereas replacement is both an admissible and a derived rule of H_s.

Since it's important to grasp the difference between admissible and derived rules, let's discuss this difference between substitution and replacement from a different point of view. The only reason why substitution is an admissible rule of H_s is that H_s is a system of logic. In such a system, the sentence parameters are allowed to stand for any indicative sentence whatsoever, including logically complex sentences. It follows that any substitution instance of a logical truth is also a logical truth. For instance, let B be any formula and P be any sentence parameter. If A is a logical truth involving P, and A' is the result of substituting B for P in A, then A' can't fail to be a logical truth, because this failure of a special case of A would show A not to be a logical truth. Since H_s is intended to capture truths of logic as its theorems, it is reasonable to expect that substitution is an admissible rule of H_s. And this expectation is borne out by M31.

Although the above reasoning shows why substitution should be an admissible rule of H_s, this reasoning does not carry over to deducibility. That is, it does not lead us to expect that if A' is the result of substituting B for P in A, then $A \vdash A'$. For instance, there is no reason to think that those formulas deducible from $\{P\}$ are all truths of logic, and hence no reason to think that the rule of substitution will yield only such formulas when applied to them.

Let's recapitulate. The rule of substitution works when applied to theorems of H_s, yielding conclusions which in this case also are theorems of H_s. (This is what is meant by saying it is admissible.) But this is no guarantee that what it does to nontheorems corresponds to any reasonable inference. In the case of substitution, this is just what happens with premisses such as P; it is not the case that $P \vdash {\sim}P$. Thus, substitution is an admissible but not a derived rule of H_s. On the other hand, replacement is not only an admissible rule of H_s, it is a derived rule. Most of the rules that we have discussed in connection with H_s are likewise derived rules of that system. For instance, since $A \supset B$, $A \vdash B$, *modus ponens* is a derived rule of H_s. For a more precise account of the notions discussed in this section, see E14 below.

15. Our treatment of deducibility in H_s enables us to give an account of the notion of *consistency*. First, it's important to realize that consistency is a quality that is properly ascribed to *sets* of sentences rather than to sentences themselves. When we tell someone that what he has said is inconsistent (i.e., when we deny that what he's said is consistent) we usually don't mean that it is inconsistent when taken by itself. Instead we mean that it's inconsistent when taken together with what he has said previously, and perhaps with other things assumed without question to be true. This is what happens, for instance, when a witness gives inconsistent evidence in court; in the course of giving evidence he says something that contradicts the body of testimony he has given previously.

In seeking to define consistency for sets of formulas of H_s it's easier to attend first to the opposite notion of inconsistency. The set of formulas $\{P, \sim P\}$ is a paradigm example of an inconsistent set; a particularly overt contradiction is exhibited between its members. However, we would also want to say that a set such as $\{P \supset Q, P, \sim Q\}$ is inconsistent even though none of its members is the negation of any other of its members. The inconsistency of this set is evident from the fact that we can deduce a contradiction from it in H_s: both $P \supset Q, P, \sim Q \vdash Q$ and $P \supset Q, P, \sim Q \vdash \sim Q$.

This suggests that we should define consistency in such a way that a set Γ of formulas of H_s is inconsistent if and only if a contradiction is deducible from it: i.e., if and only if for some formula A of H_s, $\Gamma \vdash A$ and $\Gamma \vdash \sim A$. In view of the fact that a contradiction is deducible from a set of formulas if and only if *every* formula of H_s is deducible from that set, there is a particularly simple way to make the definition. We can say that a set Γ is consistent if some formula isn't deducible from it; the consistent sets are those from which not everything is deducible.

D11. A set Γ of formulas of H_s is consistent (in H_s) if there is some formula A of H_s such that not $\Gamma \vdash A$. A set of formulas is said to be inconsistent if it is not consistent.

We can now prove as a metatheorem our claim that a set of formulas is inconsistent if and only if some formula and its negation are deducible from it.

M32. A set Γ of formulas of H_s is inconsistent if and only if for some formula A of H_s, $\Gamma \vdash A$ and $\Gamma \vdash \sim A$.
    PROOF. If Γ is inconsistent then $\Gamma \vdash B$ for all B so that in particular $\Gamma \vdash P$ and $\Gamma \vdash \sim P$. Suppose, on the other hand, that for some A, $\Gamma \vdash A$ and $\Gamma \vdash \sim A$. By M13, $A, \sim A \vdash B$ for all formulas B of H_s and so by M6, $\Gamma \vdash B$ for all formulas B of H_s; i.e., Γ is inconsistent. This proves the metatheorem.

Proving the following metatheorems about consistency is left as an exercise; the proof of M33 relies on M3.

M33. A set Γ *of formulas of* $\mathbf{H_s}$ *is consistent if and only if every finite subset of* Γ *is consistent.*

M34. $\Gamma \vdash A$ *if and only if* $\Gamma \cup \{\sim A\}$ *is inconsistent.*

M35. If Γ *is consistent, then for all formulas A of* $\mathbf{H_s}$, *either* $\Gamma \cup \{A\}$ *is consistent or* $\Gamma \cup \{\sim A\}$ *is consistent.*

If we like, we can say that a formula A of $\mathbf{H_s}$ is inconsistent if the set $\{A\}$ is inconsistent. It then turns out (E15(b)) that a formula A is inconsistent if and only if $\vdash \sim A$.

16. So far, we have dealt with two systems that purport to be formulations of the logic of implication and negation: $\mathbf{H_s}$ and $\mathbf{S_{\supset \sim}}$. Now clearly, these are very different systems, and yet it would be a strange thing if they turned out to sanction different arguments as logically correct.

In this, the final section of this chapter, we turn our attention to showing that in a sense of 'equivalence' to be made precise later, these systems are equivalent to one another. This will be our first really *intersystematic* discussion, since the metatheorems below will apply to both systems at once. Our previous metatheorems had to do only with $\mathbf{H_s}$.

Before proceeding any further, it will be a good precaution to return a moment to use and mention. This time, the problem is that $\mathbf{S_{\supset \sim}}$ was formulated before we had become self-conscious about our use of quotation marks and metavariables. Rather than being presented abstractly as the symbols of $\mathbf{H_s}$ were, via noncommital names of them, the symbols of $\mathbf{S_{\supset \sim}}$ were displayed and spoken about by means of quotation marks.

The most convenient way to eliminate the awkwardness that would result from having to speak of $\mathbf{S_{\supset \sim}}$ in one way and $\mathbf{H_s}$ in another is simply to reformulate $\mathbf{S_{\supset \sim}}$ so that its symbols and formulas are precisely those of $\mathbf{H_s}$. From here on, then, we will suppose that the definition of the formulas of $\mathbf{S_{\supset \sim}}$ is that given on p. 55, above. The deductive structure of $\mathbf{S_{\supset \sim}}$—the subordinate derivation framework of reiteration, and the four rules of implication and negation introduction and elimination—remain unchanged.

We can now say that the *formulas* of $\mathbf{S_{\supset \sim}}$ and $\mathbf{H_s}$ are the same: any formula of $\mathbf{S_{\supset \sim}}$ is a formula of $\mathbf{H_s}$, and conversely any formula of $\mathbf{H_s}$ is a formula of $\mathbf{S_{\supset \sim}}$. But of course, this isn't enough to show the two systems equivalent in any interesting sense. What we want to know is that any deduction that can be carried out in $\mathbf{H_s}$ corresponds to a derivation that can be carried out in $\mathbf{S_{\supset \sim}}$, and conversely that every derivation in $\mathbf{S_{\supset \sim}}$ corresponds to a deduction in $\mathbf{H_s}$. Let's write '$A_1, \ldots, A_n \vdash_{S_{\supset \sim}} B$' to mean that there is a derivation in

$S_{\supset\sim}$ of B from hypotheses $A_1, \ldots, A_n$. Thus if, for example, $A, B \vdash_{S_{\supset\sim}} C$, then there is some way to fill in the middle of

$$
\begin{array}{c|c}
 & A \\
 & B \\
 & \vdots \\
 & C
\end{array}
$$

so that the result is a derivation in $S_{\supset\sim}$. Our problem then reduces to two parts: to show that if $A_1, \ldots, A_n \vdash B$, then $A_1, \ldots, A_n \vdash_{S_{\supset\sim}} B$, and to show that if $A_1, \ldots, A_n \vdash_{S_{\supset\sim}} B$, then $A_1, \ldots, A_n \vdash B$.

The first of these parts is the easier, so we'll tackle it first. In order to show that if $A_1, \ldots, A_n \vdash B$ then $A_1, \ldots, A_n \vdash_{S_{\supset\sim}} B$, we will first show something apparently not so strong: that if there is a proof in H_s of a formula B, then there is a categorical derivation of B in $S_{\supset\sim}$.

M36. If $\vdash B$ then $\vdash_{S_{\supset\sim}} B$.

PROOF. We use the same technique that was employed in the proof of M31; thus, all we need to show is that if A is an axiom of H_s then A is derivable categorically in $S_{\supset\sim}$, and that if A and $A \supset B$ are derivable categorically in $S_{\supset\sim}$ then so is B.

But it's an easy matter to show that if A is an axiom of H_s then $\vdash_{S_{\supset\sim}} A$. For instance, if A is an instance of AS1, then A has the form $B \supset. C \supset B$; and the following derivation scheme shows it is derivable categorically in $S_{\supset\sim}$.

$$
\begin{array}{c|l}
 & B \\
 & \quad \begin{array}{c|c} & C \\ & B \end{array} \\
 & \quad C \supset B \\
\hline
 & B \supset. C \supset B
\end{array}
$$

And if there is a categorical derivation of A in $S_{\supset\sim}$, and another of $A \supset B$ in $S_{\supset\sim}$, we merely have to put these two derivations together in tandem and follow them by B, in order to get a categorical derivation of B.

We now know that any theorem of H_s is derivable categorically in $S_{\supset\sim}$. Let's go on to get a general result about deductions from this.

M37. If $A_1, \ldots, A_n \vdash B$ then $A_1, \ldots, A_n \vdash_{S_{\supset\sim}} B$.

PROOF. Suppose $A_1, A_2, \ldots, A_n \vdash B$; then by M10, $\vdash A_1 \supset. A_2 \supset. \cdots \supset.$

$A_n \supset B$. Applying M36, we know that $\vdash_{S_{\supset \sim}} A_1 \supset. A_2 \supset. \cdots \supset. A_n \supset B$; this means that there is a categorical derivation of $A_1 \supset. A_2 \supset. \cdots \supset.$ $A_n \supset B$ in $S_{\supset \sim}$. Coining a piece of notation, let's use '$\mathfrak{A}$' to stand for this derivation. Then the following will stand for a derivation of B from $A_1, A_2, \ldots, A_n$ in $S_{\supset \sim}$.

$$
\begin{array}{|l}
A_1 \\
A_2 \\
\vdots \\
\underline{A_n} \\
\mathfrak{A} \\
A_2 \supset. \cdots \supset. A_n \supset B \\
\vdots \\
A_n \supset B \\
B
\end{array}
$$

Thus, there is a derivation of B from $A_1, A_2, \ldots, A_n$ in $S_{\supset \sim}$; i.e., $A_1, A_2, \ldots,$ $A_n \vdash_{S_{\supset \sim}} B$, as desired.

To establish the converse of M37, we have to resort to a more roundabout reasoning. We will use an inductive argument in which a derivation is gradually transformed, by taking out one subordinated derivation after another, into a deduction in H_s. Since this construction forces us to deal with intermediate steps in the process as well as the terminal ones, we must consider hybrid arrays in which the axioms of H_s may be used, as well as the rules of $S_{\supset \sim}$.

We will say, then, that an *augmented derivation* (in $S_{\supset \sim}$) is an array like a derivation in $S_{\supset \sim}$, except that any axiom of H_s may be introduced anywhere in it. The following, for example, schematizes an augmented derivation.

$$
\begin{array}{|l}
\quad \underline{A} \\
\qquad \begin{array}{|l} \underline{\sim A} \\ \sim B \supset \sim A \supset. A \supset B \\ \sim A \supset. \sim B \supset \sim A \\ \sim B \supset \sim A \\ A \supset B \\ A \\ B \end{array} \\
\quad \sim A \supset B \\
A \supset. \sim A \supset B
\end{array}
$$

$$(\textit{xiii})$$

Notice that in this example the axioms of H_s have been used in such a way that only two hypotheses need to be made in xiii; without using any axioms, three would be needed. The idea of our argument below is that this procedure can be carried out systematically, in such a way as to eliminate *all* hypotheses.

M38. If there is an augmented derivation (in $S_{\supset \sim}$) of B from $A_1, \ldots, A_n$, then $A_1, \ldots, A_n \vdash B$.

PROOF. Suppose that there is an augmented derivation of B from $A_1, \ldots, A_n$. In the event that this augmented derivation contains any subordinated derivations (i.e., any derivations in which hypotheses are made), there will be at least one *innermost* such derivation—one to which no derivations are subordinated. This situation can be pictured as follows.

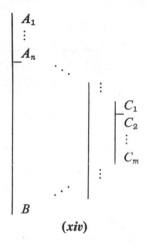

(*xiv*)

Here, $C_1, C_2, \ldots, C_m$ are the successive steps of a particular innermost derivation.

We will now outline a procedure for transforming the augmented derivation presented in xiv into an augmented derivation in which the innermost subordinated derivation

$$
\begin{array}{|l}
C_1 \\
C_2 \\
\vdots \\
C_m
\end{array}
$$

(*xv*)

has been eliminated.

The first step is to erase the line demarcating the derivation to be eliminated, and to prefix C_1 to each of the entries of this derivation; this transforms xiv into the following array.

$$
\begin{array}{l}
A_1 \\
\;\vdots \\
A_n
\end{array}
$$

$$
\begin{array}{l}
\vdots \\
C_1 \supset C_1 \\
C_1 \supset C_2 \\
\;\;\vdots \\
C_1 \supset C_m \\
\vdots
\end{array}
$$

(xvi)

Then, formulas are inserted as they are in our proof of the deduction theorem. More precisely, the step $C_1 \supset C_1$ is treated as in case 2.2 of our proof of M8; if C_i was justified by reit in xiv, steps are inserted as in case 2.1 of that proof; and if C_i was justified by *modus ponens* in xiv, it is treated as in case 3. Since xv has no derivation subordinate to it, none of its steps can be justified by an introduction rule and there is one remaining possibility: C_i may have been justified by negation elimination. In that case, a deduction in $\mathbf{H_s}$ of C_i from $\sim\sim C_i$ is to be inserted above C_i. (The existence of such a deduction is guaranteed by M14.)

The result of applying the procedure to the array presented in xv will be an augmented derivation, but one of a special sort: each of its steps will be an axiom of $\mathbf{H_s}$, or be justified by *modus ponens* or reiteration. Thus, the entire array obtained from the augmented derivation displayed in xiv will itself be an augmented derivation.

Clearly, this procedure can be applied repeatedly as long as there are subordinated derivations remaining to be eliminated. If we do this, eventually we will get an augmented derivation of B from $A_1, \ldots, A_n$ that looks like this.

$$
\begin{array}{l}
A_1 \\
\;\vdots \\
A_n \\
D_1 \\
\;\vdots \\
D_k \\
B
\end{array}
$$

(xvii)

The augmented derivation given by xvii contains no subordinated derivations, and hence no introduction rules are used in it. (This is true of $S_{\supset \sim}$ because the introduction rules for both $\supset$ and $\sim$ require subordinated derivations.) There may be uses of negation elimination, however, in xvii; these can be replaced by deductions of D_i from $\sim \sim D_i$, which, being deductions, use only axioms of H_s and *modus ponens*.

After this has been done, we obtain an array in which $A_1, \ldots, A_n$ are the only hypotheses made. Every other step is an axiom of H_s or a consequence by *modus ponens* of previous steps. In other words, the result is a *deduction* in H_s of C from $A_1, \ldots, A_n$.

Thus, $A_1, \ldots, A_n \vdash B$, as desired. The proof of M38 is now finished.

From M38 it is easy to get the converse of M37. Suppose that $A_1, \ldots, A_n \vdash_{S_{\supset \sim}} B$; i.e., suppose that there is a derivation in $S_{\supset \sim}$ of B from $A_1, \ldots, A_n$. This derivation is itself an augmented derivation, though one in which no axioms of H_s are used. Hence, by M38, we know that $A_1, \ldots, A_n \vdash B$. Thus, we have the following metatheorem.

M39. If $A_1, \ldots, A_n \vdash_{S_{\supset \sim}} B$, then $A_1, \ldots, A_n \vdash B$.

Finally, putting together M37 and M39, we have a metatheorem establishing the equivalence of H_s and $S_{\supset \sim}$.

M40. $A_1, \ldots, A_n \vdash B$ if and only if $A_1, \ldots, A_n \vdash_{S_{\supset \sim}} B$.

Reflecting on M40, you may wonder what is the point of having two systems at all. In H_s, we obtain as theorems precisely those formulas that are derivable in $S_{\supset \sim}$. So, especially since $S_{\supset \sim}$ is simpler and more natural to use, why should we bother with H_s?

But there are various kinds of simplicity, and which is best on a given occasion can depend on what we want to do with a system. $S_{\supset \sim}$ is indeed close to the way we actually reason and is by far the better of the two systems for finding derivations or for evaluating arguments in natural language. On the other hand, H_s is simpler in that it is formulated more economically. It has only one rule of inference and three axiom-schemes, and its deductions involve no nesting, being linear arrays of formulas. Thus H_s can be set up more succinctly than $S_{\supset \sim}$. By the same token, it often is easier to prove metatheorems about H_s than about $S_{\supset \sim}$, and it is chiefly for this reason that when we began to concentrate on the metatheoretic aspects of logic we also directed our attention to H_s.

Besides Hilbert-style or axiomatic systems like H_s and natural deduction systems like $S_{\supset\sim}$, there are many other sorts of systems that have been devised by logicians, many of them with special advantages of their own. And since there are many different things one might want of a system of logic, this is probably a good thing; it provides a flexibility that we would not otherwise have.

Exercises

1. What does it mean to say that A is the same as B, where 'A' and 'B' are meta-variables taking formulas of H_s as values? (The best answer would be an inductive definition.)

2. Insert quotes into the following text (*Through the Looking-Glass*, Chapter VIII).

> You are sad, the Knight said in an anxious tone: let me sing you a song to comfort you. Is it very long? Alice asked, for she had heard a great deal of poetry that day. It's long, said the Knight, but it's *very very* beautiful. Everybody that hears me sing it—either it brings the *tears* into their eyes or else—Or else what? said Alice, for the Knight had made a sudden pause. Or else it doesn't you know. The name of the song is called Haddock's Eyes. Oh, that's the name of the song, is it? Alice said, trying to feel interested. No, you don't understand, the Knight said, looking a little vexed. That's what the name of the song is *called*. The name really is The Aged Aged Man. Then I ought to have said That's what the song is called? Alice corrected herself. No, you oughtn't: that's quite another thing! The *song* is called Ways and Means: but that's only what it's called, you know! Well, what *is* the song, then? Said Alice, who by this time was completely bewildered. I was coming to that, the Knight said. The song really *is* A-sitting on a Gate: and the tune's my own invention.

3. Insert quotes in the following paragraph:
   We use $\{P, P \supset Q\} \vdash Q$ to say that there is a deduction of Q from hypotheses P and $P \supset Q$. This deduction will be an array $A_1, \ldots, A_n$ of formulas; in particular, $P, P \supset Q, Q$ is such an array. P can only take as values the sentence parameters of H_s; however, the result of putting A and B, which represent arbitrary formulas, for P and Q in $P, P \supset Q, Q$ will represent a deduction. Hence, we know that $\{A, A \supset B\} \vdash B$ for all formulas A and B of H_s.

4. Is $P_1 \vee P_2$ a formula of H_s? What about '$P_1 \vee P_2$'?

5. Restore parentheses to the following abbreviations.

   (a) $P \supset P \supset Q$
   (b) $(P \supset. Q \supset P) \supset. P \supset. \sim P \supset Q$

(c) $P \supset P \supset . P \supset P$

(d) $A \supset . B \supset A$

(e) $\sim (A \supset B) \supset A \supset \sim A \supset . A \supset B$

(f) $\sim P \supset Q$

6. Rewrite the following, eliminating all uses of '$\vee$', '$\wedge$', or '$\equiv$'.

(a) $(A \vee B) \supset . \sim A \supset B$

(b) $A \supset (A \vee B)$

(c) $(A \vee B) \supset (B \vee A)$

(d) $(A \wedge B) \supset A$

(e) $A \supset . B \supset (A \wedge B)$

(f) $(\sim A \vee \sim B) \supset \sim (A \wedge B)$

(g) $A \equiv \sim A$

(h) $(A \equiv B) \supset (\sim A \equiv \sim B)$

7. Extend the language of $\mathbf{H}_s$ to include disjunction. Give an inductive definition of the formulas of the extended language, and find axiom-schemes which make it possible to prove theorems appropriate for disjunction. What is the difference between this and *defining* disjunction, as we did in Section 11?

8. Produce derivations in $\mathbf{H}_s$ establishing the following statements.

(a) $\vdash P_1 \supset . P_1 \supset P_1 \supset . P_1 \supset P_1$

(b) $\vdash \sim P_1 \supset . P_1 \supset P_2$

(c) $\vdash P_1 \supset P_2 \supset . P_3 \supset P_1 \supset . P_3 \supset P_2$

(d) $\vdash P_1 \supset P_2 \supset . P_2 \supset P_3 \supset . P_1 \supset P_3$

(e) $P_1 \supset . P_1 \supset P_2, P_1 \vdash P_2$

(f) $P_1 \supset . P_1 \supset P_2 \vdash P_1 \supset P_2$

(g) $P_1 \supset \sim (P_2 \supset P_2) \vdash \sim P_1$

(h) $P_1 \vdash \sim \sim P_1$

(i) $\sim \sim \sim P_1 \vdash \sim P_1$

(j) $P_1 \supset . P_2 \supset \sim P_3, P_1, P_3 \vdash \sim P_2$

9. Demonstrate the following metatheorems (in each case, you may use any results established before the metatheorem in question).

(a) M4   (b) M5

(c) M6   (d) M7

(e) M10   (f) M24

(g) M25   (h) M26

(i) M27   (j) M28

(k) M30   (l) M33

(m) M34   (n) M35

10. Could a formula be an instance of both AS1 and AS2? If so, find an example; if not, show that such a formula is impossible.

11. Show that every subformula of a formula of H_s is a formula of H_s. (*Hint:* use an inductive argument.)

12. Using only M4 and M8, demonstrate the following metatheorems.

   (a) $\vdash A \supset . B \supset A$ (b) $\vdash A \supset A$
   (c) $\vdash A \supset . C \supset . B \supset C$ (d) $\vdash A \supset . B \supset B$

13. Using any metatheorem in the text (except M38, M39, and M40), establish the following.

   (a) $A \supset B \vdash \sim B \supset \sim A$ (b) $A \vdash \sim \sim A$
   (c) $\sim A \supset A \vdash A$ (d) $A \supset B, \sim A \supset B \vdash B$
   (e) $A \vee B \vdash B \vee A$ (f) $\vdash \sim A \vee A$
   (g) $A \supset B, \sim A \supset \sim B \vdash A \equiv B$ (h) $\vdash \sim (A \wedge \sim A)$
   (i) $A \wedge A \vdash A$ (j) $\sim (A \wedge B), A \vdash A \wedge \sim B$
   (k) $\sim (A \equiv B) \vdash A \equiv \sim B$ (l) $A \equiv B, \sim A \vdash \sim B$

14. In this exercise we will clarify what is meant by an *inference* and a *rule* of the system H_s. By an inference of H_s, we mean an ordered pair $\langle \Gamma, A \rangle$ where Γ is a set of formulas and A a formula of H_s. Γ is the set of *premises* and A is the *conclusion* of this inference. Thus, in the inference $\langle \{P \supset Q, P\}, Q \rangle$, Q is inferred from the premises $P \supset Q$ and P. This inference is an instance of *modus ponens*.

   A rule is a general way of passing from premises to conclusion. We will therefore understand by a rule of H_s a set of inferences of H_s. Those inferences which are members of a rule $\mathcal{R}$ are the *instances* of $\mathcal{R}$. The rule *modus ponens*, for instance, is the set $\{\langle \{A \supset B, A\}, B \rangle \mid A \text{ and } B \text{ are formulas of } H_s\}$ of inferences. This conception of a rule is so general that we can look at axiom-schemes as rules of a special sort: rules whose instances have empty premises and so are inferences of the form $\langle \varnothing, A \rangle$.

   To say that $\mathcal{R}$ is a rule of H_s is not to say that $\mathcal{R}$ is correct or valid in any way. For instance, the rule $\{\langle \{A\}, B \rangle \mid A \text{ and } B \text{ are formulas of } H_s\}$, "from anything to infer anything", is not a rule that is reasonable in any sense; nevertheless, it is a rule of H_s. We can, however, talk about *primitive, admissible*, and *derived* rules of H_s. The rule *modus ponens* is the only primitive rule of H_s, unless the three axiom-schemes are also counted as primitive rules. A rule $\mathcal{R}$ is an *admissible rule* of H_s if $\vdash A$ whenever $\langle \Gamma, A \rangle \in \mathcal{R}$ and for all $B \in \Gamma$, $\vdash B$. Thus, $\mathcal{R}$ is admissible to H_s if its addition to H_s as a primitive rule would not increase the theorems of H_s. A rule $\mathcal{R}$ is a *derived rule of H_s* if $\Gamma \vdash A$ whenever $\langle \Gamma, A \rangle \in \mathcal{R}$.

   The following are exercises involving these notions.

   (a) Show that if a rule is derivable in H_s then it is admissible in H_s.
   (b) Show that the rule $\{\langle \{A\}, B \rangle \mid A \text{ is a sentence parameter}\}$ is admissible in H_s.

(c) The empty set $\varnothing$ is a rule of $\mathbf{H_s}$. Show that it is a derived rule of $\mathbf{H_s}$.

(d) Show that the rule $\{\langle\{C,\ A \equiv B\},\ C'\rangle\ /\ C'$ is a result of replacing A by B in $C\}$ is a derived rule of $\mathbf{H_s}$. (Use M29 and M26.)

15. Prove the following.

(a) Γ is consistent if and only if it is not the case that $\Gamma \vdash P_1 \wedge \sim P_1$.

(b) $\{A\}$ is inconsistent if and only if $\vdash \sim A$.

16. Using M8 and M11, prove M6.

17. Say that $A \simeq B$ if $\vdash A \equiv B$. Show that $\simeq$ is an equivalence relation: i.e., that $A \simeq A$, if $A \simeq B$ then $B \simeq A$, and if $A \simeq B$ and $B \simeq C$ then $A \simeq C$.

18. Say that A and B are *synonymous* in $\mathbf{H_s}$ if replacement of A by B never affects provability; i.e., if whenever C' is a result of replacing A by B in C, then $\vdash C$ if and only if $\vdash C'$. Show that A and B are synonymous in $\mathbf{H_s}$ if and only if $\vdash A \equiv B$.

19. Let $\mathbf{H_s}^1$ be like $\mathbf{H_s}$, except that AS2 is replaced by the following schemes.

$$A \supset B \supset . B \supset C \supset . A \supset C$$
$$(A \supset . A \supset B) \supset . A \supset B$$

Show that $\mathbf{H_s}^1$ is equivalent to $\mathbf{H_s}$.

20. Let $\mathbf{H_s}^2$ be like $\mathbf{H_s}$ except that AS3 is replaced by the following three schemes.

$$(A \supset \sim A) \supset \sim A$$
$$A \supset . \sim A \supset B$$
$$A \supset B \supset A \supset A$$

Show that $\mathbf{H_s}^2$ is equivalent to $\mathbf{H_s}$.

21. Extend $\mathbf{H_s}$ by adding a further symbol $\wedge$ and stipulating that if A and B are formulas, then so is $(A \wedge B)$. Define a system $\mathbf{H_s}^3$ for this larger set of formulas by devising suitable axiom-schemes. Then (a) show that $\mathbf{H_s}^3$ is a *conservative extension* of $\mathbf{H_s}$; i.e., show that if A is a formula of $\mathbf{H_s}$, then $\vdash A$ if $\vdash_{\mathbf{H_s}^3} A$. (b) Using M40, go on to show that $\mathbf{H_s}^3$ is equivalent to $\mathbf{S}_{\supset \sim \wedge}$.

Problems

1. Where X and Y are strings of symbols, we say that XY is the result of *concatenating* X and Y. In order to make our treatment of $\mathbf{H_s}$ fully abstract and rigorous, we would have to make explicit the assumptions we have been making about concatenation. State some of these assumptions, and use them to show that if $A \supset B$ is $C \supset D$, then A is C and B is D, and that $A \supset \sim B$ is different from $A \supset . C \supset D$.

2. Devise an axiomatic system $H_\supset$ (with *modus ponens* its only primitive rule of inference) which is equivalent to $S_\supset$. Carry through the proof of equivalence.
3. Isolate the properties of H_s that are used in proving M29.
4. Let $S_{Q_1 \cdots Q_n}^{B_1 \cdots B_n} A \mid$ be the result of *simultaneously substituting* $B_1, \ldots, B_n$ for the respective parameters $Q_1, \ldots, Q_n$ in A. Define (in a manner analogous to D10) this notion of substitution. Then show that if $\vdash A$, then $\vdash S_{Q_1 \cdots Q_n}^{B_1 \cdots B_n} A \mid$. Try to find an argument that uses M31. Does this argument work for S_0?
5. Using 39, M4, M8, M11, M19, and M20, devise a proof of M35 simpler than the one given in the text. (*Hint:* consider the proof of M22, and note its relation to a derivation in $S_{\supset \sim}$. Then state this relation generally.)
6. If the axiom-scheme

$$A \supset A$$

were to be added to H_s, it would be *redundant*, since any instance of it is already provable in H_s. Is any one of the three axiom schemes of H_s redundant?

VI Sentence Logic:

Semantics

1. Up to this point we have made no direct use in our metatheory of the idea that language should be *about* something. In view of the fact that natural languages and mathematical notations are all used to say things (and this is surely their most important function), we should correct this neglect.

We have, of course, been careful to show how portions of English can be translated into our formal systems, and in Chapters III and IV we used this connection with natural language to justify our choice of primitive rules for S_s. This justification, however, wasn't something that we *proved*, as metatheorems were proved in Chapter V. Instead, it took place on an entirely different level. The relationship of formal to natural language is rather like the relationship of geometry to surveying practices; one establishes this relation by acquiring some theoretical knowledge of geometry and some practical knowledge of surveying, and then connecting the two. Thus, one doesn't prove in geometry that the sum of the angles of this page is 360°; this is an *applied* piece of information that springs from imposing Euclidean theory on a body of practices involving measurement, pattern recognition, and the like.

Now, the point of all this is the following. If in our discussion of how $\mathbf{H_s}$ is to be interpreted we are to maintain the standards of rigor set in the previous chapter, we shouldn't simply return to what we did in Chapter III. What we must do is to draw the "aboutness" relation up to the level of theory, so that we will have a definition of what $\mathbf{H_s}$ is about that is fully as rigorous as our definition of $\mathbf{H_s}$ itself. In this way we will obtain a *semantic* theory of our formal languages, one that treats both the languages and their "aboutness".

In general, semantic and *syntactic* theories of language are distinguished by the fact that the latter do not include an account of how things may be said with language, whereas the former do. The theory of Chapter V was syntactic, and the notions of *formula*, *proof*, *theorem*, *deduction*, *deducibility*, and *consistency* are syntactic concepts. Semantic methods have been refined in recent years to a high state of development, and include some of the most powerful and useful techniques to be found in modern logic. Like their syntactic counterparts, these semantic theories employ mathematical methods and concepts; frequently, however, these are more advanced (and sometimes, more problematic) than those used for syntactic purposes.

2. Let's launch our semantic discussion informally, with an account of truth-tables. The idea behind this technique is simply that sentence parameters stand for sentences that may be *true* or *false* in some given situation. Since, for instance, we can think of sentence parameters standing for true sentences as true, this leads us to think of the sentence parameters themselves as being either true or false. Having gone this far, we then ask what will be the truth-values of complex formulas which are made up of these parameters.

Some cases of this general question are not at all hard to settle. For instance, if P is true then $\sim P$ will be false, and if P is false, then $\sim P$ will be true. This seems to accord well with our intuitive conception of truth and falsity. Implications, though, are a bit more difficult. Suppose that we have a formula $P \supset Q$; how will its truth-value depend on the truth-values of P and Q? Well, surely $P \supset Q$ will be *false* in case P is true and Q false; there seems to be no question about this.

But the remaining three cases (P true and Q true, P false and Q true, and P false and Q false) are still unsettled. In facing up to this question we must decide what to do with examples such as the following.

> If Tucson is a city, then there is no largest even number.
> If there is a largest even number, then Tucson is a city.
> If there is a largest even number, then Tucson is a vegetable.

Such examples do not come up often in everyday specimens of reasoning, and most people encountering them for the first time would be puzzled as to their truth-values. Some might want to say that they are false or non-sensical.

But on the other hand, one *can* find examples of implications of each of these three kinds which almost anyone would want to call true. Here are some.

If there is no largest even number, then there is no largest number.

If 5 is the largest even number, then 7 is not an even number.

If 5 is the largest even number, then 6 is not an even number.

In view of these, it certainly seems as if we must *sometimes* make $P \supset Q$ true in each of these three cases. But, if we must do this *sometimes*, systematic considerations suggest that we ought to do it every time, in each of these cases.

There are several reasons that can be given in support of this claim. One of the most important of these is suggested by the inductive techniques that we developed in Chapter V. There we dealt with notions like the result of substituting A for P in B, which for complex formulas B depends on the result of substituting A for P in the component formulas of B. This leads us to be guided in our semantic theory by the *principle of truth-functionality*: the truth-value of a complex formula is completely determined by the truth-values of the simpler formulas that constitute it. This principle is the fundamental assumption on which the method of truth-tables rests. We could not compute the truth-values of formulas as we do below without relying on the principle of truth-functionality.

If we were to deny the principle of truth-functionality for formulas of the sort $P \supset Q$, we would have to say, for instance, that $P \supset Q$ is sometimes true and sometimes false when P is false and Q is false. This would force us to say that the truth-value of $P \supset Q$ depends on something besides the truth-values of P and Q. Whatever we decide this additional factor is, we would have to bring it into our semantic theory. And however we do this, we are bound to end up with a theory more complicated than one that depends on the principle of truth-functionality. This argument doesn't show that it would be foolish and misguided to deny the principle of truth-functionality, but it does indicate that it's a good idea to begin the study of logical semantics by accepting this principle.

Finally, we may note that the assumption that $P \supset Q$ is always true in case P is false or Q is true does no harm, at least in the following sense. A true implication can never allow us to infer a false conclusion by *modus ponens* from true premisses. The reason for this is that whenever $P \supset Q$ and P are both true, then Q is true, since we've already agreed to make $P \supset Q$ false in case P is true and Q false.

We can summarize the results of this discussion in tabular form as follows.

P	$\sim P$
T	F
F	T

(i)

P	Q	$P \supset Q$
T	T	T
T	F	F
F	T	T
F	F	T

(ii)

Table i gives the rule (or function) that determines the truth-value of $\sim P$ in terms of the truth-value of P. And table ii in the same way gives the function for determining the truth-value of $P \supset Q$ in terms of the truth-values of P and of Q.

3. Since P and Q are sentence parameters, what holds for them in i and ii will hold generally for *any* formulas of $\mathbf{H_s}$; for instance, we know that if $Q \supset R$ is true and $\sim P$ true, then $Q \supset R \supset \sim P$ is true. Thus, we can express i and ii more generally in the following schematic form.

A	$\sim A$
T	F
F	T

(iii)

A	B	$A \supset B$
T	T	T
T	F	F
F	T	T
F	F	T

(iv)

The rules of truth-valuation given by iii and iv are general enough to determine a unique truth-value for any formula of $\mathbf{H_s}$, given the truth-values of its constituent sentence parameters. For example, suppose P, Q, and R are assigned the truth-values T, F, and F, respectively, and consider the formula $\sim(P \supset Q) \supset \sim\sim Q \supset. P \supset R$. Since P takes T and Q takes F, $P \supset Q$ takes F (here, we use rule iv, letting A be P and B be Q). Since $P \supset Q$ takes F, $\sim(P \supset Q)$ takes T. Since Q takes F, $\sim Q$ takes T, and since $\sim Q$ takes T, $\sim\sim Q$ takes F. Proceeding in this way, we see that the truth-value of the whole formula is T. This procedure of successively determining the truth-values of larger and larger parts of the formula can be set out as follows.

$$\sim (P \supset Q) \supset \sim \sim Q \supset . P \supset R$$
$$\text{T} \quad \text{TF F} \quad \text{F FT FT} \quad \text{TF F}$$

(v)

Here, the truth-values given to P, Q, and R are written under them, and the truth-values given to complex subformulas are written under their principal connectives. (The principal connective of a formula $\sim C$ is the occurrence of $\sim$ to the left of C; the principal connective of a formula $C \supset D$ is the occurrence of $\supset$ between C and D.)

As another example, consider $\sim P \supset Q \supset Q$, where P is given the value T and Q the value F.

$$\sim P \supset Q \supset Q$$
$$\text{F TT FF F}$$

(vi)

The value given to this formula will be F, as shown in vi.

4. Examples such as v and vi illustrate how one can determine the truth-value taken by formulas in a given situation; e.g., in vi, the truth-value of $\sim P \supset Q \supset Q$ is computed for the case in which P is true and Q false. In other circumstances, $\sim P \supset Q \supset Q$ might take different truth-values. For instance, if P is true and Q true, it will be true. It is a common practice to display all these various outcomes in tables resembling i and ii; the following is an example.

P	Q		$\sim P \supset Q \supset Q$		
T	T		F	T	T
T	F		F	T	F
F	T		T	T	T
F	F		T	F	T

(vii)

In this *truth-table* for $\sim P \supset Q \supset Q$, all the various possible assignments of truth-values to P and Q appear to the left; the resultant values appear to the right. The table shows how the formula behaves truth-functionally; it is false if and only if P is true and Q is false. (In other words, it behaves just like $P \supset Q$.)

If we consider a formula in which three sentence parameters occur, we'll have to reckon with eight possible assignments of truth-values. The following

is an example of a truth-table for such a formula, showing only the resultant
value for the whole formula.

P	Q	R	$\sim(P \supset \sim R \supset . \sim(R \supset Q))$
T	T	T	F
T	T	F	T
T	F	T	F
T	F	F	T
F	T	T	T
F	T	F	T
F	F	T	F
F	F	F	T

(*viii*)

Where we have exactly one sentence parameter in a formula, the number of
rows in its truth-table will be two; where there are two parameters, it will be
four; where there are three, eight. In general, n sentence parameters will
require 2^n rows. If we wished to make a truth-table for a formula having ten
parameters, we would need 1024 rows!

5. When a natural language is used to say true or false things, it is *situations*
that make its sentences true or false. For instance, the sentence 'I was in
Rome yesterday' is not true or false until some situation is specified which
determines who is uttering the sentence and when. It is true if he was in Rome
the previous day, and false otherwise.

In the semantics of sentence logic we are only interested in what truth-
values situations give to sentence parameters. For this reason, we will think
of a situation as something that determines the truth-values of the sentence
parameters of a formula, and does nothing else. The truth-value of the formula
in a situation can then be calculated using rules iii and iv.

Now, consider an example such as the following.

P	Q	$P \supset \sim Q \supset . Q \supset \sim P$
T	T	T
T	F	T
F	T	T
F	F	T

(*ix*)

The table shows that $P \supset \sim Q \supset . Q \supset \sim P$ is true in all situations, so that this formula cannot be false under any circumstances. Let's call such formulas *valid*.

The only way a formula $A \supset B$ can be invalid is for A to be true when B is false. For this reason, where there are many implication signs in a formula, it's often easier to show it valid by showing that its antecedent is false whenever its consequent is false. Thus, in example ix, if $Q \supset \sim P$ is false, P must be true and Q true. But in that case, $P \supset \sim Q$ is false. Hence, $P \supset \sim Q$ cannot be true when $Q \supset \sim P$ is false, so $P \supset \sim Q \supset. Q \supset \sim P$ is valid. The validity of $P \supset \sim Q \supset. Q \supset \sim P$ is thus shown by the following table.

$$P \supset \sim Q \supset. Q \supset \sim P$$
$$\text{T F F T T T F F T}$$

$$(x)$$

6. Now let's redo the above material and put it into more rigorous form. Our idea is to take the notions of being true in some situation and of being true in all situations and to define them in a way that will be appropriate for proving metatheorems about them.

First we should deal with the process of assigning truth-values to parameters. Here, we must ask ourselves how many parameters need to be given values in a situation; all of them, or just some? If we say that only some parameters need to be assigned truth-values, we will have to admit that some formulas are made neither true nor false by an assignment of truth-values; these will be the formulas containing parameters without truth-values. On the other hand, in examples such as ix, above, we only bothered to assign truth-values to the parameters occurring in the formulas under consideration. It would be awkward to have to assign values to all the other parameters of $\mathbf{H_s}$ (infinitely many of them) just to determine the truth-value taken by $P \supset \sim Q \supset. Q \supset \sim P$ under an assignment.

In order to get around this difficulty we will reformulate the system $\mathbf{H_s}$, stepping once more to a higher level of generality. Instead of considering one specific *vocabulary* (i.e., the class of formulas built out of one set of sentence parameters), we will allow the deductive framework of $\mathbf{H_s}$ to be imposed on an arbitrary vocabulary. To carry out this generalization, we introduce the notion of a *morphology* for $\mathbf{H_s}$. A morphology is simply a nonempty set $\mathbf{M}$ of sentence parameters, and may be finite or infinite. Given such a morphology, the formation rules of $\mathbf{H_s}$ will determine a unique set of formulas; these will be the formulas made up of parameters drawn from $\mathbf{M}$. We can then speak of *valuations* as assigning truth-values to each parameter in a morphology $\mathbf{M}$, and it will turn out that every valuation of a morphology $\mathbf{M}$ makes every formula of **M** either true or false. Let's record definitions of these notions.

*D1. A morphology **M** for **H**$_s$ is a nonempty set of objects called sentence parameters. The notions of formula of **M**, theorem of **M**, and deducibility in **M** are defined as in Chapter V, the only change being that just sentence parameters in **M** are considered.*

As before, we use '*P*', '*Q*', and so on to range over sentence parameters and '*A*', '*B*', and so forth to range over formulas, but this time over sentence parameters and formulas of whatever morphology is under consideration.

*D2. A valuation of a morphology **M** for **H**$_s$ is a function V which assigns each sentence parameter in **M** one (and only one) of the values T and F. Where P ∈ M and V is a valuation of **M**, V(P) is the value assigned to P by V. Thus V(P) = T or V(P) = F.*

A valuation of **M** will determine a truth-value for each sentence parameter of **M**. In accordance with the law of noncontradiction (nothing is both true and false), we have specified in D2 that every parameter is assigned *at* most one of the values T and F. And observing the law of bivalence (everything is true or is false), we have ensured that every parameter of **M** is assigned *at least* one of these two values.

In accordance with rules iii and iv, every valuation of **M** assigns a truth-value T or F to every formula of **M**, however complex. When we reformulate this precisely it turns out to be an inductive definition, since the truth-value given to a formula depends on the truth-values given its subformulas.

*D3. Let V be a valuation of a morphology **M** for **H**$_s$. The truth-value V(A) of a complex formula A of **M** under V is defined according to the following rules.*

1. *If A is B ⊃ C, then V(A) = T if V(B) = F or V(C) = T, and V(A) = F otherwise.*
2. *If A is ~B, then V(A) = T if V(B) = F, and V(A) = F otherwise.*

A value T or F qualifies as the truth-value V(*A*) of *A* under the valuation V of **M** only if *A* is a sentence parameter of **M** and this value is the one assigned to *A* by V, or else *A* is a complex formula of **M** and this value can be shown by repeated applications of 1 and 2 to be the value assigned to *A*.

Recall that where *A* is a sentence parameter of **M**, V(*A*) is determined by decree; or, if you like, V(A) is specified as part of the definition of V. If A is complex, however (e.g., if A is $\sim P$ or $P \supset . P \supset \sim Q$, where P and Q are parameters of **M**), V(A) is computed from V(P) and V(Q) by means of clauses 1 and 2.

For example, suppose that V(P) = T and V(Q) = F. Then by clause 2, V($\sim P$) = F. It takes a few more steps to calculate V($P \supset . P \supset \sim Q$). By clause 2, V($\sim Q$) = T, and hence by clause 1, V($P \supset \sim Q$) = T; therefore, by clause 2, V($P \supset . P \supset \sim Q$) = T.

7. Now, if **M** is a morphology and V a valuation of **M**, it seems clear that every formula of **M** will be either true or false with respect to V and that no formula of **M** will be both true and false. Just to fix this in our minds, however, we will give a demonstration of it. As you might expect, the proof is inductive.

M1. Where M *is a morphology for* **H**$_s$ *and* V *a valuation of* M, *every formula A of* M *is given a unique value* T *or* F *by* V.

PROOF. Induce on the complexity of A (i.e., on the number of occurrences of connectives in A). If A is a sentence parameter of **M**, V gives a unique value T or F to A by D2. This furnishes the basis clause of our argument. Suppose as hypothesis of induction that all formulas B of **M** less complex than A (i.e., containing fewer occurrences of $\supset$ and $\sim$ than A) are assigned one and only one truth-value by V. Then, in case A is an implication $C \supset D$, both C and D take a unique truth-value by our hypothesis of induction; therefore so does A, by clause 1 of D3. And in case A is a negation $\sim C$, C takes a unique truth-value by the hypothesis of induction, and therefore so does A by clause 2 of D3. This completes the proof of M1.

8. D3 characterizes the fundamental semantic notion of satisfaction by a valuation V. A formula A of a morphology **M** is said to be *satisfied* by a valuation V of **M** if V(A) = T. (Here, 'satisfaction' is used in the sense of 'making good', as when we say that a thing satisfies certain criteria. To be satisfied by a valuation is to be made true by that valuation.) Now that this relation of satisfaction has been specified, we can go on to account for other semantic concepts of importance in logic. In particular, the notions of *satisfiability* (or capability of being made true) and *validity* (or incapability of being made false) are especially worth defining and investigating.

D4. A formula A of M *is satisfiable if there exists a valuation* V *of* M *such that* V(A) = T.

D5. A formula A of **M** *is valid if for all valuations* V *of* **M**, V(A) = T.

Let's consider an example or two to illustrate these definitions. Suppose that **M** = {P, Q}, set $V_1(P)$ = T, and $V_1(Q)$ = F. Let $V_2(P)$ = F and $V_2(Q)$ = T. Then the formula P is satisfiable, since some valuation of **M** (e.g., V_1) satisfies P. The negation ~P of P is also satisfiable, since some valuation of **M** (e.g., V_2) satisfies it. Likewise, P is not valid either, since there is a valuation of **M** (e.g., V_1) which fails to satisfy it. Notice that there is an implicit appeal to M1 in this reasoning: V_1 doesn't satisfy ~P because $V_1(\sim P)$ = F, so that by M1, $V_1(\sim P) \neq$ T. These examples show that there is nothing wrong with both a formula and its negation being satisfiable, though, as M1 shows, they cannot both be satisfied by the very same valuation.

To take a slightly more complicated example, ~(P ⊃ Q) is satisfiable, because V_1 satisfies it. On the other hand, it's easy to see that P ⊃ P is valid, since any valuation of **M** satisfies this formula. By the same token, ~(P ⊃ P) is not satisfiable as there is no way of making this formula true.

Probably you've noticed the relationship of truth-tables to all this. A valuation corresponds to a row of a truth-table. It turns out, then, that a formula is satisfiable if it takes a T in at least one row of its truth-table, and valid if it takes a T in all of these rows. For a simple example illustrating this, again let **M** = {P, Q}. Then there are four valuations of **M** in all, corresponding to the four rows of a truth-table for two parameters. Thus, table vii below shows that the formula ~(~P ⊃ Q) is satisfiable, since it takes the value T in the last row, and table viii shows P ⊃ ~~P to be valid.

P	Q	~(~P ⊃ Q)		P	Q	P ⊃ ~~P
T	T	F		T	T	T
T	F	F		T	F	T
F	T	F		F	T	T
F	F	T		F	F	T
		(vii)				*(viii)*

Notice that table viii is redundant, since Q does not appear in the formula P ⊃ ~~P. A row for Q was included in this table because it is supposed to correspond to the valuations of the morphology **M**, and there are four such valuations.

9. People sometimes get confused about satisfaction and satisfiability, and it may be a good idea to distinguish between them even more carefully than we have. Satisfaction is a *relation* between a formula and a valuation;

it makes no sense to speak of a formula being satisfied without regard to a valuation. On the other hand, satisfiability is a quality that may or may not be possessed by formulas; it is not a relation, and it would be meaningless to speak of a formula being "satisfiable by a valuation". In this regard *satisfaction* and *satisfiability* are like *proof* and *provability*. In at least one sense of 'proof', proof is a relation between arrays of formulas and formulas; an array of a certain sort is said to be a *proof of* its last formula. A formula is then said to be *provable* if there exists a proof of it. In general, when you have a relation that holds between things of one sort and things of another, you can always define a property pertaining to things of the first sort in terms of this relation. To do this, you consider those things of the first sort which bear the given relation to *some* thing of the second sort. This is what is done in the case of satisfiability and provability.

Satisfaction, as we have said, is a relation between formulas and valuations. Satisfiability is defined in terms of satisfaction, so that a formula is satisfiable if there is some valuation that satisfies it. Validity, on the other hand, is defined in terms of satisfaction in a slightly different way, by considering those formulas of a morphology $\mathbf{M}$ which are satisfied by *all* valuations of $\mathbf{M}$.

10. Up to now we've been indulging in a certain amount of sloppiness, and it would be best to clear this up before going ahead. When we defined satisfiability and validity, we did this with respect to a morphology $\mathbf{M}$. For instance, we said that a formula of $\mathbf{M}$ is valid if it is made true by all valuations of $\mathbf{M}$. Nevertheless, we have not spoken of "validity with respect to $\mathbf{M}$", but merely of validity. Of course, it would be very odd and unsettling if indeed it could happen that a formula were valid when regarded as a formula of one morphology and invalid when regarded as a formula of another. In order to justify our way of speaking, we must show that this sort of thing can't happen. This is just what our next metatheorem is meant to establish.

M2. Let $\mathbf{M}$ and $\mathbf{M}'$ be morphologies for $\mathbf{H}_s$, and let $\mathbf{M}' \subseteq \mathbf{M}$ (i.e., let $\mathbf{M}'$ be a submorphology of $\mathbf{M}$). Where V is a valuation of $\mathbf{M}$, let V' be the restriction of V to $\mathbf{M}'$; that is, let $V'(P) = V(P)$ for all $P \in \mathbf{M}'$, and V' be undefined for $P \notin \mathbf{M}'$. Then for all formulas A of $\mathbf{M}'$, $V(A) = V'(A)$.

PROOF. Let $\mathbf{M}, \mathbf{M}', V$, and V' be as described above. Our argument proceeds by induction on the complexity of formulas A of $\mathbf{M}'$. If A is a sentence parameter, then $V(A) = V'(A)$ by the assumptions of our theorem. Suppose as hypothesis of induction that for all formulas B of $\mathbf{M}'$ less complex than A, $V(B) = V'(B)$. Then if A is an implication $C \supset D$, $V(A)$ and $V'(A)$ are determined according to D3 from $V(C)$ and $V(D)$, $V'(C)$ and $V'(D)$. Since the hypothesis of induction guarantees that $V(C) = V'(C)$ and $V(D) = V'(D)$, we have $V(A) = V'(A)$. Similarly, if A is a negation, $V(A) = V'(A)$.

Using M2, it's easy to show, as we do in M3, that the satisfiability of a formula A does not depend on which morphology A is considered to be a formula of.

M3. Let **M** *and* **M**′ *be morphologies for* H_s *and A be a formula of both* **M** *and* **M**′. *Then there is a valuation of* **M** *that satisfies A if and only if there is a valuation of* **M**′ *that satisfies A.*

PROOF. Consider **M** ∩ **M**′; this is a submorphology of both **M** and **M**′, and A is a formula of it. It follows from M2 that there is a valuation V of **M** which satisfies A if and only if there is a valuation of **M** ∩ **M**′ (namely, the restriction of V to **M** ∩ **M**′) which satisfies A. Similarly, there is a valuation of **M**′ which satisfies A if and only if there is a valuation of **M** ∩ **M**′ which satisfies A. Therefore, some valuation of **M** satisfies A if and only if some valuation of **M**′ satisfies A.

In the same way, it's easy to show that under the same conditions every valuation of **M** satisfies A if and only if every valuation of **M**′ satisfies A. The proof of this is left as an exercise.

M4. Let **M** *and* **M**′ *be morphologies for* H_s, *and A be a formula of both* **M** *and* **M**′. *Then every valuation of* **M** *satisfies A if and only if every valuation of* **M**′ *satisfies A.*

Since satisfaction by some valuation amounts to satisfiability, and satisfaction by every valuation to validity, M3 and M4 show that we can consider these notions independently of this or that morphology; for instance, we can say simply that $P \supset Q$ is satisfiable, not satisfiable with respect to **M**. In fact, what the proof of M3 shows is that a formula A is satisfiable when considered as a formula of **M** if and only if it is satisfiable with respect to the morphology containing just the parameters in A. And M4 shows the same thing about validity. Thus, our characterization in Section 5, above, of satisfiability and validity in terms of truth-tables is also justified. Looking at the truth-table of A to see if A takes a T in some row amounts to asking whether A is satisfiable with respect to the morphology containing just the sentence parameters in A.

Notice that, although we haven't bothered to do so, the notions of *provability, derivability,* and *consistency* should also be shown to be independent of the morphology chosen. One of these problems is stated more clearly and assigned as a task to the reader in E8 below.

In view of the fact that checking the truth-table of a formula suffices to show whether it's satisfiable or not and whether it's valid or not, you may wonder why we have gone to the trouble of talking about morphologies and valuations, and choosing definitions of *satisfiability* and *validity* that must be shown to be independent of morphology. The answer is that we are interested not so much in checking whether particular formulas are satisfiable or valid as in proving general things about satisfiability and validity. For this purpose the definitions we have chosen turn out to be better than definitions using just truth-tables. And to develop the semantics of predicate logic, truth-tables no longer suffice and we will be forced to use definitions employing the notion of a valuation. So it's better to get used to them now.

11. Before turning to other matters, we should set down a few basic meta-theorems concerning satisfiability and validity. The first two of these require no explanation and may have occurred to you already. Their proof is left as an exercise.

M5. A is valid if and only if $\sim A$ is not satisfiable.

M6. A is satisfiable if and only if $\sim A$ is not valid.

Another feature of validity is that it is closed under substitution. (That is, any result of substitution in a valid formula is also a valid formula.) For instance, as soon as we know that $P \supset Q \supset. P \supset \sim Q \supset \sim P$ is valid, we know that any formula $A \supset B \supset. A \supset \sim B \supset. \sim A$ is valid. The reason for this, of course, is that where A is a formula of **M**, any valuation V of **M** must give A and B truth-values $V(A)$ and $V(B)$. But the validity of $P \supset Q \supset. P \supset \sim Q \supset \sim P$ shows that $A \supset B \supset. A \supset \sim B \supset \sim A$ will take the value T no matter what these values are.

Closure of validity under substitution follows from M7 below. Its proof is left to you; to be strictly rigorous, you should refer back to V.D10 and furnish an inductive argument.

*M7. Let A and B be formulas of **M**, and let C be the result of substituting A for P in B, where P is a sentence parameter of **M**. Then if B is valid, so is C.*

12. Other notions of great importance in logical semantics are *simultaneous satisfaction*, *simultaneous satisfiability*, and (semantic) *implication*.

All of these apply to *sets* of formulas, rather than to formulas taken one at a time.

Interest in sets of formulas arises naturally. We may be interested, say, in the set of formulas that are deducible from certain formulas posited as hypotheses. This is a syntactically defined set of formulas, since the notion of deducibility is syntactic, but it's interesting to ask semantic questions about it; for instance, are all its members true in a given situation? In terms of our semantic theory, this amounts to asking of a valuation V whether it satisfies every formula in the set, or, as we will put it from now on, whether V *simultaneously satisfies* the set.

D6. Let Γ *be a set of formulas of a given morphology* **M**, *and* V *be a valuation of* **M**. *The valuation* V *simultaneously satisfies* Γ *if* V *satisfies every formula in* Γ.

For example, let $\Gamma = \{P \supset Q, \sim Q, P \supset P\}$, and let $\mathbf{M} = \{P, Q\}$. Let $V_1(P) = T, V_1(Q) = F$, and $V_2(P) = F, V_2(Q) = F$. Then V_2 simultaneously satisfies Γ, since clearly V_2 satisfies the three formulas $P \supset Q, \sim Q$, and $P \supset P$. But V_1 does not simultaneously satisfy Γ, since there is a formula in Γ (namely, $P \supset Q$) which V_1 doesn't satisfy.

Thus, we can think of V as simultaneously satisfying Γ if V satisfies "the conjunction of formulas in Γ". But a little reflection shows that this formulation is sloppy. In the first place, even if Γ is finite, there is in general no unique way of grouping the members of Γ into a conjunction. Even though all these conjunctions can be proved to be equivalent in H_s, they are different formulas. And if Γ is infinite, things are even worse; there is no way of getting all the members of Γ into a conjunction, since all formulas (of *any* morphology) are of finite length. Nevertheless, our original idea has some value, in spite of its sloppiness, since in making it precise we arrive at some conjectures that can be proved as metatheorems.

First, we need some better notation for talking about conjunctions. Since the way we group parentheses in a conjunction really doesn't matter much, let's group at the left, so that the expression '$A_1 \wedge A_2 \wedge A_3 \wedge A_4$' abbreviates '$(((A_1 \wedge A_2) \wedge A_3) \wedge A_4)$'. So far as finite sets go, then, we have the following metatheorem.

M8. Let $\{A_1, \ldots, A_n\}$ *be a finite set of formulas of some morphology* **M**, *and let* V *be a valuation of* **M**. *Then* V *simultaneously satisfies* $\{A_1, \ldots, A_n\}$ *if and only if* V *satisfies* $A_1 \wedge \cdots \wedge A_n$.

Using the fact (which follows easily from D3) that any valuation V satisfies $A \wedge B$ if and only if V satisfies A and V satisfies B, it's simple to show inductively that V satisfies $A_1 \wedge \cdots \wedge A_n$ if and only if V satisfies A_i for all i, $1 \leq i \leq n$. From this and D6, M8 follows right away.

As far as infinite sets go, though we can't speak of conjunctions of all their members, we can speak of arbitrarily large finite conjunctions of formulas drawn from them. In this way we get the following generalization of M8.

M9. Let Γ be a set of formulas of a morphology **M**, *and let* V *be a valuation of* **M**. *Then* V *simultaneously satisfies* Γ *if and only if for all finite subsets* $\{A_1, \ldots, A_n\}$ *of* Γ, V *satisfies* $A_1 \wedge \cdots \wedge A_n$.

There are a number of ways to go about proving M9. Perhaps the simplest of these is to show (exercise 9 below), that V simultaneously satisfies Γ if and only if V simultaneously satisfies every finite subset of Γ. Then M8 can be used to get M9. But it's also easy to prove M9 directly.

Another metatheorem about simultaneous satisfaction is the following; its proof is left as an exercise.

M10. Let Γ be a set of formulas of a morphology **M** *and* V *be a valuation of* **M**. *Then if* V *simultaneously satisfies* Γ, V *simultaneously satisfies every subset of* Γ.

13. Simultaneous satisfiability stands to simultaneous satisfaction as satisfiability stands to satisfaction. When we wonder whether a set Γ of formulas is simultaneously satisfiable, we want to know whether there is some way of making all the formulas of Γ true.

D7. Let Γ be a set of formulas of **M**. Γ *is simultaneously satisfiable if there exists some valuation of* **M** *which simultaneously satisfies* Γ.

As in the case of satisfiability, we must face the task of showing that simultaneous satisfiability is independent of morphology. Here, what we first need is a result like M2.

M11. Let **M** *and* **M'** *be morphologies of* H_s *and let* **M'** *be a submorphology of* **M**. *Let* V *be a valuation of* **M** *and* V' *the restriction of* V *to* **M'** (*so that* V' *is like* V, *but is defined only for members of* **M'**). *Then for all sets* Γ *of formulas of* **M'**, V *simultaneously satisfies* Γ *if and only if* V' *simultaneously satisfies* Γ.

No induction is needed to prove M11; M2 and D6 do the trick. Having obtained M11, we can use it in the same way M2 was used to obtain M3 to get the result we want. This time we will present a proof, though again it is not difficult.

M12. Let Γ be a set of formulas of both $\mathbf{M}$ and $\mathbf{M}'$. Then there is a valuation of $\mathbf{M}$ that simultaneously satisfies Γ if and only if there is a valuation of $\mathbf{M}'$ that simultaneously satisfies Γ.

PROOF. As in the proof of M3, consider the morphology $\mathbf{M} \cap \mathbf{M}'$; Γ is a set of formulas of $\mathbf{M} \cap \mathbf{M}'$. Now, by M11 there is a valuation of $\mathbf{M}$ which simultaneously satisfies Γ if and only if there is a valuation of $\mathbf{M} \cap \mathbf{M}'$ that simultaneously satisfies Γ. Likewise, there is a valuation of $\mathbf{M}$ which simultaneously satisfies Γ if and only if there is a valuation of $\mathbf{M} \cap \mathbf{M}'$ which simultaneously satisfies Γ. So at once M12 follows.

Other results that come to mind about simultaneous satisfiability are the following, which we state without proof.

M13. If a set Γ of formulas is simultaneously satisfiable, then every subset of Γ is simultaneously satisfiable.

M14. $\{A\}$ is simultaneously satisfiable if and only if A is satisfiable.

M15. If Γ is simultaneously satisfiable and A is valid, then $\Gamma \cup \{A\}$ is simultaneously satisfiable.

14. How is simultaneous satisfiability of Γ related to satisfiability of the members of Γ? Well, if Γ is simultaneously satisfiable, all its members are satisfiable. But the converse of this is false. For instance, consider P and $\sim P$. These are both satisfiable; we can make each of them true. But we can't make them both true *at once*; the set $\{P, \sim P\}$ is not simultaneously satisfiable. So simultaneous satisfiability has to be determined by looking at the set as a whole, not at its individual members separately.

There is a bit more that can be said about this question, though. In view of M8, we know that simultaneous satisfiability of a finite set amounts to satisfiability of a conjunction of its members. In other words, $\{A_1, \ldots, A_n\}$ is simultaneously satisfiable if and only if $A_1 \wedge \cdots \wedge A_n$ is satisfiable. However, this doesn't tell us anything about infinite sets; to do this, it must be generalized. The most promising way of seeking such a generalization is to try to find an analogue of M9. In this way we arrive at the following conjecture: A set Γ of formulas is simultaneously satisfiable if and only if all of its finite subsets are simultaneously satisfiable.

Knowing as much as we do, we can say a good deal about this conjecture. On the basis of previous results (in particular, M8), we know it holds when Γ is finite. So any trouble that may arise in trying to prove it will come when Γ is infinite. Also, by M13 we can see that if Γ is simultaneously satisfiable all of its finite subsets are simultaneously satisfiable. This leaves us with the problem of settling (with special reference to the case in which Γ is infinite) whether Γ is simultaneously satisfiable if all its finite subsets are. This doesn't look so easy; consider, for instance, a case in which $\Gamma = \{A_1, A_2, A_3, \ldots\}$. Now, we can assume that for every n, $\{A_1, \ldots, A_n\}$ is simultaneously satisfiable. This only means that there is for each n a valuation V_n which simultaneously satisfies $\{A_1, \ldots, A_n\}$. But this certainly doesn't guarantee in any obvious way that there is a *single* valuation that simultaneously satisfies $\{A_1, \ldots, A_n\}$ for *every* n. And this last is what we need to prove.

For the time being, then, we will have to leave this question unsolved (it is presented, with a few hints, as a problem at the end of this chapter). But the property we are interested in here, often called *compactness*, is an extremely important one, and we will furnish in the next chapter a (rather devious) proof that a set is simultaneously satisfiable if all its finite subsets are.

15. The last semantic notion to be defined in terms of satisfaction is implication. In semantic theories implication is treated as a relation between sets of formulas, on the one hand, and formulas on the other. What we need to do is to give semantic conditions under which a formula A can be regarded as a consequence of a set Γ of formulas. We accomplish this by stipulating that Γ implies A in case A is true in every situation in which every formula in Γ is true.

D8. Let Γ be a set of formulas of **M**, *and A be a formula of* **M**. Γ *(semantically) implies A, i.e., $\Gamma \Vdash A$, if every valuation of* **M** *which simultaneously satisfies Γ also satisfies A.*

For instance, let Γ be the set $\{P, Q \supset \sim P\}$, and let **M** consist of P and Q. Then the only valuation of **M** which simultaneously satisfies Γ will make P true and Q false, and hence we know that $\Gamma \Vdash \sim Q$. Or consider the set $\Delta = \{P \supset \sim P, \sim(P \supset \sim P)\}$. In view of M1 there is *no* valuation of **M** which simultaneously satisfies Δ. Thus, vacuously, every valuation of **M** which simultaneously satisfies Δ also satisfies Q. Therefore $\Delta \Vdash Q$. To take a case where we have an infinite set, it's easy to see that for all n, $\{P_1, P_2, P_3, \ldots\} \Vdash P_1 \wedge \cdots \wedge P_n$.

16. Notice the resemblance of '$\Vdash$' to the symbol '$\vdash$' we use in talking about deducibility. This notation was chosen as a reminder that, although there is a great difference in the way the two are defined, there are many similarities between deducibility and implication. Many of the metatheorems listed below are suggested by this analogy.

*M16. Let Γ be a set of formulas of both **M** and **M**′, and let A be a formula of both **M** and **M**′. Then A is satisfied by every valuation of **M** which simultaneously satisfies Γ if and only if A is satisfied by every valuation of **M**′ which simultaneously satisfies Γ.*

This metatheorem can be proved directly in much the same way as M12 or it can be obtained more easily by using the following metatheorem, together with M12.

M17. $\Gamma \Vdash A$ if and only if $\Gamma \cup \{\sim A\}$ is not simultaneously satisfiable.

PROOF. Suppose that $\Gamma \Vdash A$. Then, with respect to some given **M** such that A and every member of Γ are formulas of **M**, $V(A) = T$ for every valuation V of **M** which simultaneously satisfies Γ. Then, by M1, for every such valuation V, $V(A) \neq F$, and so, by D3, $V(\sim A) \neq T$. Therefore, $\Gamma \cup \{\sim A\}$ is not simultaneously satisfiable, since every valuation of **M** which simultaneously satisfies Γ must fail to satisfy $\sim A$. This argument also reverses: if $\Gamma \cup \{\sim A\}$ is not simultaneously satisfiable, then every valuation of **M** which simultaneously satisfies Γ must fail to satisfy $\sim A$, and hence must satisfy A. And so we've finished the proof of M17.

The next metatheorems are all straightforward consequences of our definitions, so their proofs are not written out below. You may wish to try some of them before reading on.

M18. $\varnothing \Vdash A$ if and only if A is valid.

We will use the notation '$\Vdash A$' to signify that A is valid, exploiting in this way the fact that validity is a special case of implication.

M19. If $A \in \Gamma$, then $\Gamma \Vdash A$.

M20. If $\Gamma \Vdash A$, *then* $\Gamma \cup \Delta \Vdash A$.

M21. If $\Gamma \Vdash A$ *and* $\Delta \cup \{A\} \Vdash B$, *then* $\Gamma \cup \Delta \Vdash B$.

M22. If $\Gamma \Vdash A \supset B$, *then* $\Gamma \cup \{A\} \Vdash B$.

M23. If $\Gamma \cup \{A\} \Vdash B$, *then* $\Gamma \Vdash A \supset B$.

An interesting notion related to implication is that of *implicative closure*. The implicative closure with respect to **M** of a set Γ of formulas of **M** is the set of all formulas A of **M** which are implied by Γ. If we think of Γ as determining the class of situations in which it is true, the implicative closure of Γ will consist of those formulas that are true in all of these situations. Clearly, Γ will always be a subset of its implicative closure. But instead of developing this and other properties of implicative closure as metatheorems, we will treat this topic in the exercises for this chapter.

17. Before going on to other matters, let's return briefly to the treatment of truth-tables which we gave in Sections 3 and 4 and discuss how this may be applied to complex formulas such as $P \vee Q$. If we wish to determine the truth-table of a formula such as $\sim Q \supset (P \vee Q)$, we can do it by calculating the truth-table of $\sim Q \supset (P \supset Q \supset Q)$, which of course is the same formula.

But this makes things more complicated than need be. Once we know the truth-table of $P \supset Q \supset Q$, we can treat the formula $P \vee Q$ as a unit and calculate its truth-table directly as a function of P and Q. In other words, we can use *derived* truth-tables, which are composed out of the *primitive* truth-tables assigned to negation and implication.

The truth-table corresponding to $P \vee Q$ is the following one.

P	Q	$P \supset Q \supset Q$
T	T	T
T	F	T
F	T	T
F	F	F

(*ix*)

This turns out just as we would expect in view of our discussion of disjunction in IV.5. There we said that we would construe disjunction in an inclusive sense, so that $P \lor Q$ would be true if P is true or if Q is true or if both are true, and false if both are false. And this is just what is stated in ix.

Here, then, we have another justification of our definition of disjunction: a *semantic* justification, rather than the syntactic one of V.12. Similar justifications can be given for the definitions of conjunction and equivalence. All that is needed is to work out the truth-tables for $P \land Q$ and $P \equiv Q$, and to relate these truth-tables to the intuitive discussion of conjunction and equivalence in Chapter IV.

Of course, all of this can also be expressed in terms of the more abstract notion of a valuation. We notice that the truth-value $V(A \lor B)$ of a formula $A \lor B$ of **M** (with respect to a valuation V of **M**) is a function of the values $V(A)$ and $V(B)$ which V gives to A and B. If we like, we can express this as a metatheorem.

M24. Let A and B be formulas of **M**, *and* V *a valuation of* **M**. *Then* $V(A \lor B) =$ T *if and only if* $V(A) =$ T *or* $V(B) =$ T *(or both)*.

Similar metatheorems can be obtained for conjunction and equivalence.

18. Every formula of $\mathbf{H_s}$ corresponds to a truth-table which shows what truth-values the formula takes when its sentence parameters are assigned various truth-values. We will say that a formula *expresses* its truth-table; in case a formula has n sentence parameters it will express a truth-table for n parameters. In Section 4 we remarked that such a truth-table will have 2^n rows. In the preceding section we argued that because $P \supset Q \supset Q$ expresses the truth-table of disjunction, it is justifiable to regard '$P \lor Q$' as an abbreviation of '$P \supset Q \supset Q$'. It is this that allows us to regard formulas of the sort '$A \supset B \supset B$' as disjunctions.

This suggests that we can use truth-tables to add another dimension to the account of definition that was given in V.11. In seeking to define disjunction in $\mathbf{H_s}$, we start out with the notion of a particular truth-table for two parameters P and Q: the table ix for disjunction. We then try to find a formula of $\mathbf{H_s}$ which expresses this truth-table. In a semantic sense, what we define in D5, D6, and D7 of Chapter V are the truth-tables for disjunction, conjunction, and equivalence. In each case we do this by finding a formula of $\mathbf{H_s}$ which expresses the truth-table we have in mind.

All of this raises a general question: can a definition be found in $\mathbf{H_s}$ of *any* truth-table we can think of? More precisely, let's choose a particular infinite morphology $\{P_1, P_2, \ldots\}$. (This ensures that we have enough parameters to enable us to express truth-tables of arbitrary size.) Given any truth-table for n parameters, is there a formula of this morphology which expresses that truth-table?

Although we won't bother to give a detailed proof of this, it is indeed true that H_s has this property. This is established by presenting a method of finding, given any truth-table, a formula that expresses that table. An example or two will indicate how the method works in general. Consider the following truth-table for two parameters.

P	Q	
T	T	F
T	F	T
F	T	F
F	F	T

(x)

The left-hand rows of the table correspond to situations (the situation in which P is true and Q is true, the situation in which P is true and Q false, etc.). On the right-hand side of the table are given the resultant truth-values for these situations. A formula expressing this truth-table can be true in only two situations: the one in which P is true and Q is false, or the one in which P is false and Q is false. To express this truth-table then, we choose a formula of H_s which says just this: $(P \land \sim Q) \lor (\sim P \land \sim Q)$. Since this formula is true if and only if P is true and Q is false, or P is false and Q is false, it expresses the truth-table x.

This method works for any truth-table having at least one T in its right-hand column. For example, take a truth-table for three parameters.

P	Q	R	
T	T	T	T
T	T	F	F
T	F	T	T
T	F	F	F
F	T	T	T
F	T	F	F
F	F	T	T
F	F	F	F

(xi)

In this case the method produces the formula
$(((P \land Q \land R) \lor (P \land \sim Q \land R)) \lor (\sim P \land Q \land R)) \lor (\sim P \land \sim Q \land R)$.

In cases where there are no T's in the right-hand column, we will have tables such as the following one.

P	Q	
T	T	F
T	F	F
F	T	F
F	F	F

(xii)

These correspond to formulas that are not satisfiable, and we need only choose any such formula. For instance, $(P \wedge \sim P) \wedge (Q \wedge \sim Q)$ expresses the truth-table xii.

The general result whose proof is indicated by these examples is called the *expressive completeness* of the language of H_s: a language, or way of constructing formulas by means of connectives, is *expressively complete* with respect to truth-tables if any truth-table is expressed by some formula of the language. To give a full-scale proof of this result we would have to furnish an explicit statement of the method exemplified above and then show, by an inductive argument, that this method always produces a formula that expresses the given truth-table. Expressive completeness, by the way, is just one of many technical senses of the word 'completeness'. Logicians tend to overwork this word, and we will run across a more important sense of it in the next chapter, where we prove the semantic completeness of H_s.

There are, of course, languages other than that of H_s which are expressively complete. For instance, if we were to take negation and disjunction as primitive connectives, this language would be expressively complete. This can be shown by pointing out that implication is definable in terms of disjunction and negation, and then appealing to the expressive completeness of H_s.

On the other hand, there are many languages which are *expressively incomplete* with regard to truth-tables. An example is the pure implicative language, which is based on just one binary connective, $\supset$. With respect to a morphology **M**, the formulas of this language will be the sentence parameters of **M** together with all expressions generated by the following rule: if A and B are formulas, then so is $(A \supset B)$. To show this language expressively incomplete, one has to find some truth-table that cannot be expressed by any formula of the language. Generally, the best way to do this is to search for some property not possessed by all truth-tables which can be shown by an inductive argument to be possessed by every truth-table expressible in the language.

In the case of the pure implicative language, a good property to use is that of yielding the value T when every parameter takes the value T. Certainly the truth-table expressed by a sentence parameter P has this property, and it looks as if every formula gotten by implication from formulas expressing such a truth-table will also do so.

To prove this rigorously we use an induction on the complexity of formulas of the pure implicative language, showing that if **M** is a morphology and V the valuation of **M** which assigns every sentence parameter in **M** the value T, then for all formulas A of **M** in this language, $V(A) = T$. In the basis step of the induction A will be a sentence parameter P of **M**, and by assumption $V(A) = T$. This completes the basis step. For the inductive step, let A be $B \supset C$ and assume as inductive hypothesis that for all formulas D less complex than A, $V(D) = T$. Then $V(B) = T$ and $V(C) = T$, and it follows by D3 that $V(A) = T$.

This shows that no truth-table that yields the value F when every parameter takes the value T can be expressed in the pure implicative language. For example, the table for negation, i, is such a truth-table; negation is therefore not definable in terms of implication.

There are many ways in which these ideas could be further developed. In particular, though it's interesting to find alternative languages for sentence logic which are expressively complete, it is often more rewarding to think about expressively incomplete languages. It frequently requires ingenuity to prove such systems incomplete, and sometimes in trying to find the right property of truth-tables to use in an inductive argument, one hits on some revealing results. Also, when a language is expressively incomplete, it is interesting to try to find an axiomatic system which generates the valid formulas of the language. But we will go on to other matters now and leave these topics to the exercises and problems of this and the next chapter.

19. In the above sections we have been speaking of *languages* as well as morphologies, and though this terminology is more general than the one we will use throughout the rest of the book, perhaps we should pause to explain it. The following account is very general and abstract; what we have been doing with $\mathbf{H_s}$ is only one of its many special cases.

By a (truth-functionally interpreted) *sentential language* we will understand a set of connectives that permit the construction of complex formulas out of sentence parameters. The pure implicative language and the language of $\mathbf{H_s}$ are both languages in this sense. Each of the connectives of a sentential language must have some *degree*, which tells how many formulas it connects. Disjunction, for example, has degree 2, or is a 2-*ary* connective; negation is

1-ary. We will therefore stipulate that for each n, a sentential language possesses a set of n-ary connectives. For many numbers n, this set may be empty.

Besides these syntactic features, truth-functionally interpreted languages have a semantic side. Each of their connectives must be assigned a truth-table of appropriate size; i.e., an n-ary connective should be given a truth-table for n parameters.

We therefore say that a truth-functionally interpreted sentential language is to consist of the following components.

1. For each $n \geq 0$, a set C^n of n-ary *connectives*.
2. An assignment of a truth-value to each 0-ary connective of the language and of a truth-table having n parameters to each n-ary ($n > 1$) connective of the language.

In the case of H_s, the set of 1-ary connectives is $\{\sim\}$, the set of 2-ary connectives is $\{\supset\}$, and all the other sets are empty; there are, for instance, no 3-ary or 0-ary connectives of H_s. The truth-tables assigned to $\sim$ and $\supset$ are, of course, the tables iii and iv of Section 3, above.

The notion of a 0-ary connective may need some explaining. Since n-ary connectives correspond to functions which, given n truth-values, produce a truth-value, 0-ary connectives should correspond to functions which, given *no* truth-values, produce a truth-value. Thus, 0-ary connectives should correspond to a fixed truth-value T or F.

With respect to each morphology M, we want each sentential language to determine a unique set of formulas. One way of accomplishing this is to say that every parameter of the morphology and every 0-ary connective of the language is a formula, and that if $A_1, \ldots, A_n$ are formulas and C^n is an n-ary connective of the language ($n > 1$), then $C^n A_1 \cdots A_n$ is a formula of the language.

Using this general concept of a language, it is possible to give rigorous formulations of notions such as *expressibility of a truth-table in a language* and *expressive completeness*. But there is almost no place below where we need such a high degree of generality, and we will be able to proceed on the assumption that we are speaking only about one particular language at a time. Until Chapter VIII this will be the language of H_s.

Exercises

1. Work out the truth-tables of the following formulas and determine whether

they are valid or invalid and satisfiable or not satisfiable. (For instance, $P \supset Q$ is invalid and satisfiable.)

(a) $P \supset \sim P \supset \sim P$

(b) $\sim (P \supset P)$

(c) $\sim \sim P \supset \sim P$

(d) $P \supset Q \supset P \supset P$

(e) $\sim P$

(f) $\sim (P \supset Q \supset . \sim Q \supset \sim P)$

(g) $P \supset Q \supset P \supset . \sim P \supset Q$

(h) $\sim (P \supset Q)$

(i) $\sim (P \supset Q) \supset P$

(j) $P \supset Q \supset R$

(k) $P \supset Q \supset R \supset . \sim P \supset R$

(l) $\sim (P \supset \sim (Q \supset R) \supset . P \supset Q)$

2. Show that every formula of H_s having the following forms is valid.

(a) $A \supset . B \supset A$

(b) $(A \supset . B \supset C) \supset . A \supset B \supset . A \supset C$

(c) $\sim A \supset \sim B \supset . B \supset A$

(d) $A \supset B \supset . A \supset \sim B \supset \sim A$

(e) $A \supset . A \supset B \supset B$

(f) $\sim A \supset . A \supset B$

3. In each of the following cases, determine whether every formula of H_s of the given sort is satisfiable. If every such formula is satisfiable, show that it is; if not, give an example of a formula having the given form which is not satisfiable.

(a) A

(b) $A \supset B$

(c) $A \supset B \supset A$

(d) $A \supset B \supset B \supset B$

(e) $A \supset A \supset A \supset A$

(f) $\sim A$

4. Show that for every **M** and every valuation V of **M**, either $V(A) = T$ or $V(\sim A) = T$. (If you wish, use M1.) Go on to show that for no such **M** and V does $V(A) = T$ and $V(\sim A) = T$.

5. Prove the following metatheorems (use any results stated prior to them in the text).

(a) M5

(b) M6

(c) M8

(d) M9

(e) M10

(f) M11

(g) M13

(h) M14

(i) M15

(j) M18

(k) M19

(l) M20

(m) M21

(n) M22

(o) M23

6. Show that every valuation of any morphology simultaneously satisfies the empty set $\varnothing$.

7. Let **M** and **M'** be morphologies for H_s, and let A be a formula of **M** and $A \supset B$ a formula of **M'** such that every valuation of **M** satisfies A and every valuation of **M'** satisfies $A \supset B$. Show that for all **M''**, if B is a formula of **M''**, then every valuation of **M''** satisfies B.

8. Show that if A is a formula of both **M** and **M′**, then there is a proof of A consisting only of formulas of **M** if and only if there is a proof of A consisting only of formulas of **M′**.

9. Let Γ be a set of formulas of some morphology **M**, and let **V** be a valuation of **M**. Show that **V** simultaneously satisfies Γ if and only if **V** simultaneously satisfies every finite subset of Γ.

10. Decide the following questions by proofs or by counterexamples.

   (a) If Γ is simultaneously satisfiable and Δ is simultaneously satisfiable, is $\Gamma \cup \Delta$ simultaneously satisfiable?

   (b) If Γ and Δ are simultaneously satisfiable, is $\Gamma \cap \Delta$ simultaneously satisfiable?

   (c) If Γ and Δ are simultaneously satisfiable, is $\{A \vee B \mid A \in \Gamma$ and $B \in \Delta\}$ simultaneously satisfiable?

   (d) If Γ is simultaneously satisfiable, is $\{\sim A \mid A \in \Gamma\}$ simultaneously satisfiable?

11. Find a set Γ of formulas such that Γ is not simultaneously satisfiable, but for all members A and B of Γ, $\{A, B\}$ is simultaneously satisfiable.

12. Show that if A is not valid, then for any B, $A \supset B$ is satisfiable.

13. Show that if A is a formula of **M** such that any formula of **M** which results from A by simultaneous substitution is satisfiable, then A is valid.

14. Determine the truth-tables for conjunction and equivalence, as these connectives are defined in $\mathbf{H_s}$.

15. Give the truth-tables of the following formulas, and determine their status with regard to validity and satisfiability.

   (a) $(P \vee Q) \supset P$ (b) $P \supset ((P \vee Q) \vee (P \vee \sim Q))$

   (c) $(P \wedge Q) \wedge (R \equiv (R \supset (\sim P \vee \sim Q)))$ (d) $P \equiv (\sim P \supset P)$

   (e) $((P \vee Q) \wedge R) \equiv ((P \wedge R) \vee (Q \wedge R))$

   (f) $(P \wedge Q) \equiv P$ (g) $((P \wedge Q) \equiv P) \equiv Q$

   (h) $(P \wedge Q) \vee ((\sim P \wedge Q) \vee (P \wedge \sim Q))$

   (i) $(P \equiv Q) \equiv ((P \equiv R) \equiv R)$ (j) $\sim P \wedge Q$

16. Find a definition in $\mathbf{H_s}$ of the exclusive sense of disjunction.

17. Let $\mathrm{L_{\wedge v}}$ be the language containing just two binary connectives, $\vee$ and $\wedge$, standing for disjunction and conjunction, respectively. Show that $\mathrm{L_{v \wedge}}$ is expressively incomplete.

18. Let $L_|$ consist of one binary connective $|$, which takes the following truth-table.

P	Q	$P \mid Q$
T	T	T
T	F	T
F	T	T
F	F	F

Show (using any results mentioned in the text) that $L_|$ is expressively complete.

Problems

1. Let $L_\equiv$ consist of one binary connective $\equiv$, standing for equivalence. Show that $L_\equiv$ is expressively incomplete.
2. Show that a formula of $L_\equiv$ is valid if and only if each sentence parameter occurring in it occurs an even number of times.
3. Consider the following class-interpretation of the language of H_s: a valuation V assigns to sentence parameters certain subsets of a set X, so that $V(P) \subseteq X$; $V(A \supset B) = \overline{V(A)} \cup V(B)$ and $V(\sim A) = \overline{V(A)}$, where $\overline{Y}$ is the set of members of X which are not in Y. Say that a formula A of M is *valid* if for all sets X and all valuations V of M in X, $V(A)=X$. Show that a formula is valid under the class-interpretation if and only if it is valid in the truth-functional sense.
4. Show that if all finite subsets of a set of formulas $\Gamma = \{A_1, A_2, \ldots\}$ are simultaneously satisfiable, then Γ is simultaneously satisfiable. (*Hint:* show that under the given conditions there exist morphologies $M_1, M_2, \ldots$ and valuations $V_1, V_2, \ldots$ such that for all n, (1) V_n is a valuation of M_m; (2) for all m, if $n < m$ then M_n is a submorphology of M_m and V_n the restriction of V_m to M_n; and (3) V_n simultaneously satisfies $\{A_1, A_2, \ldots A_n\}$. Define in terms of the sequence $V_1, V_2, \ldots$ a valuation V which simultaneously satisfies Γ.)
5. Develop the sketch given in Section 18 into a rigorous proof that the language of H_s is expressively complete.

VII Sentence Logic:
Semantic Completeness

1. In the last chapter our discussion of $\mathbf{H}_s$ was almost exclusively semantic. We recalled in a few places that there is a deductive apparatus associated with $\mathbf{H}_s$, but at no point did we refer to this apparatus in developing definitions and metatheorems. Despite our neglect of this matter, however, it certainly looks as if there must exist close interrelationships of some sort between syntactic and semantic notions. Metatheorems VI.M17 to VI.M21, for instance, when compared with metatheorems V.M4 to V.M8, certainly suggest a connection between semantic implication and deducibility.

In fact, if we take a closer look at a special case of this and compare validity with provability, it begins to seem as if this relationship should be one of equivalence. It ought to be the case that every provable formula is valid and that every valid formula is provable. To see why this is so, let's try to establish a connection between validity and the notion of what a logical system is supposed to do. According to our intuitive idea of validity, a formula

122

is valid if it is true in any situation whatsoever; the truth of a valid formula is wholly independent of particular circumstances.

It's important to notice just how broad the conception of *situation* is that enters into this characterization of validity. According to the semantic theory of Chapter VI, which identified situations with valuations, situations are generated mechanically by assigning truth-values to sentence parameters; any such assignment generates a legitimate situation. This entails that the resulting conception of validity is exceedingly strict, so that most truths of common sense, of science, and even of mathematics will be rendered invalid. 'Water is wet', 'Force equals the product of mass and acceleration', and '2 + 2 = 4' will all be translated by formulas of H_s which are invalid; indeed, P is about the best translation we can manage of any of them. (This, of course, doesn't deny them status as truths, but means only that they cannot be regarded as valid in sentence logic.) However there will be some formulas, like $P \supset P$, which are valid even when situations are construed so broadly. These will be the formulas which, because of their structure as complexes built up by means of the connectives $\supset$ and $\sim$, are invariably true. The point of presenting things this way is to make it evident that the validity with which we are dealing is *logical* validity. A valid formula, in other words, is one that is true in any logically possible situation; an invalid formula is one that can be made false in some logically possible situation.

Let's relate this to the deductive apparatus of Chapter V. If this apparatus is to be at all successful in constituting a system of logic, it must not render any invalid formula provable. Something would be wrong with any logical theory that sanctioned in this way a formula that could be made false. Furthermore, a good logical theory ought to be powerful enough to generate *all* the valid formulas as theorems. It would be *incomplete* if there were some valid formula that could not be legitimized by the theory.

We arrive, then, at the following criterion for a deductive system of logic such as H_s: H_s is an adequate system of logic in case for all formulas A (of any morphology), $\vdash A$ if and only if $\Vdash A$. The relationship we are demanding between provability and validity is thus a very intimate one; we are requiring that these two concepts determine precisely the same class of formulas.

The chief business of this chapter will be to prove that this requirement is met. This divides into two problems: to show that if $\vdash A$ then $\Vdash A$, and that if $\Vdash A$ then $\vdash A$. The first of these tasks is rather easy; the second is difficult, and requires a long argument. There exist many methods of carrying out this second proof; the one we will use is among the most powerful and flexible of these. The key idea of this method is a mediating concept having both a semantic and a syntactic side: the concept of a *saturated set* of formulas.

Using this amphibious notion we will be able to pass from validity to provability.

Much of the material in this chapter will be a meditation on saturated sets. Once we have unfolded enough of the properties of these sets, the result we want will appear as a corollary.

2. Intuitively, a (sententially) saturated set of formulas is a set having the structural properties of a set of truths in some situation. That is, we arrive at the notion of a saturated set by reflecting on the properties possessed by sets of formulas of **M** such that for some valuation V of **M**, $\Gamma = \{A \mid A$ is a formula of **M** and $V(A) = T\}$. Of the many properties one might expect of such a set, we need only single out two for purposes of definition, since these two properties suffice to characterize the notion we are seeking. One of these is *completeness with respect to negation* (a set Γ of formulas of **M** is complete with respect to negation if for all formulas A of **M**, $A \in \Gamma$ or $\sim A \in \Gamma$). The other is consistency. Notice that the latter property (see V.D11) is defined in terms of the deductive apparatus of H_s.

*D1. A set Γ of formulas of **M** is **M**-saturated if:*
  1. *For all formulas A of **M**, $A \in \Gamma$ or $\sim A \in \Gamma$;*
  2. *Γ is consistent.*

From D1 a number of important characteristics of **M**-saturated sets can be developed; we begin by showing that **M**-saturated sets are deductively closed.

*M1. If Γ is **M**-saturated, A is a formula of **M**, and $\Gamma \vdash A$, then $A \in \Gamma$.*
  PROOF. Suppose that Γ is **M**-saturated and that $\Gamma \vdash A$, and assume for *reductio ad absurdum* that $A \notin \Gamma$. Then by clause 1 of D1, $\sim A \in \Gamma$, so by V.M32, Γ would be inconsistent; but this contradicts clause 2 of D1. Therefore, $A \in \Gamma$.

Using V.M4, it is easy to strengthen M1 a bit.

*M2. If Γ is **M**-saturated and A is a formula of **M**, then $\Gamma \vdash A$ if and only if $A \in \Gamma$.*

Other characteristics of **M**-saturated sets which follow easily from the definition are the following. Their proofs are left as exercises.

*M3. If Γ is **M**-saturated and A is a formula of **M**, then $A \in \Gamma$ if and only if $\sim A \notin \Gamma$.*

*M4. If Γ is **M**-saturated and A and B are formulas of* **M**, *then $A \supset B \in \Gamma$ if and only if $A \notin \Gamma$ or $B \in \Gamma$.*

*M5. If Γ is **M**-saturated and $\Gamma \subseteq \Delta$, where Δ is a consistent set of formulas of* **M**, *then $\Gamma = \Delta$.*

In view of M5, an **M**-saturated set is a set of formulas of **M** that is as large as it can get without being inconsistent. For this reason saturated sets are sometimes called *maximal consistent* sets.

3. In this section we are finally going to take notice of the fact that the theorems of $\mathbf{H_s}$ are all valid formulas. This is easy to establish by an induction on length of proof in $\mathbf{H_s}$. (To carry out such an induction, it suffices to show that every axiom of $\mathbf{H_s}$ is valid and that if premisses of *modus ponens* are valid, then the conclusion is valid as well. Recall our discussion of this following the proof of V.M31.)

M6. If $\vdash A$ then $\Vdash A$.
    PROOF. Using truth-tables, it's easy to see that every axiom of $\mathbf{H_s}$ is valid (see exercises VI.E2(a) to (c)). But also if $\Vdash A$ and $\Vdash A \supset B$ then $\Vdash B$ (see VI.E7). Therefore every theorem of $\mathbf{H_s}$ is valid.

Using M6 we can secure a number of more general results which relate syntactic and semantic notions. First, an analogue of M6 can be obtained relating deducibility and implication.

M7. If $\Gamma \vdash A$ then $\Gamma \Vdash A$.
    PROOF. Suppose that $\Gamma \vdash A$. Then by V.M3, there is a finite subset Γ' of Γ such that $\Gamma' \vdash A$. Let $\Gamma' = \{B_1, \ldots, B_n\}$. By V.M10, $\vdash B_1 \supset . \cdots \supset . B_n \supset A$, and so, using M6, $\Vdash B_1 \supset . \cdots \supset . B_n \supset A$. Thus, by repeated uses of VI.M22, $\Gamma' \Vdash A$. Finally, by VI.M20, $\Gamma \Vdash A$.

Notice that M7 is a generalization of M6. M6 is just the special case of M7 in which $\Gamma = \varnothing$.

Using M7, we can get a result linking consistency and simultaneous satisfiability; its proof is left to you.

M8. If Γ is simultaneously satisfiable then Γ is consistent.

When in Section 2 we gave a rough-and-ready characterization of M-saturation, we said that an M-saturated set is one having the structural properties of a set of formulas true in some situation. At this point we can use M8 to cash in part of this idea in the form of a metatheorem.

M9. Let V *be a valuation of some morphology* **M**, *and let* Γ *be the set of formulas satisfied by* V; *i.e.,* $\Gamma = \{A \mid A$ *is a formula of* **M** *and* V(A) = T}. *Then* Γ *is* **M**-*saturated.*

PROOF. By VI.E4, $B \in \Gamma$ or $\sim B \in \Gamma$ for all formulas B of **M**, and by M8 Γ is consistent. Hence, Γ is **M**-saturated.

4. Let's digress for a short time to reflect on what we've just done and explore some of its applications. What M6 shows is that $\{A \mid A$ is a formula of **M** and $\vdash A\} \subseteq \{A \mid A$ is a formula of **M** and $\Vdash A\}$; i.e., every provable formula is valid. Thus, if we agree that a valid formula, as we have defined validity, is a logically good formula, we know that every theorem of $\mathbf{H_s}$ is something worth proving in a system of logic. No theorem of $\mathbf{H_s}$, in other words, is undesirable.

This is sometimes expressed by saying that $\mathbf{H_s}$ has been shown to be *sound*. But if we wish to be more circumspect (and this is a good precaution to take), we will recall that M6 assumes a notion of validity that is dependent on the two-valued interpretation we developed in Chapter VI. If we had used *three* truth-values (say, T, F, and ?) or had changed the definition of validity in some other way, we might not have been able to get M6. For this reason it's better to say that $\mathbf{H_s}$ has been shown to be sound with regard to two-valued truth-tables, or with regard to its *intended interpretation*.

Now, if we read M6 negatively, it says that any formula that is *invalid* is *not* a theorem of $\mathbf{H_s}$. With this version of M6 we have at once an easy method of settling questions that have bothered us from time to time—questions as to whether certain formulas are not provable.

In Chapter V we developed elaborate techniques for showing that various formulas are provable in $\mathbf{H_s}$. Like the deduction theorem, these techniques all amount to ways of showing the existence of proofs in $\mathbf{H_s}$ by furnishing general methods for constructing these proofs. But when, for instance, the question arose in V.14 whether $P \supset \sim P$ was provable, we were stymied. We *could* show, using V.M31, that if $P \supset \sim P$ were provable, every formula would be provable. But there we had to let the matter rest, since at that time we had no method of showing the nonexistence of proofs. Certainly, manipulation of columns of formulas will not yield results of this sort. One has to look elsewhere to find some guarantee that no array of formulas can constitute a proof in H_s of $P \supset \sim P$. And our semantic interpretation provides just this sort of touchstone.

For instance, if we let $M = \{P\}$ and set $V(P) = T$, it turns out that $V(P \supset \sim P) = F$. Therefore $P \supset \sim P$ is an invalid formula and by M6 is not a theorem of H_s; no column of formulas of H_s, however long and complicated, can be a proof of $P \supset \sim P$.

In a more general vein, M7 can be used to show that certain things aren't *deducible* in H_s, since this metatheorem guarantees that if A is not implied by Γ then A is not deducible from Γ. In order to show that $P \supset Q, Q \vdash P$ is not the case, for instance, all we have to do is note that P is not implied by Q and $P \supset Q$; so we need only find a valuation (say, of $\{P, Q\}$) which makes P false and $P \supset Q$ and Q true. Well then, let $V(P) = F$ and $V(Q) = T$—this does the trick.

Similarly, M8 can be used to show certain sets of formulas consistent. Take the same morphology $M = \{P, Q\}$ as in the above example, and let Γ be the deductive closure of $\{P\}$; i.e., $\Gamma = \{A \mid A$ is a formula of M and $P \vdash A\}$. Now, the valuation V of M which makes P true and (say) Q false simultaneously satisfies Γ. We know this because V simultaneously satisfies $\{P\}$ and, by M7, $P \Vdash A$ for all $A \in \Gamma$, so that V must also satisfy every such A. Therefore Γ is simultaneously satisfiable, and so by M11 is consistent. On the other hand, Γ is not M-saturated, since, for instance, neither $P \vdash Q$ nor $P \vdash \sim Q$, so that neither $Q \in \Gamma$ nor $\sim Q \in \Gamma$. This can be shown using M7 again; it is easy to see that neither $P \Vdash Q$ nor $P \Vdash \sim Q$, and M7 therefore entails that neither $P \vdash Q$ nor $P \vdash \sim Q$.

M9, however, allows us to construct many examples of sets that are saturated. This metatheorem guarantees, for instance, that the set $\Delta = \{A \mid A$ is a formula of M and $V(A) = T\}$ is M-saturated, where V is the valuation of the above example. By seeing whether or not V satisfies a given formula of M, we can easily check whether or not that formula is a member of Δ; formulas like $P, \sim Q, P \wedge \sim Q$, and $Q \supset \sim Q$ are members of Δ, while $\sim P, P \wedge Q$, and $\sim P \vee Q$ are not.

5. By definition, every M-saturated set is consistent. But it is by no means the case that every consistent set of formulas of M is M-saturated. As in the above examples, let $M = \{P, Q\}$. Then we know by M8 that the set $\{P, \sim Q\}$ of formulas of M is consistent, but this set is clearly not complete with respect to negation and so isn't M-saturated. For instance, neither $P \supset Q$ nor $\sim(P \supset Q)$ is a member of $\{P, \sim Q\}$.

But suppose that we enlarge $\{P, \sim Q\}$; suppose, for instance, we take all the formulas of M which are deducible from this set. As it turns out, this deductive closure of $\{P, \sim Q\}$ is **M**-saturated. (It's consistent because $\{P, \sim Q\}$ is, and can be shown complete with respect to negation by an inductive argument. See E11 in this connection.)

Well, then, is it true in general that the set of formulas of **M** deducible from a consistent set will be **M**-saturated? No. For example, consider the set $\{P\}$ containing just P, and let $\Gamma = \{A \mid A$ is a formula of **M** and $P \vdash A\}$. We showed, in Section 4, that Γ isn't **M**-saturated because it contains neither Q nor $\sim Q$.

Nevertheless, it remains true that the set $\{P\}$ can be enlarged so as to obtain an **M**-saturated set. We can add $\sim Q$, for instance, and then as before take all the formulas of **M** deducible from this set. It is always true that a consistent set of formulas can be *extended to* (that is, can be enlarged to obtain) an **M**-saturated set. This is a fundamental property of saturated sets and is one of the most important steps in our proof of semantic completeness.

In carrying through a proof of this result, M11, we must venture very close to certain details of the theory of sets which are not likely to interest the nonspecialist. To keep these complications within bounds, we will assume in proving M11 that the formulas of **M** can be ordered by means of the positive integers, so that there is a list $A_1, A_2, A_3, \ldots$ of all the formulas of **M**. We will call this list the *alphabetical ordering* of the formulas of **M**.

In Chapter XIII we introduce a piece of terminology which enables us to state this assumption succinctly: if there is a list $A_1, A_2, A_3, \ldots$ of all the formulas of **M**, the set of formulas of **M** is said to be *denumerable*. The assumption that the set of formulas of **M** is denumerable may not appear to be very restrictive, and as a matter of fact most morphologies that we are apt to think of will meet this condition. However, as we will show in Chapter XIII, there do exist sets that are nondenumerably infinite—sets too large to be ordered by means of the positive integers. And if **M** itself is such a set it can be shown that the set of formulas of **M** will also not be denumerable. Although such morphologies are not covered by our proof of M11, a set-theoretic principle called the *axiom of choice* can be used to show that M11 holds for all morphologies whatsoever. We therefore will state M11 generally, though its proof for the nondenumerable case is left as a problem (P7) at the end of this chapter.

Our method of proving M11 is the one that naturally suggests itself. Given an arbitrary consistent set Γ, we try to obtain an **M**-saturated set from it by throwing formulas into it one at a time. Enlarging Γ in this way, we obtain a sequence $\Gamma_1, \Gamma_2, \Gamma_3, \ldots$ of consistent sets of formulas, where $\Gamma = \Gamma_1$. Since each stage of this sequence is obtained by adding a formula to the previous stage, $\Gamma_i \subseteq \Gamma_j$ whenever $i \le j$: earlier members of the sequence are subsets of later members.

Since for every morphology **M** the set of formulas of **M** is infinite, in general there will be no largest member of this sequence. Given any step Γ_i of the sequence, there may be a larger set Γ_j later on. We can't therefore obtain our **M**-saturated extension of Γ by talking about the "last" or "largest" step of the sequence. We can, however, collect together the formulas selected in the course of the sequence; this yields the set $\Gamma_1 \cup \Gamma_2 \cup \Gamma_3 \cup \cdots$ of formulas of **M**. And if we construct the original sequence properly, this set will be complete with respect to negation. To show it consistent, and hence **M**-saturated, we appeal to the following metatheorem.

*M10. Let $\Gamma_1, \Gamma_2, \Gamma_3, \ldots$ be any sequence of consistent sets of formulas of **M** such that if $i \le j$ then $\Gamma_i \subseteq \Gamma_j$, and let $\Delta = \Gamma_1 \cup \Gamma_2 \cup \Gamma_3 \cup \cdots$. Then Δ is consistent.*

PROOF. We will show Δ consistent by proving that all its finite subsets are consistent. Let $\Theta = \{A_1, \ldots, A_n\}$ be any finite subset of Δ. Since $\Theta \subseteq \Delta$, there is for each A_k a set $\Gamma_{f(k)}$ such that $A_k \in \Gamma_{f(k)}$. Let m be the largest of the numbers $f(1), \ldots, f(n)$; since $\Gamma_i \subseteq \Gamma_j$ whenever $i \le j$, it follows that $\Theta \subseteq \Gamma_m$. Then Θ is consistent, because Γ_m is consistent. In general, then, any finite subset of Δ is also a subset of some Γ_i and so is consistent. But then Δ is consistent, in view of V.M33.

We can now proceed with the metatheorem we first set out to prove.

*M11. Any consistent set of formulas of **M** has at least one **M**-saturated extension.*

PROOF. Let Γ be a consistent set of formulas of some morphology **M**, and let $A_1, A_2, A_3, \ldots$ be the alphabetical ordering of the formulas of **M**. Define a sequence $\Gamma_1, \Gamma_2, \Gamma_3, \ldots$ of sets inductively, by letting $\Gamma_1 = \Gamma$ and continuing the sequence according to the following rule.

Let $\Gamma_{i+1} = \Gamma_i \cup \{A_i\}$ if $\Gamma_i \cup \{A_i\}$ is consistent, and let $\Gamma_{i+1} = \Gamma_i \cup \{\sim A_i\}$ otherwise.

The set Γ_{i+1} is thus constructed from Γ_i by testing the alphabetically ith formula A_i of **M** for consistency with Γ_i. If this formula can be added consistently to Γ_i, Γ_{i+1} is obtained by doing so. If A_i cannot be added consistently to Γ_i, then $\sim A_i$ is added to Γ_i.

We will use induction on i to show that for every i, the set Γ_i is consistent. The fact that Γ_1 (i.e., Γ) is consistent furnishes the basis step of the induction.

Suppose as inductive hypothesis that Γ_i is consistent. Then by V.M35 either $\Gamma_i \cup \{A_i\}$ is consistent or $\Gamma_i \cup \{\sim A_i\}$ is consistent. Now, if $\Gamma_i \cup \{A_i\}$ is consistent then Γ_{i+1} by definition is $\Gamma_i \cup \{A_i\}$ and so is consistent. If $\Gamma_i \cup \{A_i\}$ is not consistent, then $\Gamma_i \cup \{\sim A_i\}$ is consistent and is Γ_{i+1} by definition, and so again Γ_{i+1} is consistent. In either case, Γ_{i+1} is consistent, and the induction is complete.

Let $\Delta = \Gamma_1 \cup \Gamma_2 \cup \Gamma_3 \cup \cdots$, and let B be any formula of $\mathbf{M}$; B must appear in the alphabetical ordering of the formulas of $\mathbf{M}$, and so is A_j for some j. We have defined things so that either $B \in \Gamma_{j+1}$ or $\sim B \in \Gamma_{j+1}$, and thus $B \in \Delta$ or $\sim B \in \Delta$. The set Δ is therefore complete with respect to negation. Since Δ meets the conditions of M10 it also is consistent and so is $\mathbf{M}$-saturated. We have arranged things from the beginning so that $\Gamma \subseteq \Delta$, and Δ is therefore an $\mathbf{M}$-saturated extension of Γ, as desired. This completes the proof of M11.

Since every $\mathbf{M}$-saturated set is consistent by definition, we can make M11 a bit stronger.

M12. A set of formulas of $\mathbf{M}$ is consistent if and only if it has an $\mathbf{M}$-saturated extension.

6. Continuing our investigation of $\mathbf{M}$-saturated sets, let's return to the original intuitive characterization we gave of them in Section 2, where we said that $\mathbf{M}$-saturated sets were to be like sets that consist of those formulas true in some situation. In M9 we were able to make good a part of this characterization by showing that every set of formulas which is the set of formulas made true by some valuation of $\mathbf{M}$ is $\mathbf{M}$-saturated. But if our definition of $\mathbf{M}$-saturation is really successful, the converse of M9 should also hold: it should be true that every $\mathbf{M}$-saturated set of formulas can be characterized as the set of formulas made true by some valuation or other of $\mathbf{M}$.

Our next metatheorem establishes that this is so. The central idea of its proof is to use the properties of an $\mathbf{M}$-saturated set itself in order to define a valuation of $\mathbf{M}$ which makes true every formula in the given set.

M13. Let Γ be an $\mathbf{M}$-saturated set of formulas of $\mathbf{M}$. Then there exists a valuation V of $\mathbf{M}$ such that $\Gamma = \{A \mid A$ is a formula of $\mathbf{M}$ and $V(A) = T\}$.

PROOF. Let V be defined by letting $V(P) = T$ if $P \in \Gamma$ and $V(P) = F$ if $P \notin \Gamma$.

This determines the valuation V exhaustively, since all there is to a valuation of $\mathbf{M}$ is an assignment which gives truth-values to sentence parameters in **M**. Therefore, in view of VI.D3, the truth-value $V(A)$ assigned to any formula A of **M** by V is also determined, so that these values are now beyond our control. We can find things out about them, but can't change them. We will now go on to discover that, in fact, satisfaction by V coincides with membership in Γ for all formulas of **M**, however complex; that is, for all formulas A of **M**, $V(A) = T$ if and only if $A \in \Gamma$.

Since our definition of V guarantees that this is so in case A is a sentence parameter of **M**, an inductive argument suggests itself. For the basis step of the induction, we want to show that for all $P \in$ **M**, $V(P) = T$ if and only if $P \in \Gamma$. And this holds because that is the way we defined V.

In the inductive step, we assume that for all formulas B less complex than A, $V(B) = T$ if and only if $B \in \Gamma$. We want to show that $V(A) = T$ if and only if $A \in \Gamma$. Here, there are two cases: either A is an implication or a negation.

First, then, if A is $B \supset C$, we know by VI.D3 that $V(A) = T$ if and only if $V(B) = F$ or $V(C) = T$. But by VI.M1 and the hypothesis of induction, $V(B) = F$ if and only if $B \notin \Gamma$ and $V(C) = T$ if and only if $C \in \Gamma$. Hence, $V(B) = F$ or $V(C) = T$ if and only if $B \notin \Gamma$ or $C \in \Gamma$. But by M4 this holds if and only if $B \supset C \in \Gamma$; i.e., if and only if $A \in \Gamma$. Therefore, $V(A) = T$ if and only if $A \in \Gamma$.

Second, if A is $\sim B$, we know by VI.D3 that $V(A) = T$ if and only if $V(B) = F$. But by VI.M1 and the hypothesis of induction, $V(B) = F$ if and only if $B \notin \Gamma$. But by M3, this holds if and only if $\sim B \in \Gamma$; i.e., if and only if $A \in \Gamma$. Therefore, again $V(A) = T$ if and only if $A \in \Gamma$.

So in both cases we have $V(A) = T$ if and only if $A \in \Gamma$, and our inductive argument is complete. We have shown that for all formulas A of **M**, $V(A) = T$ if and only if $A \in \Gamma$. But this means that $\Gamma = \{A \mid A$ is a formula of **M** and $V(A) = T\}$; thus, there is a valuation of **M** (namely, V) such that Γ is the set of formulas of **M** made true by V. And this is what was to be shown.

Putting together M12 and M13, we have the following necessary and sufficient semantic condition for **M**-saturation.

M14. A set Γ of formulas **M** *is* **M**-*saturated if and only if there exists some valuation* V *of* **M** *such that* Γ *is the set of formulas of* **M** *satisfied by* V: $\Gamma = \{A \mid A$ *is a formula of* **M** *and* $V(A) = T\}$.

7. Now let's return to the problem of semantic completeness and try to locate ourselves with respect to the overall argument. In Section 4, we showed that every formula provable in H_s is valid, so that every theorem of H_s is something we want to be able to prove. On the other hand, it would be nice

to know whether every formula we want to be able to prove is in fact provable: is every valid formula a theorem of H_s? This is called the problem of
completeness, because if some valid formula weren't provable in H_s there
would then be something partial and inadequate about our formulation of
the system. It would be *incomplete* with regard to its semantic interpretation.
If this were so, we'd have to reformulate H_s—perhaps by adding more axioms
—in order to be able to prove all the valid formulas.

The question of soundness (of a deductive system, with respect to a semantic interpretation) thus amounts to whether we can prove *too much*; i.e.
whether we can prove any formulas that are invalid with respect to the interpretation. The question of semantic completeness, on the other hand, amounts
to whether we can prove *enough*; i.e., whether we can prove all the valid
formulas.

We now want to know whether H_s is semantically complete with respect to
its intended interpretation, and so we ask whether all valid formulas A (of
some arbitrary M) are also provable. If we were to seek a direct proof of this,
we would try to use the fact that A is valid to show that A is provable. We
would thus look for a general method for turning a truth-table for A which
takes only T's on its right-hand side into a proof of A in H_s. It is possible to
formulate such a method, although the details are rather complicated and
tedious.

An indirect method of proof, on the other hand, turns out to be more
fruitful. In this approach we try to show that if A is not provable in H_s it
is invalid. This suggests the following sort of argument. First, try to devise a
systematic procedure of trying to find a proof in H_s of an arbitrary formula
A. Then show that if this procedure fails to work, there is a valuation that
makes A false. Actually, systems of natural deduction lend themselves to this
approach better than Hilbert-style systems such as H_s. This is indicated by
the fact that in the natural-deduction systems one has a good idea, just from
looking at a formula A, of what a proof of A must look like if there is a proof
at all. And this sort of demonstration of semantic completeness can be made
to work for the systems of Chapter IV (see P1 for hints).

But we'll use still another argument, one that turns on the metatheorem
we proved in the last section. This argument uses only results that we have
already obtained: M13, in combination with M11, enables us to show that
any formula of H_s that is not provable has a falsifying valuation. The idea is
this: consider a formula A (of some morphology M) which is not provable in
H_s. Then $\{\sim A\}$ is consistent. (This follows from the special case of V.M34
in which Γ is $\varnothing$.) Then, by M11, $\{\sim A\}$ has an M-saturated extension Δ. But
by M13, there is a valuation V of M which satisfies those and only those

formulas of **M** which are in Δ. So V doesn't satisfy A, since A is not in Δ (if A were in Δ, this set would be inconsistent). So A is invalid. Hence, every formula that is not provable is invalid, and therefore (finally) every valid formula is provable. This, in a nutshell, is our proof of semantic completeness. In the next section we will present this proof more generally and so obtain completeness as a corollary of a stronger result.

8. The first metatheorem of this section is the converse of M8.

M15. Let Γ be any set of formulas of a morphology **M**. *If Γ is consistent, then Γ is simultaneously satisfiable.*

PROOF. Suppose that Γ is consistent. By M11, Γ has an **M**-saturated extension Δ. By M13, there is a valuation V of **M** such that $\Delta = \{A \mid A$ is a formula of **M** and $V(A) = T\}$. Now, if $B \in \Gamma$ then $B \in \Delta$, and hence $V(B) = T$. So V satisfies every formula in Γ; i.e., simultaneously satisfies Γ. Therefore Γ is simultaneously satisfiable.

Together with M8, M15 establishes that consistency and simultaneous satisfiability are equivalent in a very strong sense; these notions apply to precisely the same sets of formulas. These two notions are therefore, at bottom, different ways of looking at the same thing. And M16, below, is thus our first result stating the equivalence of syntactic and semantic concepts.

M16. Let Γ be any set of formulas of a morphology **M**. *Γ is consistent if and only if Γ is simultaneously satisfiable.*

Using M16, we can go on to verify similar relationships between other pairs of syntactic and semantic concepts. First, let's make good the "analogy" discussed in VI.15 between deducibility and implication by showing that these are also equivalent.

M17. Let Γ be any set of formulas of a morphology **M** *and A be any formula of* **M**. *Then $\Gamma \vdash A$ if and only if $\Gamma \Vdash A$.*

PROOF. By V.M34, $\Gamma \vdash A$ if and only if $\Gamma \cup \{\sim A\}$ is inconsistent. But by M16, $\Gamma \cup \{\sim A\}$ is inconsistent if and only if $\Gamma \cup \{\sim A\}$ is not simultaneously satisfiable. And by VI.M15, $\Gamma \cup \{\sim A\}$ is not simultaneously satisfiable if and only if $\Gamma \Vdash A$. Putting these together, it follows that $\Gamma \vdash A$ if and only if $\Gamma \Vdash A$, and M17 is proved.

When we proved M7, we already obtained half of M17. What is new about

M17 is the following piece of information, which is sufficiently important to record separately as a metatheorem.

M18. If Γ ⊩ A then Γ ⊢ A.

   This metatheorem states that if Γ ⊩ A, then there exists a deduction in H_s of A from Γ. But intuitively, to say that Γ ⊩ A is to say that A is true in every situation in which all the members of Γ are true; and, surely, this means that (in a semantic sense) A is entailed by any theory in which all the members of Γ are postulated. What M18 tells us is that whenever A is a consequence of Γ in this sense, there is a deduction in H_s of A from Γ. According to M18, then, every argument that is worth deducing in H_s *can* be deduced in H_s. Thus, what is established here is a sort of completeness, more general than the sort we discussed above in Section 7. Sometimes this strong kind of completeness is called *completeness as to consequences*, or *argument-completeness*. We will simply call it *strong semantic completeness*. M18 shows the strong semantic completeness of H_s with respect to its intended interpretation. In contrast with this, a system is said to be *weakly complete* relative to an interpretation if every formula of the system which is valid with respect to the interpretation is provable. There exist systems of logic which are weakly complete with respect to certain interpretations, but not strongly complete with respect to these interpretations (see XI.P1, below). Hence, it's important to distinguish these two notions of completeness.
   Finally, the equivalence of provability in H_s with validity (M19) and the weak semantic completeness of H_s (M20) can be obtained as special cases of M17 and M18.

M19. ⊢ A if and only if ⊩ A.
   PROOF. By M17, ∅ ⊢ A if and only if ∅ ⊩ A. Therefore, by V.M2 and VI.M18, ⊢ A if and only if ⊩ A.

M20. If ⊩ A then ⊢ A.

   Since in Chapter V we showed directly that the natural deduction system $S_{⊃~}$ is equivalent to H_s, the results of this chapter apply also to the former system. In particular, using M17 and V.M40, we have the following metatheorem.

M21. {$A_1, \ldots, A_n$} ⊩ B if and only if $A_1, \ldots, A_n$ ⊢$S_{⊃~}$ B.

9. Besides being an interesting and important result (or cluster of results) in its own right, the semantic completeness of H_s is also useful in solving other problems concerning H_s and its intended interpretation. In this section we'll discuss several of these applications.

One semantic problem that we have not yet settled is the question of compactness raised in VI.14. We are now in a position to show that H_s is indeed compact with respect to its intended interpretation.

M22. (*Compactness*). *A set Γ of formulas is simultaneously satisfiable if and only if every finite subset of Γ is simultaneously satisfiable.*

PROOF. By M16, Γ is simultaneously satisfiable if and only if Γ is consistent. By V.M33, Γ is consistent if and only if every finite subset of Γ is consistent. And again by M16, every finite subset of Γ is consistent if and only if every finite subset of Γ is simultaneously satisfiable. Hence, Γ is simultaneously satisfiable if and only if every finite subset of Γ is simultaneously satisfiable, as desired.

Using M22, it is easy to get the following result, which is another form of compactness. Its proof is left as an exercise.

M23. If $\Gamma \Vdash A$, then $\Gamma' \Vdash A$ for some finite subset Γ' of Γ.

As another example of how to apply semantic completeness, we will show how to use it to obtain the *interpolation theorem* for H_s. This theorem says that if $\vdash A \supset B$, then if A and B share any sentence parameters there is a formula C containing only parameters common to A and B and such that $\vdash A \supset C$ and $\vdash C \supset B$. (We leave it as an exercise to show that if A and B share no parameters and $\vdash A \supset B$, then $\vdash \sim A$ or $\vdash B$.) Interpolation theorems are very important results in their own right, and have many uses in advanced areas of logic.

M24. If $\vdash A \supset B$ and there are some parameters occurring in both A and B, then there is a formula C which contains only parameters common to A and B and such that $\vdash A \supset C$ and $\vdash C \supset B$.

PROOF. Let $\mathbf{M}$ be the set of parameters occurring in A, and $\mathbf{M}'$ be the set of parameters occurring in B. By hypothesis, $\mathbf{M} \cap \mathbf{M}' \neq \varnothing$, so let $\mathbf{M} \cap \mathbf{M}' = \{Q_1, \ldots, Q_n\}$; also, let $\mathbf{M} \cup \mathbf{M}'$ be $\mathbf{M}''$. Since $\mathbf{M}''$ is finite, there is only a finite number of valuations of $\mathbf{M}''$ and hence there are only finitely many of these valuations which satisfy A; let these be $V_1, \ldots, V_k$. (If there are *no* such valuations, then $\sim A$ is valid, and hence by M18, $\vdash \sim A$. We can therefore take

C to be $Q_1 \wedge \sim Q_1$, so that we will have $\vdash A \supset C$ and $\vdash C \supset B$. Thus we can suppose without loss of generality that there is at least one valuation of $\mathbf{M}''$ satisfying A.) Use these valuations V_i in the following way to construct a formula C: let $D_1{}^i$ be Q_1 if $V_i(Q_1) = T$ and $\sim Q_1$ if $V_i(Q_1) = F$; let $D_2{}^i$ be Q_2 if $V_i(Q_2) = T$ and $\sim Q_2$ if $V_i(Q_2) = F$, and so forth. Let C^i be $D_1{}^i \wedge \cdots \wedge D_n{}^i$, and finally take C to be $C^1 \vee \cdots \vee C^k$. The formula C has been constructed (as you may verify) so that all of the valuations V_1 through V_k satisfy C; hence, for all valuations V of $\mathbf{M}''$, $V(C) = T$ if $V(A) = T$, and so $A \supset C$ is valid. Therefore, by M18, $\vdash A \supset C$.

Now, all that is left to be shown is that $\vdash C \supset B$. Suppose for *reductio* that for some valuation V of $\mathbf{M}'$, $V(C \supset B) = F$; then $V(C) = T$ and $V(B) = F$. Since $V(C) = T$, $V(C^i)$ must be T for some i, and hence for all j, $1 \le j \le n$, $V(Q_j) = V_i(Q_j)$. That is, V coincides on $\mathbf{M} \cap \mathbf{M}'$ with V_i. Now let V' act like V on $\mathbf{M}'$, and like V_i on $\mathbf{M} - \mathbf{M}'$; that is, let $V'(P) = V(P)$ if P is in $\mathbf{M}'$, and let $V'(P) = V_i(P)$ if P is in $\mathbf{M}$ but not in $\mathbf{M}'$. The valuations V' and V_i are identical on $\mathbf{M}$, and so, by VI.M2, V' satisfies A if and only if V_i does, since A is a formula of $\mathbf{M}$. But V_i was chosen so that $V_i(A) = T$; hence, $V'(A) = T$. And by the same reasoning, since V' and V coincide on $\mathbf{M}'$ and B is a formula of $\mathbf{M}'$, $V'(B) = F$. But this is impossible, since by assumption $A \supset B$ is valid.

Therefore for every valuation V of $\mathbf{M}'$, $V(B) = T$ if $V(C) = T$; hence, $C \supset B$ is valid. By M6, $\vdash C \supset B$, and our proof is finished.

We've saved the most obvious application of the completeness results for last. This, of course, is their use in deciding whether various formulas of $\mathbf{H_s}$ are provable or not. Since M19 tells us that validity is a necessary and sufficient condition of provability, we need only check the truth-table of a formula in order to see whether or not it's provable in $\mathbf{H_s}$ or, for that matter, in $\mathbf{S}_{\supset \sim}$.

When confronted, for instance, with a formula such as $\sim(P \equiv Q) \supset . P \supset Q \supset Q$, we no longer need to try to find a proof of it in $\mathbf{H_s}$ or even to show by means of the metatheorems of Chapter V that there is a proof of it. All we need do is to verify that this formula is valid and at once we know it's provable in $\mathbf{H_s}$. Similarly, when we are given $\sim(P \equiv Q) \supset . P \supset Q \supset P$, we check its truth-table and, finding it invalid, we know it isn't provable in $\mathbf{H_s}$.

It is generally easier to test for validity by means of truth-tables than to try to show more directly that the given formula is provable. But besides being easier, the semantic method has a far greater advantage: in case a formula is *not* provable, the truth-table test will show that it isn't provable. The syntactic methods of Chapter V are no good for this at all. They only work when one wants to show of a provable formula that it does, in fact, have a proof. If in the exercises for Chapters IV and V we had mixed in unprovable formulas with provable ones and asked you to prove the ones that could be proved, you'd have had a hard time, unless you already knew something about truth-tables.

What the method of truth-tables gives us, then, is a mechanical or automatic way of deciding, in a finite number of steps, whether any given formula of H_s is provable or not. The procedure is mechanical because the rules for constructing truth-tables are completely explicit and leave no room for ingenuity. And it halts in a finite number of steps because every formula of H_s by definition contains a finite number of parameters, and a truth-table for n parameters will contain 2^n rows. Thus, every truth-table of a formula of H_s is finite. Such a method is called a *decision procedure*, and a system is said to be *decidable* if there exists a decision procedure for it. We have, then, the following metatheorems.

M25. H_s *is decidable.*

M26. $S_{\supset \sim}$ *is decidable.*

These metatheorems may seem less useful to you than the actual procedure itself, which certainly is a handy thing to have in working with these systems. Nevertheless, the mere existence of such procedures is of interest, because some well-known systems of logic can be shown to be *undecidable*. Thus M25 and M26 do serve to contrast H_s and $S_{\supset \sim}$ with other systems that have no decision procedures.

   10. Considering the fact that checking for validity is a much easier way of telling whether or not something is provable, you may have begun to wonder why we went to so much trouble in previous chapters to develop the syntactic notions of provability and deducibility. Don't M19 and M17 show that these notions are redundant? It's almost as if we were taking pains to make the study of logic difficult by treating everything in two different ways and by choosing to discuss the harder way first.

   Well, it *is* true, of course, that it would have been much easier to discuss sentence logic in terms of truth-tables alone. And, if the purpose of everything we have done up to now had been only to acquaint you with this sort of logic, that would probably have been a better way to do it. But all along our aim has been to do much more than just this. We've tried to do the theory of classical sentence logic in such a way that the techniques and results we developed in the course of our investigation will apply to other areas of logic. In other words, all this material has really been an introduction to the concepts and methods used by modern logicians, as applied to just one kind of logical system. There really would have been no point in devoting so many pages to classical sentence logic otherwise; as the truth-table technique shows, the whole thing is pretty simple. But precisely because it *is* so simple, it's a good example to cut one's logical teeth on.

This does not yet settle the question of why we need two distinct approaches which turn out to characterize the same thing. We can begin to answer this question by saying that logicians really do use both syntactic and semantic techniques, so that we must discuss both in order to give a comprehensive account of the concepts actually employed by logicians. But this doesn't go far enough; we should try to explain *why* both approaches are used.

One thing that necessitates the use of both is the fact that in some cases they are *not* equivalent. For instance, in so-called *higher-order* logics—logics in which one can quantify over predicates and so say things such as 'John has all the qualities of a good executive'—it turns out that there must be a discrepancy between any notion of provability remotely resembling the provability of H_s and the corresponding notion of validity. These systems are semantically incomplete. In situations of this sort one *has* to use both methods, since they give different results.

But even in cases where one has semantic completeness, there is some point in doing logic both ways. Even though they are equivalent, the two approaches are different enough so that they complement one another. Each furnishes valuable sources of insight into the subject that would be lacking if only one method were used. Thus, in M23 we employed a syntactic result to obtain a semantic metatheorem, and in M24 we used semantic methods to obtain a syntactic result. Direct proofs of either of these metatheorems would not have been easy. So the result is mutual support rather than redundancy. (Compare this to the situation in quantum physics, where wave mechanics and matrix mechanics complement each other in a similar way). Together, the semantic and the syntactic approaches provide much more stability to a logical theory than either would afford by itself.

Exercises

1. Check the following with regard to provability in H_s.

   (a) $\sim P \lor (\sim P \supset (P \lor Q))$
   (b) $(P \equiv Q) \equiv (R \equiv (R \equiv Q))$

(c) $((P \equiv Q) \equiv (R \equiv (R \equiv Q))) \equiv P$
(d) $(P \wedge (Q \wedge (R \vee P))) \equiv ((P \wedge Q) \wedge R)$
(e) $\sim(P \vee (P \supset Q)) \supset \sim R$
(f) $(P \equiv (P \vee Q)) \vee Q$

2. Decide the following statements, one way or another.

   (a) $\{P \supset Q, P \equiv \sim R\} \vdash R \vee Q$
   (b) $\{P \vee (Q \wedge R), P \equiv \sim Q\} \vdash R$
   (c) $\{P \wedge (Q \vee R), \sim(R \vee P)\} \vdash \sim Q$
   (d) $\{P \equiv \sim Q\} \vdash \sim(P \equiv Q)$
   (e) $\{P \supset Q, \sim Q \supset R, R \supset \sim P\} \vdash \sim P$
   (f) $\{P \vee (Q \wedge (R \vee S))\} \vdash (P \vee Q) \wedge (P \vee R)$

3. Check the following with regard to consistency in $\mathbf{H_s}$.

   (a) $\{P, Q \supset P, \sim Q \supset \sim R, R\}$
   (b) $\{\sim(P \supset (Q \vee P)), P \equiv R\}$
   (c) $\{\sim\sim P, \sim(R \supset P)\}$
   (d) $\{A \supset B \mid A, B$ are formulas of $\{P, Q\}\}$
   (e) $\{A \vee B \mid A, B$ are formulas of $\{P, Q\}$ and $P \vdash A$ and $Q \vdash B\}$
   (f) $\{A \mid A$ is a formula of $\{P, Q\}$ and not $\vdash A\}$

4. Is there a derivation in $\mathbf{S_{\supset\sim}}$ of P from $P \vee Q$? Give reasons for your answer.

5. Show that a set Γ of formulas of $\mathbf{M}$ is simultaneously satisfiable if and only if Γ has at least one $\mathbf{M}$-saturated extension. Use any metatheorems proved in this chapter.

6. Choose an appropriate formula of some morphology and show that neither it nor its negation is provable in $\mathbf{H_s}$.

7. Show that if a formula A is provable in $\mathbf{H_s}$, then $\sim A$ is not provable in $\mathbf{H_s}$.

8. Prove the following metatheorems (use any results established previously).

   (a) M3   (c) M5   (e) M23
   (b) M4   (d) M8

9. Settle the following questions by proofs or counterexamples.

   (a) If $\vdash A \vee B$ then $\vdash A$ or $\vdash B$.
   (b) If A and B are formulas of $\mathbf{M}$ and $\vdash A \equiv B$, then, where V_1 and V_2 are any valuations of $\mathbf{M}$, $V_1(A) = V_2(B)$.
   (c) If A is satisfiable, then any substitution instance of A is satisfiable.
   (d) A is satisfiable if and only if not $\vdash \sim A$.
   (e) Let X be a set consisting of sets of formulas of $\mathbf{M}$, such that for all $\Gamma, \Delta \in X$, $\Gamma \subseteq \Delta$ or $\Delta \subseteq \Gamma$. Let $\Theta = \{A \mid$ for some $\Gamma \in X, A \in \Gamma\}$. Then

Θ is simultaneously satisfiable if every set in X is simultaneously satisfiable.

10. Show that if $\Gamma \vdash A$ (where Γ is a set of formulas of M and A a formula of M) and V is a valuation of M which simultaneously satisfies Γ, then V satisfies A.

11. Let Γ be a set of formulas of M which is deductively closed (if $\Gamma \vdash A$ and $A \in M$ (and not both), then $A \in \Gamma$). Show if all parameters P of M either $P \in \Gamma$ or $\sim P \in \Gamma$, then Γ is M-saturated. (*Hint:* Use induction on the complexity of A to show that for all formulas A of M, $A \in \Gamma$ or $\sim A \in \Gamma$.)

12. Show that a set Γ of formulas of M is M-saturated if and only if (1) Γ is deductively closed; (2) for some formula A of M, $A \notin \Gamma$; and (3) for all formulas A and B of M, if $A \lor B \in \Gamma$ then $A \in \Gamma$ or $B \in \Gamma$.

13. Let $M = \{P, Q, R\}$. Prove M11 for M, without using any results of this chapter (i.e., show directly that any consistent set Γ of formulas of M has an M-saturated extension. The fact that M is finite in this special case makes possible a much simpler proof than the one given in the test). *Hint:* See E11.

14. Use compactness and weak completeness to obtain strong completeness (i.e., using M22 or M23 and M20 and results of previous chapters, prove M18).

15. Let V_1 and V_2 be valuations of M and let $\Gamma = \{A \mid A$ is a formula of M and $V_1(A) = T$ and $V_2(A) = T\}$. Show that if $\Gamma \vdash A$ and A is a formula of M, then $A \in \Gamma$.

16. Show that if $\vdash A \supset B$ and A and B share no sentence parameters, then either $\vdash \sim A$ or $\vdash B$.

17. Let the language of $H_\supset$ consist only of the binary connective $\supset$, and let $H_\supset$ have the following axiom-schemes.

$$A \supset. B \supset A$$
$$(A \supset. B \supset C) \supset. A \supset B \supset. A \supset C$$
$$A \supset B \supset A \supset A$$

The one rule of inference of $H_\supset$ is *modus ponens*. Show, by an argument similar to the one given in this chapter, that $H_\supset$ is semantically complete in the strong sense: if $\Gamma \Vdash_{H_\supset} A$, then $\Gamma \vdash_{H_\supset} A$.

Problems

1. Give a direct proof that if $A_1, \ldots, A_n \Vdash B$, where $A_1, \ldots, A_n$, and B are formulas of $S_{\lor \sim}$, then $A_1, \ldots, A_n \vdash_{S_{\lor \sim}} B$. *Hint:* Devise a systematic procedure for

eliciting a contradiction from $\{A_1, \ldots, A_n, \sim B\}$ using dis elim, neg elim, reit, and the procedure of obtaining $\sim C$ and $\sim D$ by subordinating derivations

$$\begin{array}{c|l} & C \\ \hline & \sim(C \vee D) \\ & C \vee D \end{array} \quad \text{and} \quad \begin{array}{c|l} & D \\ \hline & \sim(C \vee D) \\ & C \vee D \end{array}$$

wherever one has a step $\sim(C \vee D)$. Show if this procedure succeeds, there is a derivation of B from $A_1, \ldots, A_n$ in $\mathbf{S}_{\vee\sim}$ and that if it fails, there is a valuation falsifying $(A_1 \wedge \cdots \wedge A_n) \supset B$.

2. Use the above result to show directly that any valid formula is a theorem $\mathbf{S}_{\supset\sim}$.

3. Show (using any results established in the text) that $\mathbf{S}_s$ is semantically complete.

4. Show that if not $\vdash A$ then the system $\mathbf{H}_s{}^A$ obtained from $\mathbf{H}_s$ by adding every substitution instance of A as an axiom is *absolutely inconsistent*. That is, show that any formula whatsoever is provable in $\mathbf{H}_s{}^A$.

5. Let L be a language, say with two connectives, one 1-ary connective N and one 2-ary connective O. L is to be interpreted by correlating N and O with operations in a *matrix* for L. Such a matrix is a nonempty set M, together with two operations (or functions) f and g (f taking members of M into members of M, and g taking pairs of members of M into members of M), and a subset D of M (the *designated* elements of M). The notion of a valuation in M of a morphology and of the value $V(A)$ assigned to a formula A of a morphology M by a valuation V of M are defined by generalizing the corresponding defini- tions in Chapter VI. A formula A of M is satisfied by a valuation V of M if the value $V(A)$ is designated, and is *valid* if it is satisfied by every valuation of M. Let Γ be a set of formulas of L (Γ may be thought of as a set of "theorems"). A matrix M for L is said to be *characteristic* for Γ if for all formulas A of L, A is valid in M if and only if $A \in \Gamma$.

   Show that if Γ is closed under substitution (i.e., if whenever $A \in \Gamma$ and B is a substitution instance of A, then $B \in \Gamma$) then there is some characteristic matrix for Γ.

   (*Hint:* Define a relation $\simeq$ of synonymy relative to Γ, as in V.E18, and show that $\simeq$ is an equivalence relation. Let the equivalence classes of this relation be the elements of a matrix M, and define operations and a set of designated elements of this matrix so that it characterizes Γ.)

6. Show that the system $\mathbf{S}_0$ of Chapter I is semantically *incomplete*; i.e., find a valid formula of $\mathbf{S}_0$ that is not provable in $\mathbf{S}_0$.

7. Where X is a set of sets, a *chain* in X is a subset Y of X such that for all $U, V \in Y$, $U \subseteq V$, or $V \subseteq U$. A chain Y of X is *maximal in* X if for all chains U of X, $U = Y$ if $Y \subseteq U$. The *Hausdorff maximal principle* states that every set X of sets possesses at least one chain which is maximal in X; this principle

is known to be equivalent to the axiom of choice. Show that the Hausdorff maximal principle implies that every consistent set Γ of formulas of **M** has an **M**-saturated extension, for **M** of any cardinality. (*Hint:* Consider a chain that is maximal in the set of all consistent extensions of Γ.)

VIII Predicate Logic with Identity: Notation and Informal Semantics

1. The pattern we followed in Chapters II to VII sets a model for the development of a logical theory. First and most important, the formal language to be studied by the theory should be clearly defined and its connections with ordinary language accounted for. In other words, we must explain how to recognize formulas and how to translate English sentences into them. To the extent that we fail in either of these respects, we will have no clear notion of what our theory is about.

We then want to account for valid reasoning by characterizing those patterns of formulas which correspond to logically correct arguments. Here we must use our native sense of validity in English, and try to make our system an accurate model of reasoning which actually occurs in everyday situations. The chief insight required for this task concerns the importance of hypotheses in everyday reasoning. Recognition of this point leads us to construct a formal apparatus for keeping track of hypotheses, and this in turn provides a general framework in which formal reasoning can be presented. Logicians have suggested a variety of notations for displaying relations among hypotheses and their consequences; Fitch's notation, with its apparatus of subordinate derivations, is one of the most perspicuous of these. Once a framework of this sort has been selected, it's necessary to examine examples of valid arguments in English to determine what special rules of inference are needed in the formal system.

All of the above tasks can be carried out with reference only to examples. We can understand what the formulas are and how they can stand for sentences of natural language by being given a number of examples of formulas and translations. Similarly, we can learn from instances how to recognize and construct derivations. This approach to logic has its limitations, however, and to obtain a deeper understanding of logical systems we must formulate them with mathematical rigor and begin to prove things about them. In this way we build up a body of metatheorems about notions such as provability and deducibility. This can be done directly with natural deduction techniques, or with axiomatic systems of the kind we studied in Chapter V.

After a metatheoretic treatment of the syntax of a logical system it remains necessary to work out a semantic theory of the system. Such a theory will supplement our intuitive idea of what the formulas of the system are about with a mathematical theory of their meaning. Also it should provide a rigorous definition of notions such as satisfaction, validity and implication. When a logical theory has developed to this extent, its final test will be the establishment of the equivalence of provability and validity, or better, of deducibility and implication, as in Chapter VII.

In short, the following components should be present in a good logical theory: a formal language; an account of how to translate expressions of natural language into the formal language; a system of natural deduction; a syntactic account of notions such as provability, deducibility, and consistency; a semantic account of notions such as satisfaction, validity, implication and simultaneous satisfiability; and, finally, proofs of soundness and semantic completeness.

In presenting a theory of predicate logic with identity, we will follow this same line of development. The task of this chapter is to revise the formal language of sentence logic to obtain the more complex language of predicate logic with identity and to indicate how the formulas of this language can stand for English sentences.

2. Let's begin by considering some senses of the English word 'is'. For example, take the following inferences.

$3 \cdot (4 + 2)$ is $(3 \cdot 4) + (3 \cdot 2)$.

$12 + 6$ is $(3 \cdot 4) + (3 \cdot 2)$.

Therefore $3 \cdot (4 + 2)$ is $12 + 6$.

(i)

Texas is large.

Alaska is large.

Therefore Texas is Alaska.

(ii)

Common sense indicates that the first of these inferences is good and the second bad. The two premisses of i assert that $3 \cdot (4 + 2)$ and $(3 \cdot 4) + (3 \cdot 2)$ are the same number, and that $12 + 6$ and $(3 \cdot 4) + (3 \cdot 2)$ are the same number. It follows that $3 \cdot (4 + 2)$ is $12 + 6$. It is asserted by the premisses of ii, however, that Texas and Alaska share the property of being large. From this it doesn't follow that Texas is Alaska.

Although these two arguments are superficially similar, there are two very different senses of 'is' at stake in them. A good piece of evidence for this is that we can substitute 'equals' or 'is identical to' for 'is' in '$3 \cdot (4 + 2)$ is $(3 \cdot 4) + (3 \cdot 2)$' without changing the meaning of this premiss, whereas 'Texas equals large', being ungrammatical, has little if any meaning, much less the meaning of 'Texas is large'.

Let's call these two senses of 'is' the 'is' *of identity* and the 'is' *of predication*. The first sense occurs with a predicate noun and is used to assert sameness or identity. The latter sense occurs with a modifying predicate of some sort and is used to assert that the predicate applies to the subject.

3. The above examples indicate that these two senses of 'is' should be kept separate in distinguishing valid from invalid inferences. For this reason we want our formal system to distinguish identity from predication, so that the underlying differences between i and ii will be brought out clearly. As a start let's say that $=$ is a symbol of our new language and that, where a and b are names of the language, $a=b$ is a formula. We will think of $a=b$ as expressing the identity of whatever is named by a and by b.

This means that '$=$' will be ambiguous, having two senses in our metalanguage. Sometimes we will use it in speaking of formulas such as $a=b$. When, for instance, we say '$a=b$ is a formula' we're using '$=$' as a metalinguistic constant which stands for a sign of our new object-language. On the other hand, we have used '$=$' in previous chapters to express equality of sets or numbers, as in '$\{A, B\} \cap \{C, B\} = \{B\}$'. Here, '$=$' is used as an abbreviation in our metalanguage for 'is equal to'. Though in the future we will use '=' in both ways, this ambiguity should cause no confusion, since it's always easy to tell from context which sense of '=' is intended.

The fact that we are to have formulas such as $a=b$ in our object-language already tells us a great deal. This formula doesn't appear to be truth-functionally complex; it contains no hidden implications or negations. The nearest we could come to translating it in $\mathbf{H_s}$ would be to treat it as a sentence parameter P. From the standpoint of sentence logic, then, this formula is not complex, since it contains no parts. But our new way of talking about it *does* show it to be complex. The formula is made up of two names, a and b, and the identity sign $=$. Here, then, we can already see one way in which our new logical system is more sensitive than $\mathbf{H_s}$. It allows us to display relationships such as that between $a=b$ and $b=a$, something that cannot be done just with sentence parameters.

We now have a way of handling the 'is' of identity: '2 + 2 is 4' would be rendered, say, by $a=b$. But what about the 'is' of predication? How, for instance, will we render 'Alaska is large?' If we were to remain faithful to the structure of the English, we would probably use something like 'a *is* P' to denote the translations of sentences such as '3 is prime'. We would then have expressions a, *is*, and P in our object-language, corresponding, respectively, to the subject, verb, and predicate adjective of the original.

However, it turns out to be more economical, and more consistent with our notation for identity, not to have any special symbol for the 'is' of predication. We will translate 'Alaska is large' by a formula such as Pa, and will let concatenation do the work in our system of the English verb.

4. So far our formal system has the following components which were not present in sentence logic. (1) Namelike symbols such as a and b. We will call these symbols *individual constants*, since we think of them as fixed (constant) names of individuals. (2) The symbol $=$. Like $\supset$, this is a *logical symbol*—one that will figure essentially in the axioms of our new formal system. The grammar of $=$, however, is unlike that of $\supset$. The identity-sign $=$ links namelike expressions such as a and b rather than formulas, such as Pa or $a=b$; we will not regard the expression $Pa = a=b$ as a formula of our system. $Pa \equiv a=b$, on the other hand, is a perfectly good formula, but is not at all the same expression as $Pa = a=b$. (3) Symbols such as P. These can be attached to individual constants such as a to make formulas: in this case, the formula Pa. (We will generalize this part of the system after a short while.) Symbols such as P will be called *predicate parameters*.

Using the means now at our disposal, we can make formulas such as the following.

$$\sim a = a$$
$$Pb \supset . \; Qa \supset a = b$$
$$a = b \supset . \; b = c \supset a = c$$

Naturally, formulas such as these can be used as translations of English sentences. For instance, examples i and ii, above, might be translated into the formal language by letting a_1 stand for '$3 \cdot (4 + 2)$', a_2 for '$(3 \cdot 4) + (3 \cdot 2)$', a_3 for '$12 + 6$', b_1 for 'Texas', b_2 for 'Alaska', and P for 'large'. We then obtain iii, below, as a translation of i, and iv as a translation of ii.

$$
\begin{array}{cc}
a_1 = a_2 & Pb_1 \\
a_3 = a_2 & Pb_2 \\
\hline
a_1 = a_3 & b_1 = b_2 \\
(iii) & (iv)
\end{array}
$$

At least, we've now succeeded in distinguishing the two inferences with which we started. Translated into formal notation, i and ii are entirely different. And later, when we come to specify a method of proof for this language, we will be able to derive iii but not iv.

5. Let's look now at some English examples that involve a direct object as well as a subject.

(v)   2 is less than 3

(vi)   Alaska is larger than Texas.

We can translate these into our notation by formulas such as Pa and Qb, where a stands for '2' and b for 'Alaska'. But although these translations are correct, they are not very complete. In particular, consider v. Whether or not this sentence is true depends as much on the meaning of '3' as it does on the meaning of '2' and yet we have given '2', the subject of the English sentence, a preferred role in our translation. There seems to be no reason for doing this.

There is a further consideration. If we insist on paying attention only to the subjects of English sentences in translating them into formal notation we'll run into problems with inferences like the following:

2 is less than 3.
$2 = 1 + 1$.
$3 = 2 + 1$.
Therefore $1 + 1$ is less than $2 + 1$.
(vii)

This inference clearly is valid; logical considerations ensure that its conclusion will be true if its premises are. But if we force ourselves to translate '2 is less than 3' by *Pa*, letting *a* stand for '2' and *P* for 'less than 3', we obtain

$$Pa$$
$$a=b$$
$$c=d$$
$$\overline{}$$
$$Qc$$
$$(viii)$$

as a translation of vii. Here *b* stands for '1 + 1', *c* for '3', *d* for '2 + 1', and *Q* for 'less than 2 + 1'.

But viii can't be regarded as a valid inference: its premises might very well be true while its conclusion is false. For instance, the inference

2 is less than 3
$$2 = 1 + 1$$
$$1 = 0 + 1$$
Therefore 2 + 1 is less than 0 + 1
$$(ix)$$

is just as well represented by viii as is vi. And ix is obviously invalid.

This is an indication that the formula *Pa* does not represent enough detail of the sentence '2 is less than 3'. We must somehow capture more of the structure of this sentence in order to distinguish inferences such as ix from vii.

What we've neglected, of course, is the *relational* character of '2 is less than 3': its dependence on *both* of the names '2' and '3'. To remedy this we should translate v by a formula such as *Rac*, which contains counterparts of both '2' and '3'. Here, *R* stands for 'less than', and, as above, *a* stands for '2' and *c* for '3'. Now we can translate the inference vii so that the formal inference we obtain also looks valid. What we get is this.

$$Rac$$
$$a=b$$
$$c=d$$
$$\overline{}$$
$$Rbd$$
$$(x)$$

This way of handling relations looks very much like the notation used by mathematicians. For '2 is less than 3', for example, they write '2 < 3'. If we turn this into ' < 23', we get something resembling '*Rab*'. ' < 23', of course, would be bad notation since '23' ordinarily denotes the number twenty-three. No similar ambiguities, however, result from our metalinguistic notation '*Rab*', which we use rather than '*aRb*' because of systematic considerations.

We have now been driven to acknowledge that there are various kinds of predicate parameters: *singulary* predicate parameters, which apply only to one term at a time, and *binary* predicate parameters, which apply to two terms at a time. But there is no need to stop here; we will need ternary predicate parameters to translate sentences such as '3 is between 2 and 4', and quaternary predicate parameters to translate sentences like '1 is further from 9 than 2 is from 8'. Indeed, there is no good reason for stopping *anywhere*, for then there would be a number n such that we couldn't express n-ary relations in our formal language. And this would be an unwelcome expressive inadequacy.

We therefore must allow for the possibility of n-ary predicate parameters for any number n. Where P is an n-ary predicate parameter and $a_1, \ldots, a_n$ are individual constants, $Pa_1 \cdots a_n$ will be a formula of our language.

6. In discussing symbols such as a and b, we called them individual constants and said that they are regarded as fixed names of individuals. You may perhaps have wondered why we didn't speak of them instead as individual *parameters*. Certainly, this would be more consistent with our previous terminology. The reason why we did not do this is that besides individual constants, we will have other symbols in our system which we'll call individual parameters.

In systems of logic there is actually very little difference between constants and parameters. We can begin to explain this difference, however, by taking as an example what we ourselves said in the last sentence of Section 5: where P is an n-ary predicate parameter and $a_1, \ldots, a_n$ are individual constants, $Pa_1 \cdots a_n$ will be a formula of our language. We had started with the idea that we would allow 1-ary predicate parameters, and 2-ary predicate parameters. We wanted to generalize this to arbitrary numbers, and so we said we would allow n-ary predicate parameters and use them to make formulas like $Pa_1 \cdots a_n$. What we did here was to use a parameter 'n' standing for numbers.

When we talk about one and two, we use the terms 'one' and 'two' as individual constants; these words are fixed by linguistic convention as names of certain numbers. When we use 'n', however, we are trying to express something general; 'n' enables us to say things about *arbitrary* numbers, precisely because it isn't the name of any particular number. We can't say things like 'Pick an arbitrary number, say, 37', because 37 has many properties not possessed by all numbers, and so we use a letter such as '*n*' here. We can call this '*n*' a *parameter*, not because it's the name of any such thing as a "parametric number", but because we are free to let '*n*' denote any number we like. Since '*n*' is not a conventional constant, like '1', '2', and '3', we can regard as unsettled the question of which number is named by '*n*'.

Our next step will be to add to our formal language *individual parameters* such as *u*, *v*, and *w*. As in natural languages these parameters will be used in order to carry out general reasoning. For reasons that will become clear as we go along, we must require that infinitely many of these individual parameters are available in our object-language.

Individual parameters will function grammatically very much like individual constants. For instance, where P is a 1-ary predicate parameter, Pu will be a formula, just as Pa is; and where Q is a binary predicate parameter, Quv, Qau, Qua, and so on are formulas; so too are $u=a$, $u=v$, and $a=v$.

In general, then, we want to say that if P is an n-ary predicate parameter and each of $t_1, \ldots, t_n$ is either an individual parameter or an individual constant, then $Pt_1 \cdots t_n$ is a formula. To say things of this sort it is convenient to call any individual constant or individual parameter a *term*, and to use the metavariables '*r*', '*s*', and '*t*' to range over terms.

7. When parameters are used in mathematical reasoning, a qualifying phrase is often added to explain *how* they are being used. For instance, rather than saying merely

(*xi*) $$n + 1 = m$$

a person who wishes to make his meaning more precise may say

(*xii*) $$\text{For some } m, n + 1 = m$$

or even

(*xiii*) $$\text{For all } n, \text{ there is an } m \text{ such that } n + 1 = m.$$

The way in which such qualifications are added to sentences containing parameters is very important. For instance, if we change the order of the qualifications in xiii, we get a false statement about numbers

(*xiv*) $$\text{There is an } m \text{ such that for all } n, n + 1 = m,$$

whereas xii is true. And again, even though

(*xv*) $$\text{For all } n, n \text{ is even or } n \text{ is odd}$$

and

(*xvi*) $$\text{For some } n, n \text{ is even or } n \text{ is odd}$$

are both true, their meaning seems significantly different.

A general statement involving parameters, then, is ambiguous unless from context or the conventions of the language it is clear how the parameters are to be understood. In order to see what xi means, for instance, you have to know in what way it is to be qualified.

The final step in deploying our formal language will be to add a means of qualifying formulas. Of the many sorts of qualification that could be chosen for this purpose, we will use only the two that figure in the above examples: universal and existential qualification. Since these have to do with the *quantity* of things satisfying a given condition, they are called *quantifiers*.

In mathematical English it is customary to express quantification as in xiii to xvi, by means of phrases involving parameters. If we were to follow this practice in our formal language we might use

$$(u)Pu$$

to represent a universal quantification of *Pu*, and

$$(\exists u)Pu$$

to represent an existential quantification of *Pu*. The formal expression $(\exists u)Pu$ would then stand for 'For some *n*, *n* is less than 10' if *Pu* stood for '*n* is less than 10', and $(u)Pu$ would stand for 'For all *n*, *n* is less than 10'.

If we were to adopt this notation we would soon come to realize that there is an enormous difference between the roles played by *u* in, for instance, $(\exists u)Pu$ and *Pu*. Intuitively, the difference is this: the truth-value of *Pu* will depend in general on what individual *u* denotes, whereas the truth-value of $(\exists u)Pu$ has nothing to do with the denotation of *u*—it depends only on whether there is something having the property corresponding to *P*. To know whether *Pu* is true or false, we in general have to know what *u* names; to know whether $(\exists u)Pu$ or $(u)Pu$ is true or false, we never need to know what *u* names.

These two uses of *u* are usually called *free* and *bound* uses. The parameter *u* is free in *Pu*, and is bound in $(\exists u)Pu$ and in $(u)Pu$. If we were to allow both these uses of parameters in formulas, things would get very complicated when we came to formulate rules of derivation for quantifiers. In doing this we would have to make messy restrictions involving the distinction between bound and free uses of parameters, and although it's possible to state these rules correctly, they wouldn't be easy to remember or to work with.

For this reason we will depart from mathematical usage in defining our formal language and will use different symbols in quantifying formulas. We will call these symbols *individual variables,* and will represent them by letters such as '*x*', '*y*', and '*z*'. Otherwise we will use the notation suggested above, so that $(\exists x)Px$ is an existential and $(x)Px$ a universal quantification of *Pu*.

The expressions $(\exists u)Pu$ and $(u)Pu$, on the other hand, are not formulas at all, nor is Px a formula.

The left part of $(x)Px$, namely (x), is called a *universal quantifier* (in the variable x). It does the job of signaling that the variable x in Px is to be interpreted universally: it *universally quantifies* the expression Px. Likewise, $(\exists x)$ is an *existential quantifier* (in the variable x). In the formula $(\exists x)Px$ it *existentially quantifies* the expression Px.

Like sentence connectives such as $\sim$ and $\supset$, the universal and existential quantifiers provide means of constructing complex formulas. The following are some formulas that can be built up in this way.

Puv	$(\exists x)\sim(\exists y)\sim(z)(z=x \lor z=y)$
$(x)Pxv$	$(x)((\exists y)Qyx \lor (z)\sim Pxyz)$
$(\exists y)(x)Pxy$	$(x)(y)(Pxy \supset Pyx)$
Pww	$(x)(y)(Py \supset. x=x \supset y=u)$
$(z)Pzz$	$\sim Pbuu \supset (x)(\exists y)Qxy$
$(\exists y)(x)Pxy \supset (z)Pzz$	$(x)Px \supset (x)Qx$
$Pu \supset Qu$	$(x)(\exists y)x=y$
$(x)(Px \supset Qx)$	$(\exists y)(x)x=y$

The grammar of our formal language, however, will prevent formulas such as $(\exists u)Pu$, in which an individual parameter is bound by a quantifier, or $(x)Qxy$, in which an individual variable is not bound by a quantifier, from being formulas. In setting things up in this way we have diverged from the practice of many logicians, especially in the United States. Perhaps the most common usage is to allow formulas in which individual variables need not be bound by quantifiers and to speak of *free* and *bound* occurrences of individual variables. In this case individual parameters aren't needed at all: free occurrences of individual variables correspond to individual variables in our sense and bound occurrences of individual variables to individual parameters. This alternative is simpler, in that it eliminates the need for a separate category of parameters. But the approach that we have chosen is to be preferred in several respects: it makes it unnecessary to distinguish between free and bound occurrences of variables and, as we remarked above, it greatly simplifies the rules for introducing and eliminating quantifiers in derivations.

8. The translation of sentences from natural languages into our new notation is nowhere nearly as straightforward as it is in the case of sentence logic. This is partly due to the fact that there are more complexities in our formal language, so that we naturally have to take more factors into account in translating into this language. But there is more to it than just this. The whole apparatus of quantifiers was originally developed with reference to mathematical jargon such as 'for all n there is an m such that $n < m$', which is a rather narrow and regimented offshoot of plain English. Since a good deal of this regimentation of mathematical language is for the sake of clarity in the presentation of reasoning, it isn't surprising that it's possible to develop a formal language into which mathematical reasoning can be translated with a great deal of success.

It's also not entirely surprising that a good deal of manipulating is sometimes needed to translate more colloquial sorts of English into formal notation. Often, such a translation can't be direct and natural; you first have to reconstruct the English sentence in some way before rendering it in formal notation. (We'll give some examples of this sort below.) This means that at times it's rather difficult to cling to the idea that any indicative English sentence has one and only one best translation into formal language.

At this juncture it's important to avoid saying either "So much the worse for natural language" or "So much the worse for formalized language"; either of these extremes would be wrong. It would be foolish to ignore the defects of our formal language, pretending that it enables us to formulate a perfect theory of reasoning. But it would be equally wrong to ignore the wonderful success of these logical techniques in the areas to which they do apply.

Situations of this sort are common in science. A theory will be developed which applies beautifully to a particular subject matter, but which is less successful in accounting for other things which scientists think it ought to account for. It's natural in such cases to try to develop the theory so that it will apply equally well to these new areas. In view of its success, however, the old theory is treated with respect in this enterprise; one tries to grasp what is essential and important in the theory and to preserve these features in modifying it.

In recent years many logicians have been working along these lines and have completed a great deal of promising research concerning temporal uses of language, questions, commands, subjunctive conditionals, and locutions having to do with knowledge, belief, and perception. All of this work, however, accepts the theory we will develop here as its starting-point and foundation. Thus, although the system we will discuss in this book isn't the last word, it is by no means out of date and in fact must be learned in order to understand current research in logic.

With respect to the translation of English into formal language, this means that we should try to acquaint ourselves with the limitations of what can be rendered in the formal language. Although this enterprise may suggest certain shortcomings of the logical system, we will hold these in abeyance in order to cultivate other areas of the theory. But at the same time we shouldn't allow ourselves to become blind to these shortcomings. They exist, and furnish many challenging problems for logicians.

9. Let's start with a simple example.

(xvii)   Every football player on the field is Irish.

Although the word 'if' doesn't appear explicitly in xvii, implication is involved implicitly in this sentence. This is shown by the fact that we can paraphrase xvii accurately by saying 'If any football player is on the field, then he is Irish'. Once xvii has been restated in this way, it looks as if its translation should be a result of universally quantifying an implication. But before we can proceed further with the translation we have to decide what values our individual variables are to range over. In translating sentences that involve quantification this is as important as specifying which names the individual constants are to represent. In the present case we could choose any one of a number of domains for the individual variables; for instance, people on the field, football players, people, or physical objects.

First, suppose that our individual variables can take only people on the field as values. In this case, if we let P stand for 'football player' and Q for 'Irish', we obtain

(xviii) $(x)(Px \supset Qx)$

as our rendition of xvii. On the other hand, if we take the set of all football players to be the domain of the individual variables, we will need a predicate parameter to represent 'on the field', say R. We then get

(xix) $(x)(Rx \supset Qx)$

as our translation. Now, if we enlarge this domain so that it will include all people, we must include in the translation an explicit limitation to football players on the field. We then get something like

(xx) $(x)((Px \wedge Rx) \supset Qx)$

or, equivalently,

(xxi) $(x)(Px \supset. Rx \supset Qx)$.

If we widen the domain to include all physical objects (in a sense of 'physical object' which includes people) we can still use xx as a translation of xvii. Or, if we want to be fussy, we could let S stand for 'person' and use

(xxii) $(x)((Sx \wedge Px \wedge Rx) \supset Qx)$.

Certainly, if we continue to widen the domain (say, to include numbers or ideas as well as physical objects) we need not change our translation of xvii any more.

Which of these translations is best? To some extent this depends on contextual factors. It may be, for instance, that we wish to translate other sentences as well as xvii and to use the same domain for quantifiers in all of them. This may force us to use a very large domain and result in a translation such as xx. On the other hand, translations such as xix could be perfectly adequate for some purposes. In any case, though, xxii is overly complicated as a translation of xvii; the use of the predicate parameter S is entirely superfluous.

In choosing a domain it is a good rule to make it wide enough so that all the predicates used in the English sentence will be represented in the translation—but not to make the domain *too* wide. On this rule a good domain for xvii, taken by itself, would be the set of all people.

There are locutions of English, such as 'everyone', 'whenever', and 'wherever', which seem to function as specifications of the domain. If these words appear in a sentence to be translated, you would want to let the domain consist of persons, times, or places, unless other considerations make it necessary to select a wider domain. Take, for example,

(*xxiii*)   Wherever it's hilly, it's difficult to build.

Suppose we let P stand for 'hilly at' and Q for 'difficult to build at'. Then, letting our domain consist of all places, we can translate xxiii as follows.

(*xxiv*) $(x)(Px \supset Qx)$

The following sentence is an example in which we are forced to make the variable range over a more inclusive domain.

(*xxv*)   Whenever anyone employed at the factory is late to work, he is docked five dollars.

Here we have to talk about all persons as well as all times. Since we've provided in our formal language only for one sort of individual variable, we can't have one variable ranging over times and another over persons. So to translate xxv we must think up some domain which contains all places and all times, and must use explicit conditions in the translation to get the effect of the locutions 'whenever' and 'anyone'. Perhaps the most natural domain to use here is the set-theoretic union of the set of places and the set of times; i.e., the set of all things which are places or times. Then, if we let P stand for 'person', Q for 'employee at the factory', T for 'time', R for 'late to work at the factory at', and S for 'docked five dollars at', our rendition of xxv is

(xxvi) $(x)(Tx \supset (y)(Py \supset. Qy \supset. Ryx \supset Syx)).$

10. To get an idea of the amount of regimentation that has taken place here, let's translate xxvi back into English as literally as possible. We then get something like 'For all x, if x is a time then if y is an employee at the factory then if y is late to work at the factory at x then y is docked five dollars', where it is understood that the variables 'x' and 'y' range over people together with times. This is rather awkward and ugly prose, but doesn't seem to involve any great distortion in the meaning of xxv.

It may have occurred to you, however, that our translation of xxv could have been further refined. We could have regarded 'he is docked five dollars' as involving a relation between a person and a number rather than just a property pertaining to persons. In translating xxv we would then use a 2-ary predicate parameter, say S, to represent this relation. But when we try to say what relation S represents, we find ourselves tongue-tied: we can't say

(xxvii) S stands for 'is docked dollars'.

This brings to light a defect in our way of describing translations; it doesn't work well for relations. To take another example, if we wished to represent 'Sam ate lunch in Joe's diner at twelve o'clock' we would have to say something like

(xxviii) P stands for 'ate lunch in at',

which is nonsense. Our policy needs to be overhauled.

The trouble with xxvii and xxviii is that they give no indication of where names have been taken out of 'he is docked five dollars' and 'Sam ate lunch at Joe's diner at twelve o'clock' in passing to a relation. We can therefore solve our difficulties by using dashes and dots to indicate where names have been removed. Instead of xxvii, we'll say

(xxix) Suv stands for '... is docked ___ dollars'

and, instead of xxviii,

(xxx) $Puvw$ stands for '... ate lunch in ___ at ___'.

We will make one small exception to this in translating mathematical sentences such as 'For all i there is a j such that $i < j$'. Rather than using dashes and dots in such cases, it's more natural to use letters such as 'n'

and '*m*'. Where our translation, then, is $(x)(\exists y)Pxy$, we'll say that *Puv* stands
for '*n* is less than *m*'.

Let's use our new convention to present the revised translation of xxv. The
translation is

(***xxxi***) $(x)(Tx \supset (y)(Py \supset. \ Qy \supset. \ Ryx \supset Syax)),$

where *Tu* stands for '... is a time', *Pu* for '... is a person', *Qu* for '... is
an employee at the factory', *Suvw* for '... is docked ___ dollars at ___ ',
and *a* for 'five'. This, of course, is a slightly better translation than xxvi, since
it reveals more of the structure of xxv. However, our addition of a constant
standing for 'five' forces us to enlarge the domain. The reason for this is
that 'five' is a name of a number, not of a person or a time. And we will
require that *only individual constants that stand for names of things in the
domain of the individual variables can occur in translations*. In other words,
the domain must include everything that is spoken about. So, in example
xxxi we must let the domain consist of persons, times, and numbers. That is,
the domain will be the set {x / x is a person or x is a time or x is a number}.

11. There are many different ways of expressing universality in English;
the examples we have given above hardly begin to give an idea of their variety.
First, there are words such as 'any', 'all', 'ever', and 'whoever', which are
frequently used to say universal things. The sentences

(***xxxii***)   Any mathematician can add

(***xxxiii***)   All mathematicians can add

(***xxxiv***)   Every mathematician can add

(***xxxv***)   Whoever is a mathematician can add

all say the same thing, and would all be translated by a formula such as
$(x)(Px \supset Qx)$. Here, *Pu* represents '... is a mathematician' and *Qu* represents '... can add'. We can let the domain consist of all persons.

But the indefinite and the definite article are also used to secure universality,
as in the following proverbs.

(***xxxvi***)   A penny saved is a penny earned.

(***xxxvii***)   The man who loves well lives well.

Again, both of these will be translated by formulas of the kind $(x)(Px \supset Qx)$.

Sometimes the plural is used to indicate universality, as in

(***xxxviii***)   Opossums are marsupial,

which like our other examples can be rendered by $(x)(Px \supset Qx)$. If we changed this example to

(xxxix) Opossums are marsupials,

we might continue to translate this by $(x)(Px \supset Qx)$. Or we could proceed on the assumption that the 'is' in xxxix is an 'is' of identity. This leads to a translation such as

(xl) $(x)(Px \supset (\exists y)(x=y \land Qy))$.

In cases such as this where two different formulas seem equally good as translations of an English sentence, we are led to expect that these formulas may be logically equivalent. And indeed, after we formulate a deductive apparatus for our new formal language, we'll be able to show these translations of xxxix equivalent.

Sometimes the singular is used instead of the plural to express universality, as in

(xli) Man is born free.

Without too much distortion of meaning we can regard this as equivalent to 'All men are born free'. Its translation will then again be a formula like $(x)(Px \supset Qx)$. Locutions such as those involved in xxxviii and xli are, however, very tricky and treacherous; it is very seldom that they can be straightforwardly translated into our formal language. In Section 19, below, we discuss some of the difficulties associated with expressions of this kind.

Another way of saying something universal is illustrated by

(xlii) Those the gods love die young.

If we let Pu represent 'the gods love ...' and Qu represent '... dies young', we get the familiar formula $(x)(Px \supset Qx)$ as a translation of xlii. Here, the domain consists of persons.

It's possible to do more sophisticated things with xlii. For instance, we could construe 'dies young' as 'there is a time at which ... dies, and ... is young at that time', and 'the gods love ...' as 'every god loves ...'. We then get a translation of the sort $(x)(Px \supset. (y)(Qy \supset Ryx) \supset. (\exists z)(Sz \land Txz\,Uxz))$. Here Pu stands for '... is a person', Qu for '... is a god', Ruv for '... loves ___', Su for '... is a time', Tuv for '... dies at ___' and Uuv for '... is young at ___'. The domain might consist of persons, gods, and times. There is, however, some risk of distortion here: in particular, being loved by the gods might not involve a unanimous decision. If it's more like being approved by a committee, one might be loved by the gods and yet not loved by all the gods.

Finally, it may be surprising that words like 'none', 'nobody', and 'never' are also often used to express universality. For instance,

(*xliii*)   None of the apples in the basket is good

would be translated by

(*xliv*) $(x)((Px \land Qx) \supset \sim Rx)$,

where *Pu* stands for '... is an apple', *Qu* for '... is in the basket', and *Ru* for '... is good'. The domain can consist, say, of foodstuffs.

12. Words such as 'some', 'someone', 'somewhere', 'something', and the phrase 'there is' are fairly reliable indicators of existential quantification. A very simple example is

(*xlv*)   Some philosophers are worth knowing.

Grammatically, this looks very similar to

(*xlvi*)   All philosophers are worth knowing.

But when rendered formally, these two appear very different. Example xlv takes the form

(*xlvii*) $(\exists x)(Px \land Qx)$,

while xlvi takes the form

(*xlviii*) $(x)(Px \supset Qx)$.

Here, *Pu* stands for '... is a philosopher' and *Qu* for '... is worth knowing'; we can let the domain consist of all people.

Why does xlvii involve conjunction rather than implication? The reason is that xlv asserts a conjunction: that someone is both a philosopher and worth knowing. Rather than saying that everyone who is worth knowing is a philosopher, xlv says only that among philosophers, there is at least one who is worth knowing. Far from being a translation of xlv, the formula

(*xlix*) $(\exists x)(Px \supset Qx)$

says something that we would hardly ever want to say in English: that there is someone who is worth knowing or not a philosopher.

While xlv and xlvi are fresh in our minds, let's consider two kindred sentences.

(*l*)   Some philosopher isn't worth knowing.

(*li*)   No philosophers are worth knowing.

Like xlv, l is translated by means of conjunction and existential quantification: its translation is $(\exists x)(Px \wedge \sim Qx)$. The translation of li is $(x)(Px \supset \sim Qx)$. Formally, then, the relationship between l and li is like the relationship between xlv and xlvi.

Another example in which the existential quantifier figures is

(lii) There is someone in the next room.

This simply takes the form $(\exists x)Rx$, where Ru stands for '... is in the next room'; the domain here still consists of all persons. If we add a condition to lii and consider a sentence such as

(liii) There is someone sick in the next room,

we again get a translation, say $(\exists x)(Rx \wedge Sx)$, like xlvii. Here Su stands for '... is sick'.

With expressions like liii it often is difficult to specify a domain; take

(liv) There is something wrong with the car,

for instance. If we translate this by $(\exists x)Px$, letting Pu stand for '... is wrong with the car', what is the domain? Perhaps it should consist of defects or impairments, or perhaps, more generally, of "qualities" or "states of affairs". It's easy to see that problems of this sort can soon turn into questions of ontology or descriptive metaphysics.

In some cases of this kind, it's best to reconstruct the sentence a bit before putting it in formal notation. Consider, for instance,

(lv) There is something good to be said for everyone.

For most purposes it may do to translate this by

(lvi) $(x)Px,$

where Pu stands for '... is good in some way'. Here we can let the domain consist just of persons. If, however, we wish to get more structure in our translation, we might construe lv as saying that everyone has some good quality, and render it by

(lvii) $(x)(Px \supset (\exists y)(Qy \wedge Ry \wedge Sxy)),$

where Pu stands for '... is a person', Qu for '... is a quality'. Ru for '... is good', Suv for '... has ___', and the domain consists of persons and qualities.

Uses of the indefinite article in English are often to be translated by existential quantifiers, as in

(lviii) Jim owns a brown hat.

This can be rendered by $(\exists x)(Px \wedge Qx \wedge Rax)$, where a stands for 'Jim', Pu for '... is a hat', Qu for '... is brown', and Ruv for '... owns ___'. The domain can consist of persons together with articles of clothing.

In Section 11 we pointed out that sentences involving words like 'none' and 'nobody' can be translated using universal quantifiers. Alternatively, they can be translated by using existential quantifiers. A sentence such as

(lix)   Nobody in Indiana has heard of Latzko,

for instance, may be rendered by either of the following two formulas.

(lx) $(x)(Px \supset \sim Qxa)$

(lxi) $\sim(\exists x)(Px \wedge Qxa)$

These two formulas are equally acceptable as translations of lix. In the next chapter, we'll be able to prove them logically equivalent.

13. Many English examples require both universal and existential quantifiers. An example is

(lxii)   Every dog has its day.

We will take this in a literal rather than a metaphorical sense; letting Pu represent '... is a dog', Qu represent '... is a day' and Ruv represent '... has ___', we get

(lxiii) $(x)(Px \supset (\exists y)(Qy \wedge Rxy))$

as a translation of lxii. The domain can consist in this case of animals together with time intervals.

A similar example is

(lxiv)   Every afternoon at four o'clock there is a concert.

Let Pu stand for '... is an afternoon', Qu for '... is a concert', and a for '4 o'clock'. We also need something to stand for '... occurs at ___ on ___'; let's use $Ruvw$. Our domain will consist, say, of events, time intervals, and hours. (More exactly, the time intervals would be restricted to some period that could usually be inferred from the context in which lxiv is used; e.g., to the summer of 1968.) The translation of lxiv will then be

(lxv) $(x)(Px \supset (\exists y)(Qy \wedge Ryax)).$

A slightly different example is

(lxvi)   He who has an unhappy child is himself unhappy.

The translation of this can take either of the two equivalent forms

(lxvii) $(x)((\exists y)(Pyx \wedge Qy) \supset Qx)$

(lxviii) $(x)(y)((Pyx \wedge Qy) \supset Qx),$

where *Puv* represents '... is a child of ___', and *Qu* represents '... is unhappy'. Taking 'he' in lxvi to mean 'one', we can let the domain consist of all persons.

Notice how different

(lxix) He who has only unhappy children is himself unhappy.

looks from this when it is rendered into formal notation. Its translation is

(lxx) $(x)((y)(Pyx \supset Qy) \supset Qx).$

14. Pronouns do much the same work in English that is done in our formal language by individual variables and constants. In a formula such as $(x)(Px \supset Qx)$, the fact that the same individual variable occurs in two places is crucial. Likewise, in $(x)(y)(Pxy \supset Pyx)$, recognition that x and y are different variables and occur in different ways in Pxy and Pyx is essential to an understanding of the formula.

Similar recognition needs to be made with pronouns in English sentences, although the rules for identifying and distinguishing occurrences of pronouns are much more complex. We will illustrate this point with some examples.

In the sentence

(lxxi) If anyone is taller than John he is very tall,

we naturally assume that 'he' should be connected with 'anyone' rather than with 'John', and therefore we translate this sentence by

(lxxii) $(x)(Pxa \supset Qx),$

where *a* stands for 'John', *Puv* for '... is taller than ___' and *Qu* for '... is very tall', rather than by

(lxxiii) $(x)(Pxa \supset Qa).$

We prefer lxxii as a translation because of what we feel the meaning of lxxi should be, rather than from anything in the grammar of the sentence. This is indicated by the fact that we would want to translate

(lxxiv) If anyone is taller than John he is shorter than someone.

by a formula such as

(lxxv) $(x)(Pxa \supset (\exists y)Qay).$

Here we have connected 'he' with 'John' in lxxiv.

Some further examples are

(lxxvi)   John knows a man and dislikes him

and

(lxxvii)   John knows a man who dislikes him.

In lxxvi, 'him' connects with 'a man', and we get a translation $(\exists x)(Pax \wedge Qax)$ where a stands for 'John', Puv for '... knows ___' and Quv for '... dislikes ___'. In lxvii, 'him' connects with 'John' (and 'who' with 'a man'), and we obtain $(\exists x)(Pax \wedge Qxa)$ as a translation.

More complicated examples that illustrate similar points are the following three.

(lxxviii)   No one loves him whom he fears.

(lxxix)   No one loves him who fears him.

(lxxx)   No one loves him who fears himself.

In lxxviii 'whom' connects with 'him' and 'he' with 'no one'. In lxxix 'who' connects with the first 'him' and 'no one' with the second. In lxxx 'himself' connects with both 'him' and 'who'. If we let Puv stand for '... loves ___' and Quv for '... fears ___' we then should translate these three in the following different ways.

(lxxxi) $(x)(y)(Qxy \supset \sim Pxy)$

(lxxxii) $(x)(y)(Qxy \supset \sim Pyx)$

(lxxxiii) $(x)(y)(Qyy \supset \sim Pxy)$

In cases where it isn't clear how to connect pronouns in an English sentence there may be two genuinely different ways of rendering the sentence formally. This is a clear indication that the sentence is ambiguous or even muddled. An example is

(lxxxiv)   If anyone is taller than John he isn't very tall.

This might be translated by $(x)(Pxa \supset \sim Px)$ or by $(x)(Pxa \supset \sim Pa)$. A worse example of this sort of thing is the sentence 'A man who works for someone whose dog bit someone else hit him on the head after he had told him not to'. When such sentences come up in conversation or prose they usually meet with disapproval as being unclear and in bad style. An advantage of the grammar of our formal language is that it's arranged so that blunders of this sort can't even be expressed.

15. Often, hidden relations must be brought to light in English sentences when translating them into formal notation. Some of the examples we considered above involved this sort of thing; lxiv is one. Another is the sentence

(lxxxv) Larry met a stranger wearing an overcoat.

Let's make the domain consist of persons together with pieces of clothing, and let *a* stand for 'Larry', *Puv* for '... met ___', *Quv* for '... wore ___', and *Ru* for '... is an overcoat'. There is something suspicious about letting *Su* stand for '... is a stranger' and translating lxxxv by $(\exists x)(Pax \land Sx \land (\exists y)(Ry \land Qxy))$. The difficulty with this is that it doesn't make sense to say that someone is a stranger unless it is specified to whom. Suppose in this instance it is meant in lxxxv that the man was a stranger *to Larry*. We then get a more accurate translation by letting *Tuv* stand for 'is acquainted with', and rendering '... is a stranger' by $\sim Tau$:

(lxxxvi) $(\exists x)(Pax \land \sim Tax \land (\exists y)(Ry \land Qxy))$.

The sentence

(lxxxvii) Larry met an uncle wearing an overcoat

presents a similar problem. This could mean that Larry met an uncle of his (i.e., of Larry's) or just an uncle of someone's. To determine which was meant, we would have to know more about the context of lxxxvii.

But in any case, we can represent both of these senses formally, letting *Tuv* stand now for '... is an uncle of ___'. The first sense is then captured by $(\exists x)(Pax \land Txa \land (\exists y)(Ry \land Qxy))$, and the second by $(\exists x)(Pax \land (\exists z)Txz \land (\exists y)(Ry \land Qxy))$.

A more complicated example of disguised relations is

(lxxxviii) All the inhabitants of the village lost some of their belongings.

Here the disguised relation has to do with 'belongings'. It would be a great mistake to introduce a predicate parameter for '... is a belonging' in translating lxxxviii; we would then have no way of accounting for the locution 'their belongings'. Rather, we must use the relation '... belonged to ___'. Letting *Puv* stand for this, *Qu* for '... is an inhabitant of the village', and *Ruv* for '... lost ___', and letting the domain consist of physical objects, we can translate lxxxviii by

(lxxxix) $(x)(Qx \supset (\exists y)(Pyx \land Rxy))$.

16. It's plain that the way quantifiers are placed in a formula with respect to connectives and other quantifiers will have a great deal to do with the

formula's significance. Consider, for instance, the following three pairs of
formulas.

(xc)	$(x)(\exists y)Pxy$
(xci)	$(\exists y)(x)Pxy$
(xcii)	$(x)(Qx \lor Rx)$
(xciii)	$(x)Qx \lor (x)Rx$
(xciv)	$(x)\sim Qx$
(xcv)	$\sim(x)Qx$

The notion of the *scope* of an occurrence of a quantifier in a formula is convenient to use in discussing examples such as these. The scope of an occurrence
of a quantifier in a formula is the part of that formula on which the occurrence of the quantifier acts. In xcii, for instance, the scope of the only occurrence of (x) is the expression $Qx \lor Rx$; in xciii the scope of the first occurrence
of (x) is Qx.

The differences between xc and xci, xcii and xciii, and xciv and xcv can
easily be represented in English. Suppose, for example, that our domain
consists of all persons and that *Puv* stands for '... knows ___', *Qu* for '... is
liberal' and *Ru* for '... is conservative'. Then these examples can be rendered formally as follows.

(xcvi)	Everyone knows someone.
(xcvii)	Someone knows everyone.
(xcviii)	Everyone is liberal or conservative.
(xcix)	Everyone is liberal or everyone is conservative.
(c)	No one is liberal.
(ci)	Not everyone is liberal.

The scope of quantifiers plays an important role in translating sentences
from English into formal notation. It isn't always easy to place quantifiers
correctly, owing to the fact that in English the rules that determine distinctions of scope are rather complicated. Also these rules permit the formation of
sentences that are ambiguous in that they cannot be translated correctly
unless further information is furnished.

A good example of this is the sentence

(cii)	I wouldn't do that for anybody.

To resolve the ambiguity here, it's sufficient to hear the sentence spoken. When spoken with a rising intonation on the last two syllables, it would be translated by $\sim(x)Px$, where Pu stands for 'I would do that for …'. But when spoken with a falling intonation on the last two syllables, it would be translated by $(x)\sim Px$.

A similar example is

(ciii)   All that glitters is not gold.

In its intended sense, this sentence would be rendered by a formula such as $\sim(x)(Px \supset Qx)$. But the intended sense of the grammatically similar sentence

(civ)   All that perishes is not divine

is translated by a formula such as $(x)(Px \supset \sim Qx)$.

The words 'any' and 'every' are often used to signal distinctions of scope. An example is

(cv)   If anyone votes for Greene, he will win a moral victory.

We may contrast this with

(cvi)   If everyone votes for Greene, he will win a moral victory.

Let a stand for 'Greene', Puv for '… votes for ___' and Qu for '… will win a moral victory'. We can let the domain consist of all persons. In both sentences, 'he' should be connected with 'Greene'. Now, cv claims that Greene will win a moral victory if at least one person votes for him, and so can be translated by either of the following two formulas.

(cvii) $(x)(Pxa \supset Qa)$

(cviii) $(\exists x)Pxa \supset Qa$

(We will be able to prove these equivalent in the next chapter.) On the other hand, cvi says that Greene will win a moral victory if he gets *all* the votes; its translation is then

(cix) $(x)Pxa \supset Qa.$

As a final example, consider

(cx)   There is a remedy for every sickness.

The most natural way to construe this would yield a formula of the sort $(x)(Px \supset (\exists y)Qxy)$ as a translation. But cx could conceivably be used to assert the existence of a panacea, in which case its translation would be a formula of the sort $(\exists y)(x)(Px \supset Qxy)$. We often use locutions such as 'the same' or 'one' to indicate that scope is to be taken in the latter of these two ways; e.g., the second sense of cx would be more clearly expressed by

(cxi)   There is a single cure for every sickness.

Still, there remains a residual ambiguity in cxi. It might be used to say that every sickness has one and only one remedy.

Scope is a serious matter; it's obvious that a small difference in scope (e.g., the difference between xciv and xcv) can make an enormous change in meaning. For this reason it's important to carefully check any translation of an English sentence to make sure that the intended scope has been achieved.

17. None of the examples that we have considered so far have involved identity in any significant way. Identity, however, does figure prominently in the translation of many sentences from natural language. For instance, 'any' is frequently used to mean 'any other', as in the sentence

(cxii)   John is taller than anyone in the room.

Even if John is in the room, cxii is not meant to imply that he is taller than himself. It's short for 'John is taller than anyone else in the room', and so should be translated by

(cxiii) $(x)(\sim x = a \supset Pax)$,

where a stands for 'John' and Puv for '... is taller than ___'.

A similar example is

(cxiv)   Monday is the first day of the week.

To simplify things, let the domain consist of just days of the week. Also, let a stand for 'Monday' and Puv for '... comes earlier in the week than ___'. The formula cxiii will then serve as a translation of cxiv.

Often the plural commits us to the existence of more than one thing of a certain kind, as in

(cxv)   There are some cats in that bag.

If we take this to mean that there are *at least two* cats in the bag, the formula $(\exists x)(Px \wedge Qx)$ is inadequate as a translation of cxv. (Here Pu stands for '... is a cat' and Qu for '... is in that bag'.) A far better translation is

(cxvi) $(\exists x)(\exists y)(\sim x = y \wedge Px \wedge Qx \wedge Py \wedge Qy)$.

Generalizing the strategy used in this translation we could find formal ways of representing expressions such as 'there are at least three', 'all but one', and 'there are more than one but fewer than five'.

Since different occurrences of the same individual constant or variable in a formula are always connected as referring to the same thing, a formula $(\exists x)Pxx$ means that something bears a certain relation to *itself*. For instance, if *Puv* stands for '... employs ___' and the domain consists of all persons, $(\exists x)Pxx$ will correspond to 'Someone is self-employed'.

Reflexive pronouns such as 'himself', 'herself', and 'itself', and generally the word 'self', are clues that an English sentence should be translated by a formula with two or more occurrences of the same individual variable or constant. In translating such sentences, you usually go from a particular sentence (e.g. 'John employs himself') to a relation which can relate different things (John and Roger can stand in the relation expressed by '... employs ___'). Then you can say that a thing is related to itself by putting a term at more than one place in an expression ('John employs John'). This can then be readily translated into formal notation.

An example illustrating everything we have said in this section is the sentence

(*cxvii*)   Anyone who looks after himself can trust himself to look after others.

We can translate this by letting *Puv* stand for '... looks after ___', *Quv* for '... can trust ___ to look after ____', and the domain consist of all persons. The formula that then emerges is

(*cxviii*) $$(x)(Pxx \supset (y)(\sim x=y \supset Qxxy)).$$

18. The meanings of many English sentences depend flagrantly on the context in which they are used; they involve the here and now. Some typical examples of this dependence are the following sentences.

(*cxix*)   I am older than you.
(*cxx*)   Norman is thirty-five years old.
(*cxxi*)   It rained yesterday.
(*cxxii*)   That cap fits this jar.
(*cxxiii*)   The mayor was present at the banquet.

To understand a use of cxix we must know who is speaking and who is being addressed. To understand a use of cxx we must know when it took place; if we knew only that cxx was asserted between 1965 and 1970, we wouldn't be able to tell how old Norman is. Similarly, cxxi is intelligible only with respect to a time and a place; we must know where and when it is used to see what it means. In cxxii and cxxiii, contextual features determine the reference of terms such as 'that cap' and 'the mayor'. This would typically be accomplished by pointing while uttering cxxii. In the case of cxxiii, there are many indicators that could establish which mayor and which banquet are singled out; these will usually occur in previous conversation.

These examples show that, in general, one can't speak of English sentences as having a noncontextual meaning. These sentences can be used on different occasions, and they take on meanings that vary from occasion to occasion. Example cxix means one thing when Warren says it to Agatha, and another when Agatha says it to Warren. The features of an occasion which are most relevant in conferring meaning are those that are suggested by the above examples: speaker, addressee, time, place, and "indicational features" which serve to point out the reference of various terms, especially demonstratives such as 'this' and 'that'.

People sometimes get the idea that when English is translated into formal notation, these "occasion-bound" features should be eliminated in some way or other. According to this view of formalization, in translating a sentence such as cxix you first have to find out that Warren is saying it to Agatha, and then translate it by Pab, where a stands for 'Warren' and b for 'Agatha'. And similarly, the translation of cxxi would have to contain an explicit reference to some date and location.

This policy adds nothing to the clarity of translation and a good deal to its complexity. It's much easier to suppose in translating an English sentence by a formula that the formula takes on meaning with respect to whatever occasion gives meaning to the English sentence. Thus, when we translate cxix by Pab, we need only say that a stands for 'I' and b for 'you'. Similarly, we can translate cxxii by Qcd, letting c stand for 'the mayor', d for 'the banquet', and Quv for '. . . attended ___'. In doing this sort of thing we need only make sure that when we translate several sentences at once, they must all be determined by one and the same occasion.

Examples cxxi and cxxiii do suggest one limitation on translation into our formal language: we can't represent any connection between different tenses of the same verb in rendering English into formal notation. For instance, in translating

(*cxxiv*)   Helen was a citizen of England and is a citizen of Canada

we must use wholly different formulas, say Puv and Quv, to stand for '. . . was a citizen of ___' and '. . . is a citizen of ___'. Letting a stand for 'Helen', b for 'England', and c for 'Canada', we then get $Pab \land Qac$ as a translation of cxxiv. This captures some of the structure of the sentence, but fails to represent any relation between being a citizen and having been a citizen.

Sentences such as

(*cxxv*)   The battle of Trafalgar took place before the battle of Waterloo

raise special problems. Let *a* stand for 'the battle of Trafalgar' and *b* for 'the battle of Waterloo'. When we translate cxxv by *Pab*, should we say that *Puv* stands for '. . . occurs before ___' or for '. . . occurred before ___'? We can use the former translation if we believe that cxxv is a timeless truth; i.e., one whose truth-value doesn't change from time to time. Otherwise we should use the latter translation. This leads us to ask whether cxxv can be true *before* the battle of Trafalgar; this is a philosophical problem which raises profound issues about time. Here is another case in which the task of translation leads us directly into philosophy.

19. Before concluding our account of translation, we should discuss more fully some of the difficulties that can arise in translation. Although the examples that we will choose can give only a rough idea of the limits of sensible translation, they may help to provide a feel for the ways in which distortion may arise when English is squeezed into formal notation.

Back in Section 11, we remarked that constructions involving the plural can sometimes be tricky. An example is

(*cxxvi*)   Carrots are good to eat.

It would be a blunder to translate this by a formula such as $(x)(Px \supset Qx)$; cxxvi doesn't mean that all carrots are good to eat. For instance, the fact that a rotten carrot isn't good to eat doesn't make cxxvi false. Perhaps, then, cxxvi means that *most* carrots are good to eat, or that *almost all* carrots are good to eat. Even though this idea is superficial in some respects, it still can't be handled by our formal language. The best we can do in translating 'Almost all carrots are good to eat' is to represent it by *P*. Another way of construing cxxvi would be to say that it means that *as a rule* any carrot is good to eat, or that *all things being equal* any carrot is good to eat. But again, we can't do better than *P* in rendering this formally.

An even worse example than this is

(*cxxvii*)   The dog is man's best friend.

Plainly this doesn't mean that any dog is any man's best friend, or that any dog is some man's best friend, or any variant of this. And even if we translate cxxvii by *Pa*, letting *a* stand for 'the dog', we still are in difficulties, since we have to say what sort of thing "the dog" is. Again, it seems that the best we can do is *P*.

Adjectives aren't always all they seem to be. The usual pattern for translating a sentence such as 'Sam is a brown dog' is $Pa \wedge Qa$, where a stands for 'Sam', Pu for '... is brown', and Qu for '... is a dog'. But if we do this to

(*cxxviii*)   Beatrice is a small elephant

we are, in effect, paraphrasing it as

(*cxxix*)   Beatrice is small and Beatrice is an elephant,

which is absurd. Perhaps the best we can do in translating cxxviii is to let Pu stand for '... is small, for an elephant', Qu for '... is an elephant', and a for 'Beatrice', and to render it by $Pa \wedge Qa$.

A similar example is

(*cxxx*)   That's a fake diamond.

We want to construe this as saying something like 'That looks like a diamond, but isn't a diamond' before translating it.

The trouble with adverbs is that it's almost always impossible to represent them as separate from the verb. For instance, take

(*cxxxi*)   She skates well.

About the best we can do with this is to use Pa to translate it, letting Pu stand for '... skates well' and a for 'she'. If we try to find a translation in which the adverb is separated from the verb, we might first paraphrase cxxxi by

(*cxxxii*)   She skates and does it well.

We would then find ourselves quantifying over actions or abilities or something of the sort. There is nothing intrinsically wrong with this, but doing it raises philosophical problems that would have to be considered if we were to take this translation seriously. In particular, we would have to ask questions such as "What are actions?" and "What is it to do an action?"

20. Like most healthy areas of inquiry, logic has its frontiers and areas of controversy and doubt, as well as its safe and secure territory. Although our account of translation in this chapter has carried us out to the boundaries, when we turn in the next chapter to the problem of characterizing valid inference by means of derivations we will want to minimize all problems connected with translation. This will make it much easier to tell good from bad arguments.

In Chapter IX, then, we will confine ourselves entirely to mathematical material in selecting examples; our domain will always consist of the non-negative integers 0, 1, 2, and so on.

Exercises

1. Which of the following are formulas?

(a) $(x)(x)(x)x = x$

(b) $u = a$

(c) $x = a$

(d) $(\exists x)x$

(e) $(\exists x)u$

(f) $(\exists x)Px$

(g) $(\exists y)Pu$

(h) $(x)(\exists y)Pxy \lor \sim(\exists y)(x)Qx$

(i) $Pab = Qb$

(j) $(\exists x)(a = b \lor (Px \land (x = a \land Pa)))$

(k) $Qab \supset (\exists P)Pab$

(l) $(Pw \equiv Pw) \equiv (\exists x)(x = y \land Py)$

2. Translate the following into formal notation, specifying in each case what the predicate parameters and individual constants you use are standing for, as well as the domain of the individual variables.

(a) All oaks are deciduous.

(b) Margaret is unhappy.

(c) John and Susan are married.

(d) None of the glasses in this shipment is broken.

(e) None but the wise are free.

(f) Bill knows everyone in St. Louis worth knowing.

(g) No one in St. Louis Bill doesn't know is worth knowing.

(h) A jest breaks no bones.

(i) Every day she is at home someone calls her.

(j) Every cloud has a silver lining.

(k) Anyone who buys a pair of pants without trying them on is an optimist or a blockhead.

(l) It is only the ignorant who despise education.

(m) A rolling stone gathers no moss.

(n) No one tries harder than he does.

(o) No one who doesn't love himself loves anyone.

(p) No one who doesn't love himself loves everyone.

(q) No man but a blockhead ever writes except for money.

(r) Food good enough for anybody is good enough for everybody.

(s) Γ implies A if and only if A is made true by every valuation by which every formula in Γ is made true.

(t) Wisdom is the only virtue.

(u) The same shoe does not fit every foot.

(v) Patience is the best remedy for every trouble.

(w) Everyone here is going in the same car.

(x) There are some remedies worse than the disease.

(y) If he obeys the law, everyone who owns a restaurant will not refuse to serve anyone in it on account of his race.

(z) No one will win the nomination unless everyone on the committee has no objection to him.

3. The following translations are in general more difficult. Treat those that can be translated as in E2; explain why those that cannot be translated are untranslatable.

(a) Everyone in the next room is sitting or standing.

(b) Nothing is said now that has not been said before.

(c) If the shoe fits, put it on.

(d) Whatever lacks knowledge cannot move towards an end if it be not directed by some being endowed with knowledge and intelligence.

(e) He who laughs last laughs best.

(f) There is something going on downtown tonight.

(g) I always keep a glass of water at hand.

(h) If no one obeys, then who will rule?

(i) Harris is the clerk who waited on me, and no one will dare to deny it.

(j) There is nothing which has been contrived by man by which so much happiness is produced as by a good tavern or inn.

(k) If anyone writes me, forward the letter to me.

(l) He is the man on the far right.

(m) A formula A of **M** is valid if V satisfies A, for any valuation V of **M**.

(n) Harold's wife feels groggy whenever she hasn't had enough sleep.

(o) At least three congressmen are over eighty years old.

(p) In Turkey there are two wives with the same husband.

(q) No one knows whether Marlowe is the author of *Hamlet*.

(r) If it rains today, everyone going to the picnic will be sorry.

(s) He believes that every anarchist wears a beard.

(t) Whoever made these tracks walked with a limp.

(u) Most donkeys are stubborn.

(v) A man who left a coat of his at the theatre returned later for it.

(w) All but one of my children are boys.

Problems

1. Devise a formal language which generalizes the one developed in this chapter by providing for *function parameters*. Such a parameter would stand, for instance, for the symbol '+' in '2 + 2 = 4'. Here '2 + 2' is a complex term. Give inductive definitions of *term* and of *formula* for this language.

2. How should sentences be translated which seem to involve terms which don't refer to anything? A classic example of this is 'The present king of France is bald'.

3. Is there any good way to translate any of the following sentences into formal notation?

(a) If at any time nothing were in existence, then nothing would ever exist.

(b) Santa Claus doesn't exist.

(c) He is every inch a king.

(d) Words once spoken can never be recalled.

(e) There is no genius without some touch of madness.

(f) The cheetah runs faster than the greyhound.

(h) Doctors are patient.

(i) Cigarettes are unhealthy.

(j) Ewes give milk for lambs to drink.

IX Predicate Logic with Identity: Natural Deduction Techniques

1. Now that we have an idea of what the language of predicate logic looks like and of how to translate English sentences into this language, we want to develop a proof procedure for it. As before, we'll start with a system of natural deduction. The development of this system will follow pretty much the same pattern it did in Chapters III and IV; by considering how we in fact reason about universality, existence, and identity, we will try to devise introduction and elimination rules for universal quantification, existential quantification, and identity.

In order to carry out this program we must first develop a metalinguistic notation for dealing with predicate logic. In particular, we need some way of describing the processes of universal and existential quantification. Let's consider once more the relationship between an English sentence involving an individual parameter, say

(*i*) $$n < n + 1$$

and an explicitly universal sentence obtained from it, such as

(ii) For every n, $n < n + 1$.

In translating i and ii into formulas, we must translate the occurrences of 'n' in i by an individual parameter, and the occurrences of 'n' in ii by an individual variable. If we let Puv stand for '$n < m + 1$', we then obtain

(iii) Puu

and

(iv) $(x)Pxx$

as translations of i and ii. We will say that iv is a *universal quantification* of iii.

Now we must ask a general question: given an arbitrary formula A, how do we obtain a universal quantification of it? We can begin to answer this question by describing in general terms what happened in passing from iii to iv; we first exchanged all occurrences of an individual parameter u in A for occurrences of an individual variable x, and then prefixed a universal quantifier (x) to the resulting expression. In particular, we get the expression Pxx (which, by the way, is not a formula) by substituting x for u in iii. Then we prefix (x) to Pxx to obtain iv.

Before we say anything more about universal quantification, let's take a closer look at this notion of substitution of individual variables for individual parameters in formulas. What we will now define is a more general notion of substitution of individual variables for individual parameters in *expressions*; i.e., in strings of symbols of our formal language which may or may not be formulas. We will use 'X' and 'Y' as metavariables ranging over expressions.

Where X is any expression, x an individual variable, and u an individual parameter, Y is *the result of substituting x for u in X* if Y is obtained by replacing every occurrence of u in X by an occurrence of x. Notice that this is very like substitution of formulas for sentence parameters, except that now we're substituting individual variables for individual parameters. Coining a new notation for talking about this sort of substitution, let's use '$X\,^x/u$' for the result of substituting x for u in X. For substitution in formulas, we will use notation such as '$A\,^x/u$'. (The symbol '/' is meant to suggest division. To remember how to use this notation, think of $A\,^x/u$ as obtained from A by "factoring out" u and "multiplying" by x.) Although $A\,^x/u$ will not in general be a formula, $(x)A\,^x/u$ will always be a formula.

In view of what we said above, it's tempting to go on to say that $(x)A\,^x/u$ will always be a universal quantification of A, but first there is one anomalous case that must be ruled out. It may happen that there are universal quantifiers (x) buried in A and that there are occurrences of u within the scope of these quantifiers. In cases of this sort, things go wrong when x is substituted for u in A. For instance, let A be the formula

(v) $\qquad\qquad\qquad\qquad \sim Pu \supset (x)(Px \supset \sim Pu).$

We can understand v more clearly if we regard it as the translation of an English sentence, say

(vi) $\qquad$ If n is not even then if any k is even n is not even.

The sentence vi evidently is true; if a number is not even, it will still be not even in case any number k is even. Not only is vi true, but we will soon be able to derive v as a theorem of logic.

010 However, if we substitute x for u in the formula v, we obtain the expression $\sim Px \supset (x)(Px \supset \sim Px)$. Then prefixing a universal quantifier (x), we get

(vii) $\qquad\qquad\qquad\qquad (x)(\sim Px \supset (x)(Px \supset \sim Px)).$

This formula corresponds to the English sentence 'If any number is not even then any number which is even is not even', which plainly is false. There are many numbers that are not even, but it is false that any even number is not even.

This example shows that we must not allow vii to count as a universal quantification of v. For vii is false, even though the formula v is true universally, in the same sense that vi is true for all values of n. There is yet another way of looking at what has gone wrong here. If we universalize a formula A with respect to an individual parameter u by passing to a formula $(x)A \, {}^x/u$, we should expect the outermost universal quantifier to act on occurrences of x in $(x)A \, {}^x/u$ at just those places where in A there was an occurrence of u. Otherwise $(x)A \, {}^x/u$ will not generalize what is said by A about the values of u. But in vii, the outermost quantifier does *not* act on the rightmost occurrence of x. This is because its action is blocked by a second quantifier (x). Owing to this accident, vii is not a universal quantification of v.

To exclude cases such as this, we will introduce the notion of u being *free for x in A*. An individual parameter u is free for an individual variable x in a formula A if there are no occurrences of u within the scope of a quantifier (x) or $(\exists x)$ in A. (Notice that u isn't free for x in the formula v.) If u is free for x in A, then difficulties of the sort we discussed above will not arise when we pass from A to $(x)A \, {}^x/u$. The outermost quantifier (x) acts on occurrences of x in $A \, {}^x/u$ at every place where u occurs in A, since there are no hidden quantifiers in A to block the effect of the quantifier.

We will therefore stipulate that $(x)A \, ^x/u$ is a universal quantification of A provided that u is free for x in A. This makes $(x)Pxx$ a universal quantification of Puu and $(y)(\sim Py \supset (x)(Px \supset \sim Py))$ a universal quantification of $\sim Pu \supset (x)(Px \supset \sim Pu)$. But it rules out $(x)(\sim Px \supset (x)(Px \supset \sim Px))$ as a universal quantification of $\sim Pu \supset (x)(Px \supset \sim Pu)$ and $(y)\sim(y)Pyy$ as a universal quantification of $\sim(y)Puy$.

For convenience in this and later chapters of this book, we will always assume when we use the notation '$(x)A \, ^x/u$' that u is free for x in A. This convention will save us the trouble of having always to use clauses like 'provided u is free for x in A'. In order to be thoroughly explicit, however, we will often state provisions of this kind in formulating rules, stating meta-theorems, and the like.

2. The relation of a formula to its universal quantification is one of two syntactic notions of crucial importance in predicate logic; the other is the relation of a universal formula to its *instances*. The relation between the sentences

(viii)   For every n, if $n > 2$ then $n > 1$

and

(ix)   If $2 > 2$ then $2 > 1$

or between

(x)   Every citizen has responsibilities

and

(xi)   If Jones is a citizen then Jones has responsibilities

is what we have in mind here. The sentences ix and xi are instances of the universal sentences viii and x; viii and x express universal things of which ix and xi, respectively, are particular cases.

It may occur to you that instantiation is just universal quantification in reverse, so that A will be an instance of B if and only if B is a universal quantification of A. This, however, is false; sometimes A is an instance of B, but B is not a universal quantification of A. To see how this can be so, let's render the above examples formally. Letting Puv stand for 'm is greater than n', a for '1', and b for '2', we obtain

(xii) $(x)(Pxb \supset Pxa)$

and

(xiii) $Pbb \supset Pba$

as translations of viii and ix. And letting Qu stand for '... is a citizen', Ru for '... has responsibilities', and c for 'Jones', we get

(*xiv*) $(y)(Qy \supset Ry)$

and

(*xv*) $Qc \supset Rc$

as translations of x and xi.

One reason why xii and xiv aren't universal quantifications of xiii and xv, respectively, is that b and c are individual constants rather than individual parameters. One difference between universal quantification and instantiation, then, is that you can only universally quantify with respect to individual parameters, whereas you can instantiate with any term. But there is a much more important difference than this, as can be seen by substituting u for b in xii and xiii to obtain the following formulas.

(*xvi*) $(x)(Pxu \supset Pxa)$

(*xvii*) $Puu \supset Pua$

We surely want to say here that xvii is an instance of xvi; it expresses a particular case of the universal claim made by xvi. But xvi is not a universal quantification of xvii; it is not obtained by substituting x for u in xvii and prefixing the quantifier (x) to the resulting expression. In other words, xvi does not stand to xvii as $(x)A\ ^{x}/u$ stands to A.

Nevertheless, xvi is a universal quantification of another formula; in particular, of

(*xviii*) $Pvu \supset Pva.$

If we let A be xviii, then $(x)A\ ^{x}/v$ is xvi. If we regard xvi in this way as a universal quantification of xviii, it's easy to describe the relation between xvi and its instances such as xvii; the formula xvii is obtained from xviii by substituting u for v.

Here we are using a slightly different kind of substitution, in which an individual parameter v is exchanged for an individual parameter u. More generally, we can speak of substituting an individual term s for an individual term t in an expression X; this is defined just like substitution of an individual variable for an individual term in an expression. Where X is any expression and s and t are terms, Y is *the result of substituting s for t in X* if Y is obtained by replacing every occurrence of t in X by an occurrence of s. We'll use the same notation for this kind of substitution, so that '$A\ ^s/t$' will stand for the result of substituting s for t in the formula A.

We can now describe the relation of xvi to xvii. First, let A be xviii; i.e., A is $Pvu \supset Pva$. Then xvi is $(x)A\ ^x/v$ and xvii, an instance of A, is $A\ ^u/v$. Generalizing this, we can say that the instances of a formula $(x)A\ ^x/v$ are those formulas of the kind $A\ ^t/v$. This works for our other examples as well. If we let example x be $(x)A\ ^x/v$, A will be $Pvb \supset Pva$ and xi will then be the result $A\ ^b/v$ of substituting b for v in A. Similarly, if we let example xii be $(y)A\ ^y/w$, A will then be $Qw \supset Rw$ and xv will be $A\ ^c/w$.

Notice that according to the convention we have established regarding the notation '$(x)A\ ^x/u$', $A\ ^t/u$ will be an instance of $(x)A\ ^x/u$ only if u is free for x in A. This requirement is as important for instantiation as it is for universal quantification. If it were dropped, we would run into cases in which we would have to say that B is an instance of A, even though A can translate a true and B a false sentence. For an example of this, see XI.E14.

In these sections we have clarified the notions of a *universal quantification* of a formula and an *instance* of a universally quantified formula. We can summarize our results as follows. Where A is any formula, $(x)A\ ^x/u$ is a universal quantification of A with the individual variable x with respect to the individual parameter u. And where $(x)A\ ^x/u$ is a universally quantified formula and t an individual term, $A\ ^t/x$ is an instance of $(x)A\ ^x/u$. Both cases are subject to the restriction that u must be free for x in A.

3. Now let's turn to the problem of formulating a rule of universal quantification introduction. In other words, we are asking how we reason to universally quantified conclusions. As in Chapters IV and V we will work with examples from mathematics such as the following argument, in which it is shown that for all n, if $n < 2^n$ then $n + 1 < 2^{n+1}$.

1. Suppose that $m < 2^m$, where m is an arbitrary number.
2. Then $m + 1 < 2^m + 1$.
3. But $1 \leq 2^m$.
4. By step 3, $2^m + 1 \leq 2^m + 2^m$.
5. By 2 and 4, $m + 1 < 2^m + 2^m$.
6. But $2^m + 2^m = 2 \cdot 2^m$ and $2 \cdot 2^m = 2^{m+1}$.
7. By 6, $2^m + 2^m = 2^{m+1}$.
8. By 5 and 7, $m + 1 < 2^{m+1}$.
9. In view of steps 1 to 8, if $m < 2^m$ then $m + 1 < 2^{m+1}$.
10. Hence for all n, if $n < 2^n$ then $n + 1 < 2^{n+1}$.

$$(xix)$$

Steps 2 to 8 of this argument are justified by mathematical considerations or by rules for identity. Putting off questions about identity until later, we're left with steps 1, 9, and 10. Now, step 9 is a consequence of steps 1 to 8 by the rule of implication introduction. If we put this part of xix into our formal notation and display it in the format of Chapters III and IV, steps 1 to 8 will therefore be entries of a subordinated derivation. Step 9 will then be a categorical consequence of this derivation, as follows.

$$
\begin{array}{ll}
1 & \quad\left\lceil\; Puu \right. \\
  & \qquad \vdots \\
8 & \quad\left\lfloor\; Quu \right. \\
9 & \quad Puu \supset Quu \\
10 & \quad (x)(Pxx \supset Qxx)
\end{array}
$$

$$(xx)$$

Our translation of these four steps is obtained by letting Puv stand for 'i is less than 2^j', and Quv for '$i + 1$ is less than 2^{j+1}'. (It may occur to you that there are better ways of translating xix—and in fact, there are—but xx is good enough for our present purposes. One factor that makes translation of such examples a bit awkward for us is that there are no *function parameters* in our formal language; i.e., symbols corresponding to mathematical expressions such as '$+$'. In this connection, see VIII.P1.)

It is in step 10 of the argument that a universally quantified conclusion is introduced. The form of this inference appears to be as follows.

$$
\frac{A}{(x)A\;^x/u}
$$

This is merely a matter of passing from a formula to one of its universalizations.

But there must be more than this to the rule of universal quantification introduction, since surely we can't be justified in universalizing in this fashion under *any* circumstances. If we were permitted to pass without any restriction to $(x)A\;^x/u$ from A, we could easily derive $Qu \supset (x)Qx$ categorically, as follows.

$$
\begin{array}{ll}
1 & \quad\left\lceil\; Qu \right. \\
2 & \quad\left\lfloor\; (x)Qx \right. \\
3 & \quad Qu \supset (x)Qx
\end{array}
$$

$$(xxi)$$

But this plainly isn't the sort of thing we would want to have in a system of logic; it has many unwelcome consequences. Using this principle, for instance, we could show that $1 = 2$, as follows. Suppose that $1 = m$. Then (by the argument of xxi), for all n, $1 = n$. Hence $1 = 2$. This absurdity indicates that there must be something wrong with xxi.

In order to see what it is that makes xix a good argument and xxi a bad one, let's try an analogue of xxi in English. Suppose we take Qu to stand for 'n is even'. Then xxi would correspond to an argument like the following.

1. Suppose that m is even.
2. Then all numbers are even.
3. Hence if m is even, all numbers are even.

Here, the difficulty isn't hard to spot; it has to do with the fact that the parameter 'm' in step 1 doesn't stand for an *arbitrary* number. In supposing that m is even, we've made assumptions about m that do not hold for all numbers, and so we are quite unjustified in universalizing with respect to 'm' in step 2. This fallacy is just like proving that every triangle is equilateral by saying "Let ABC be an arbitrary triangle" (meanwhile drawing an equilateral triangle, and labeling it 'ABC'), and then continuing, "This triangle is equilateral; therefore all triangles are equilateral." The flaw in both arguments consists in universalizing an unwarranted assumption involving an individual parameter.

In xix, on the other hand, no such error has been made; step 9, the only premiss for universalization in this argument, is derived *categorically*, using only assumptions that hold generally for numbers. An assumption about m is indeed made in step 1 of the argument, but this assumption is discharged by an application of implication introduction before any universalization takes place.

What we want to do in our formal system is to ensure that universal quantifier introduction with respect to an individual parameter u is used only in cases where no assumptions involving u are operative. A good way to carry this out is to add a new structural device to the format of derivations. We will use vertical lines flagged with a parameter as *barriers* across which no formula containing free occurrences of that parameter can be reiterated. These lines serve to exclude any unwarranted assumptions from being used for purposes of generalization. Our formulation of the rule of universal quantifier introduction will require that the premiss of any instance of the rule must be hedged by one of these lines. Schematically, the rule looks like this.

$$
u \left|
\begin{array}{l}
\vdots \\
\vdots \\
A \\
\vdots \\
\end{array}
\right.
$$

$$(x)A \, ^x/u$$

Let's say that an individual parameter u is *arbitrary* in any step that occurs to the immediate right of a line flagged with u. Then the rule of universal quantifier introduction (uq int) permits one to infer $(x)A \, ^x/u$, provided that u is arbitrary in some previous occurrence of A as a step in the derivation, and, of course, that u is free for x in A.

Going back now to example xxi, we can see that step 2 of this example is not a legitimate application of uq int. As we have formulated this rule, to get $(x)Qx$ as a step in this derivation we would have to get Qu inside a barrier flagged with u, like this.

$$
\left|
\begin{array}{l}
\underline{Qu} \\
u \left|
\begin{array}{l}
\\
Qu
\end{array}
\right.
\end{array}
\right.
$$

But there doesn't seem to be any way to do this: it certainly can't be done by reiteration, since Qu can't be reiterated through the barrier.

On the other hand, if we discharge the hypothesis of this argument, we can universalize with respect to u; but now the conclusion of the derivation is $(x)(Qx \supset Qx)$, not $Qu \supset (x)Qx$. The following is thus a correct derivation.

$$
\begin{array}{lll}
1 & u \left| \; \right| \, Qu & \text{hyp} \\
2 & \; | \; Qu \supset Qu & \text{1, imp int} \\
3 & (x)(Qx \supset Qx) & \text{2, uq int}
\end{array}
$$

4. Here are some examples of derivations in which the rule of universal quantifier introduction is used in combination with rules for sentence connectives. Annotating these examples is left as an exercise.

$$
\left|
\begin{array}{l}
\underline{Pa} \\
u \left|
\begin{array}{l}
\underline{Pu} \\
Pu \lor Pv \\
\end{array}
\right. \\
Pu \supset (Pu \lor Pv) \\
Pa \\
Pa \land (Pu \supset (Pu \lor Pv)) \\
(y)(Pa \land (Py \supset (Py \lor Pv)))
\end{array}
\right.
$$

(xxxii)

$$
\left|
\begin{array}{l}
\underline{Pu} \\
u \left|
\begin{array}{l}
\underline{Qu \land Qa} \\
Qa \\
\end{array}
\right. \\
(Qu \land Qa) \supset Qa \\
(x)((Qx \land Qa) \supset Qa) \\
Pu \land (x)((Qx \land Qa) \supset Qa)
\end{array}
\right.
$$

(xxiii)

$\sim (\exists x)Px$

u

$\sim (\exists x)Px$

$(y) \sim (\exists x)Px$

(xxiv)

w

$Pw \lor Pv$

Pw

v

Pw

$(x)Pw$

$(x)Pw \lor Pv$

Pv

$(x)Pw \lor Pv$

$(x)Pw \lor Pv$

$(Pw \lor Pv) \supset ((x)Pw \lor Pv)$

$(y)((Py \lor Pv) \supset ((x)Py \lor Pv))$

(xxv)

Examples xxiv and xxv involve what is called *vacuous quantification*; certain formulas in these examples are quantified with respect to variables that do not occur in them. Nothing we have said about formulas excludes this sort of thing, and we will regard $(x)Pa$ and $(x)Quv$, for instance, as perfectly good formulas, even though there is really no point to the quantifier in such cases. Although such expressions are redundant and rather pointless, they are not ungrammatical in our formal system. (One reason for this is that allowing them makes the system's *formation rules*—the rules determining what counts as a formula—simpler.) It will turn out according to our deductive theory that vacuous quantifications have no logical effect on formulas; we will be able to derive $A \equiv (x)A \, {}^x/u$ categorically whenever u does not occur in A.

5. Using only one of the rules for universal quantification, we can't derive very much; the above examples really aren't very complicated. What we need, of course, is a rule of universal quantifier elimination. To see this rule in action, let's consider an argument in which we're required to reason *from* a universally quantified step. Suppose, for instance, that we want to show that if every number whose square is less than 30 is less than 6, then every number whose square is less than 20 is less than 6. We might argue in the following way.

1. Suppose that for all n, if $n^2 < 30$ then $n < 6$.
2. Suppose that $m^2 < 20$, for an arbitrary number m.
3. By step 1, if $m^2 < 30$, then $m < 6$.
4. But $20 < 30$.
5. So, by steps 2 and 4, $m^2 < 30$.

6. By steps 3 and 5, $m < 6$.

7. Therefore, if $m^2 < 20$ then $m < 6$.

8. But m was arbitrary; so for all k, if $k^2 < 20$ then $k < 6$.

(*xxvi*)

Let's translate xxvi into formal notation by letting *Puv* stand for '$j^2 < k$'; *Qux* for '$j < k$'; and *a*, *b*, and *c* for '6', '20', and '30', respectively. We then get the following derivation.

$$
\begin{array}{ll}
1 & \;\; (x)(Pxc \supset Qxa) \\
2 & \quad u\;\; \;\;\; Pub \\
3 & \qquad\;\; (x)(Pxc \supset Qxa) \\
4 & \qquad\;\; Puc \supset Qua \\
5 & \qquad\;\; Qbc \\
6 & \qquad\;\; Puc \\
7 & \qquad\;\; Qua \\
8 & \quad\;\; Pub \supset Qua \\
9 & \;\; (y)(Pyb \supset Qya)
\end{array}
$$

(*xxvii*)

Steps 5 and 6 of xxvii are warranted by mathematical considerations, and step 9 by the rule of universal quantifier introduction. The other steps, except for 4, are justified by structural rules or rules for sentence connectives. Step 4, at which the universal hypothesis made in step 1 is used, was obtained by an inference taking the following form.

$$\frac{(x)A\,^{x}/v}{A\,^{u}/v}.$$

In other words, this step is simply an instantiation by an individual parameter u. In general, we will allow instantiation by any term to be justified by the rule of universal quantifier elimination, so that the form of this rule will be as follows.

$$
\begin{array}{l}
\vdots \\
(x)A\,^{x}/u \\
\vdots \\
A\,^{t}/u
\end{array}
$$

The rule of universal quantifier elimination (uq elim) allows us to pass in a derivation to any formula of the sort $A\ ^t/u$, provided that there is a previous step $(x)A\ ^x/u$ in the derivation, and, of course, that u is free for x in A.

6. With the rules of universal quantifier introduction and elimination, together with the rules of S_s, we have a system of logic that is much more advanced and powerful than sentential systems and we can construct derivations of considerable complexity. But let's start with some simple examples.

1	$(x)\sim\sim Px$	hyp
2	u $(x)\sim\sim Px$	1, reit
3	$\sim\sim Pu$	2, uq elim
4	Pu	3, neg elim
5	$(x)Px$	4, uq int

(*xxviii*)

1	$(x)Px$	hyp
2	u $(x)Px$	1, reit
3	Pu	2, uq elim
4	$(y)Py$	3, uq int

(*xxix*)

1	$(x)(Px \supset Qx)$	hyp
2	$(x)Px$	hyp
3	u $(x)(Px \supset Qx)$	1, reit
4	$(x)Px$	2, reit
5	$Pu \supset Qu$	3, uq elim
6	Pu	4, uq elim
7	Qu	5, 6, m p
8	$(x)Qx$	7, uq int
9	$(x)Px \supset (x)Qx$	2–8, imp int

(*xxx*)

1	$(x)((\exists x)Px \supset Qx)$	hyp
2	$(\exists x)Px$	hyp
3	u $(\exists x)Px$	2, reit
4	$(x)((\exists x)Px \supset Qx)$	1, reit
5	$(\exists x)Px \supset Qu$	4, uq elim
6	Qu	3, 5, m p
7	$(x)Qx$	6, uq int
8	$(\exists x)Px \supset (x)Qx$	2–7, imp int

(*xxxi*)

7. We now need to find rules for the existential quantifier. Since the elimination rule turns out to be more complicated, let's begin with existential quantifier introduction, and ask ourselves how we reason to existential conclusions. To take a very simple example, suppose we want to show that for every number there is some number that is identical to it; i.e., every number is identical to some number. We can do this as follows.

1. Let k be an arbitrary number; $k = k$.
2. Therefore there exists an n such that $k = n$.
3. So for all m there is an n such that $m = n$.

(xxxii)

Letting u stand for 'k', x for 'n', y for 'm', and the domain consist of nonnegative integers, we obtain the following translation of xxxii.

$$
\begin{array}{c|l}
1 & \underline{u=u} \\
2 & (\exists x)u=x \\
3 & (y)(\exists x)y=x \\
\end{array}
$$

(xxxiii)

When the time comes for us to discuss the logical rules for identity, we'll be interested in the justification of step 1 of this argument. For the present, however, we are interested in step 2, in which an existentially quantified formula is introduced: $(\exists x)u=x$ is inferred from $u=u$. Our problem is to find the general form of the inference; we will then have succeeded in formulating the rule of existential quantifier elimination.

First, the conclusion could be any existentially quantified formula $(\exists x)A \ ^x/u$. This is the general form of existentially quantified formulas; any such formula is the result of substituting an individual variable x for a parameter v in some formula A in which u is free for x, and then prefixing $(\exists x)$. For instance, $(\exists x)u=x$ is $(\exists x)u=v \ ^x/v$.

Now, the premiss $u=u$ of this inference is also obtained from $u=v$ by substitution: $u=u$ is the result of substituting u for v in $u=v$. In step 2 of xxxiii, then, a conclusion $(\exists x)A \ ^x/v$ is obtained from a premiss $A \ ^u/v$. And the following rule of existential quantifier introduction is only a slight generalization of this.

$$
\begin{array}{|l}
A \ ^t/v \\
\vdots \\
(\exists x)A \ ^x/v
\end{array}
$$

Whenever we have obtained a formula $A \ ^t/v$ as an item in a derivation, the rule of eq int permits us to write down $(\exists x)A \ ^x/v$, provided v is free for x in A.

This rule is very similar to universal quantifier elimination; uq elim permits you to infer any instance of $(x)A \ ^x/v$ from $(x)A \ ^x/v$, while eq int permits you to infer $(\exists x)A \ ^x/v$ from any instance of $(x)A \ ^x/v$. We can regard an instance $A \ ^t/v$ of $(x)A \ ^x/v$ as translating an English sentence about some particular thing, say, 'Henry is overweight'. This can then be universally quantified to obtain $(x)A\ ^x/v$ (corresponding to 'Everyone is overweight' when the domain consists of all persons), or existentially quantified to obtain $(\exists x)A\ ^x/v$ ('Someone is overweight'). Instances such as $A\ ^t/v$ stand logically between their universal and existential quantifications; they can be derived from their universal quantifications by uq elim, and from them their existential quantifications can be derived by eq int.

Here are some examples of derivations using the rule of eq int.

1	$\sim(Pu \lor \sim Pu)$	hyp
2	Pu	hyp
3	$Pu \lor \sim Pu$	2, dis int
4	$\sim(Pu \lor \sim Pu)$	1, reit
5	$\sim Pu$	2–4, neg int
6	$Pu \lor \sim Pu$	5, dis int
7	$(\exists x)(Px \lor \sim Px)$	6, eq int

(*xxxiv*)

1	$(x)Pxa$	hyp
2	Paa	1, uq elim
3	$(\exists y)Pyy$	2, eq int

(*xxxv*)

1	$(\exists x)Px \supset Qa$	hyp
2	Pu	hyp
3	$(\exists x)Px$	2, eq int
4	$(\exists x)Px \supset Qa$	1, reit
5	Qa	3, 4, m p
6	$Pu \supset Qa$	2–5, imp int
7	$(x)(Px \supset Qa)$	6, uq int

(*xxxvi*)

1	$\sim(x)\sim Px$	hyp
2	$\sim(\exists x)Px$	hyp
3	Pu	hyp
4	$(\exists x)Px$	3, eq int
5	$\sim(\exists x)Px$	2, reit
6	$\sim Pu$	3-5, neg int
7	$(x)\sim Px$	6, uq int
8	$\sim(x)\sim Px$	1, reit
9	$\sim\sim(\exists x)Px$	2–8, neg int
10	$(\exists x)Px$	9, neg elim

(*xxxvii*)

The last of these examples contains a moral. When set the problem of deriving $(\exists x)Px$ from $\sim(x)\sim Px$, it's natural to try to obtain the conclusion $(\exists x)Px$ by eq int from Pu. But if you try to do this, you'll find that it's no easy matter, and the longer you try, the more doubtful it will seem that there is a derivation of Pu from $\sim(x)\sim Px$. And when eventually we have developed a semantic theory of this language, we will in fact be able to show that there is no such derivation.

This means that the indirect argument we used in xxxvii was indispensable; we had to use some form of *reductio ad absurdum* to get the desired result. Since this often happens with existentially quantified formulas, it's a good idea to be prepared to try such methods when attempting to work out a problem in which a formula $(\exists x)A\,{}^x/u$ is to be derived. In this respect, existential quantification resembles disjunction.

8. The next rule in line is *existential quantifier elimination*. Here, we must consider cases in which we argue *from* an existentially quantified premiss. To take a simple example, suppose we want to show that if there is some number greater than 21, then there is some number greater than 15. This is how we might reason.

1. Suppose that for some number $n, n > 21$.
2. Let k be such a number; $k > 21$.
3. But $21 > 15$.
4. By 2 and 3, $k > 15$.
5. Therefore, for some $n, n > 15$.

$$(xxxviii)$$

We can translate this by letting Quv stand for 'j is greater than k', a for '21', and b for '15'. The domain will consist of nonnegative integers.

$$
\begin{array}{ll}
1 & \underline{(\exists x)Qxa} \\
2 & Qua \\
3 & Qab \\
4 & Qub \\
5 & (\exists x)Qxb
\end{array}
$$

$$(xxxix)$$

Step 1 of this argument is plainly a hypothesis. Steps 3 and 4 are justified by mathematical considerations, and step 5 follows from step 4 by eq int. This leaves step 2; should we say that this follows from step 1 by eq elim? That is, is

$$
\frac{(\exists x)Qxa}{Qua}
$$

an instance of eq elim? If so, it looks as if the rule eq elim should take the following form.

$$\frac{(\exists x)A \ {}^x/v}{A \ {}^t/v}.$$

(*xl*)

Existential quantifier elimination would then permit one to infer any instance $A \ {}^t/x$ of $(x)A \ {}^x/v$ from $(\exists x)A \ {}^x/v$, provided that v is free for x in A.

To construe the rule of eq elim in this way would be a terrible mistake. It would undo the whole distinction between existential and universal quantification by allowing us to "derive" $(x)A \ {}^x/u$ from $(\exists x)A \ {}^x/u$, as follows.

$$
\begin{array}{ll}
1 & (\exists x)A \ {}^x/u \\
2 & u| \quad (\exists x)A \ {}^x/u \\
3 & \quad | \quad A \\
4 & (x)A \ {}^x/u
\end{array}
$$

(*xli*)

Except for step 3, all the steps of this "derivation" follow by rules we have already accepted. Step 2 follows from step 1 by reit, since there are no occurrences of u in $(\exists x)A \ {}^x/u$. Step 4 follows from step 3 by uq int. But what xli purports to show is obviously invalid since there are many cases in which $(\exists x)A \ {}^x/u$ is true, while $(x)A \ {}^x/u$ is false. Some numbers are less than 10, but not all numbers are less than 10; some people are over six feet tall, but everyone isn't over six feet tall.

These difficulties all come from step 3 of xli, which employs the rule xl. To correct them we must abandon xl as a formulation of eq elim and go back to our original example, xxxviii. If we pay more attention to the details of this argument, we may be able to extract a correct account of existential quantifier elimination.

One thing we neglected in passing from xxxviii to xxxix was the word 'let' in step 2. This signals that a hypothesis has been made here: step 2 of xxxviii could as well have read 'Suppose that k is such a number; $k > 21$'. But in putting the argument into the natural deduction format, we failed to make step 2 a hypothesis. If we correct this, we get the following rendition of xxxviii.

$$
\begin{array}{ll}
1 & (\exists x)Qxa \\
2 & \quad Qua \\
3 & \quad Qab \\
4 & \quad Qub \\
5 & \quad (\exists x)Qxb
\end{array}
$$

(*xlii*)

The trouble with xlii is that it no longer places the conclusion properly. In our original argument, the result that some number is greater than 15 was a consequence *only* of the assumption that some number is greater than 15. To reproduce the reasoning of xxxviii we somehow have to discharge the further assumption that k is greater than 21.

A good way to manage this is simply to formulate the rule of existential quantifier elimination so that it will yield the conclusion we want. In the case under consideration, then, the rule will let us infer $(\exists x)Qxb$ in the main derivation. We then obtain the following derivation from xlii.

$$
\begin{array}{ll}
1 & (\exists x)Qxa \\
2 & \quad Qua \\
3 & \quad Qab \\
4 & \quad Qub \\
5 & \quad (\exists x)Qxb \\
6 & (\exists x)Qxb \\
\end{array}
$$
(*xliii*)

Generalizing this example leads to the following pattern.

$$
\begin{array}{l}
\vdots \\
(\exists x)A\ ^{x}/u \\
\vdots \\
\quad A \\
\quad \vdots \\
\quad B \\
\quad \vdots \\
\vdots \\
B \\
\end{array}
$$
(*xliv*)

This pattern tells us a good deal about the rule of eq elim. To reason from an existentially quantified premiss $(\exists x)A\ ^{x}/u$ to a conclusion B, try to obtain B under the hypothesis A. Existential quantifier elimination then permits A to be discharged as a hypothesis, yielding the desired conclusion, B.

But there are a number of ways in which the pattern xliv can be misused. As with universal quantifier introduction, we will have to exclude these abuses by putting restrictions on the parameter u.

First, as in uq int, we can't allow formulas containing the parameter u to be reiterated into the derivation headed by A. If we were to permit reiterations of this sort, we could "derive" $(\exists x)(Px \wedge \sim Px)$ from $(\exists x)Px$ and $(\exists x)\sim Px$, as follows.

1	$(\exists x)Px$	hyp
2	$(\exists x)\sim Px$	hyp
3	$\sim Pu$	hyp
4	$(\exists x)Px$	1, reit
5	Pu	hyp
6	$\sim Pu$	3, reit
7	$Pu \wedge \sim Pu$	5, 6 conj int
8	$(\exists x)(Px \wedge \sim Px)$	7, eq int
9	$(\exists x)(Px \wedge \sim Px)$	
10	$(\exists x)(Px \wedge \sim Px)$	

$$(xlv)$$

Here, step 9 follows from steps 4 and 5 to 8 according to xliv, and step 10 follows from steps 2 and 3 to 9 according to xliv. But this argument would be wholly unwelcome in any system of logic. We don't want $(\exists x)(Px \wedge \sim Px)$ to be derivable from $(\exists x)Px$ and $(\exists x)\sim Px$, because this would lead to absurdities. For instance, some numbers are even and some are not even, but nevertheless it isn't the case that some numbers are both odd and even. Some people are octogenarians and some are not octogenarians, but no one is both an octogenarian and not an octogenarian.

This means that we must amend xliv by inserting a barrier for the parameter u. In this way we arrive at the following scheme for existential quantifier elimination.

This scheme gives a correct account of the rule of eq elim. This rule permits us to infer B in a derivation whenever there occurs previously in that derivation a step $(\exists x)A \; ^x/u$ and a derivation of B from A guarded by a barrier for the parameter u. The barrier to the left of the subordinate derivation ensures that no formulas containing free occurrences of u will be reiterated into this derivation. But there is a further job that this barrier does for us. We will regard it as acting in both directions, so that it will prohibit formulas containing the forbidden parameter from crossing from right to left.

Without this restriction, we could go astray by "deriving" $(x)Px$ from $(\exists x)Px$ in the following way.

$$
\begin{array}{ll}
1 & \quad (\exists x)Px \qquad\qquad\qquad\quad \text{hyp} \\
2 & \quad u|\;\;(\exists x)Px \qquad\qquad\quad\; \text{1, reit} \\
3 & \qquad\quad u|\qquad\quad Pu \qquad\quad \text{hyp} \\
\\
4 & \quad\;\;\; Pu \\
5 & \quad (x)Px \qquad\qquad\qquad\quad \text{4, uq int}
\end{array}
$$

$$(\textbf{\textit{xlvi}})$$

Since Pu contains an occurrence of u, step 4 of xlvi does not follow by eq elim from step 2 and the derivation consisting of step 3; this is because Pu is moved to the right through the barrier. This attempt to derive $(x)Px$ from $(\exists x)Px$ therefore fails.

The rule of eq elim may seem complicated, but with a little practice it isn't difficult to use. One thing that makes the rule easy to remember is that, like the other quantifier rules, it makes good sense. Suppose that B contains no occurrences of a parameter u. In using eq elim to obtain B from an existentially quantified premiss $(\exists x)A \; ^x/u$, we try to derive B from A behind a barrier for u. But if we succeed in doing this, we can also use imp int and uq int to derive $(x)(A \; ^x/u \supset B)$, as follows.

$$
\begin{array}{l}
u|\qquad\quad A \\
\quad\;\;\;\;\;\;\;\; \vdots \\
\quad\;\;\;\;\;\;\;\; B \\
\quad\; A \supset B \\
(x)(A \; ^x/u \supset B)
\end{array}
$$

Applying the rule of eq elim thus amounts to inferring B from $(\exists x)A \; ^x/u$ and $(x)(A \; ^x/u \supset B)$, provided that B contains no occurrences of u. This is a very natural and plausible inference, as can be seen from considering an example of it in English.

Someone here took the jewels.
If anyone here took the jewels, he has them.
Therefore someone here has the jewels.

Later, when we have developed a semantic theory of quantification, we will have no difficulty in showing inferences of this sort to be valid.

There is still another way to justify the rule of eq elim. If we look at $(\exists x)A\,^x/u$ as equivalent to $\sim(x)\sim A\,^x/u$, eq elim then corresponds to a *derived rule* allowing us to infer conclusions from $\sim(x)\sim A\,^x/u$. This derived rule follows readily from universal quantifier introduction and the rules for negation. In this connection, see E5 below.

9. The system of natural deduction consisting of the rules of S_s together with the four quantifier rules is worthy of a name; let's call it S_p. The following examples illustrate the use of eq elim in combination with the other rules of S_p. Only the first two derivations are annotated, and filling in reasons in the others is left as an exercise.

1	$(x)(Px \supset Qa)$	hyp
2	$(\exists x)Px$	hyp
3	$u\quad Pu$	hyp
4	$(x)(Px \supset Qa)$	1, reit
5	$Pu \supset Qa$	4, uq elim
6	Qa	3, 5, m p
7	Qa	2, 3–6, eq elim
8	$(\exists x)Px \supset Qa$	2–7, imp int

(xlvii)

In using the rule of eq elim, it's convenient to simply flag the subordinate derivation with a parameter, rather than writing the barrier as a separate line. If we simplify xlvii by doing this, it looks as follows.

$(x)(Px \supset Qa)$
$(\exists x)Px$
$u\quad Pu$
$(x)(Px \supset Qa)$
$Pu \supset Qa$
Qa
Qa
$(\exists x)Px \supset Qa$

(xlviii)

From now on we'll write applications of eq elim in this way, as in the following examples.

1	$(\exists x)(Px \supset (x)Qx)$	hyp
2	$(x)Px$	hyp
3	$(\exists x)(Px \supset (x)Qx)$	1, reit
4	$u \mid Pu \supset (x)Qx$	hyp
5	$(x)Px$	2, reit
6	Pu	5, uq elim
7	$(x)Qx$	4, 6, m p
8	$(x)Qx$	3, 4–7, eq elim
9	$(x)Px \supset (x)Qx$	2–8, imp int

$$(xlix)$$

$(\exists x) \sim Px$
$(x)Px$
$(\exists x) \sim Px$
$v \mid \sim Pv$
$(x)Px$
Pv
$(x)Px$
Pv
$\sim Pv$
$\sim (x)Px$
$\sim (x)Px$
$\sim (x)Px$

$$(l)$$

$(\exists x)(y)(z)Pxyz$
$u \mid (y)(z)Puyz$
$(z)Puuz$
$Puuu$
$(\exists x)Pxxx$
$(\exists x)Pxxx$

$$(li)$$

10. Having formulated rules for the two quantifiers, we must now devise rules for identity. Unlike the quantifiers and connectives of H_p, identity is introduced by a rule that requires no premisses whatsoever. We've already given an example of an application of this rule in natural language; see xxxii above, where we concluded in the very first step of the argument that $k = k$. The rule of *identity introduction* (id int) will then allow us to write any formula $t = t$ at any place in a derivation. Using this rule, we can carry out the following derivations.

1	$a = a \supset (x)Px$	hyp		1	$u \mid u = u$	id int
2	$a = a$	id int		2	$(\exists y)u = y$	1, eq int
3	$(x)Px$	1, 2, m p		3	$(x)(\exists y)x = y$	2, uq int

$$(lii) \qquad\qquad (liii)$$

1	$a=a$	id int		1	$a=a$	id int
2	$(\exists x)x=a$	1, eq int		2	$(\exists x)x=x$	1, eq int

$$(liv) \qquad\qquad\qquad\qquad (lv)$$

11. We have also met with instances of the rule of identity elimination; the earliest of these uses was in example IV.i. Identity elimination is also employed in example xiv of this chapter, where we inferred that $2^n + 2^n = 2^{n+1}$, since $2^n + 2^n = 2\cdot 2^n$ and $2\cdot 2^n = 2^{n+1}$. In these examples the conclusion is reached by "substitution of equals for equals". For instance, to get '$2^n + 2^n = 2^{n+1}$', replace '$2\cdot 2^n$' by '$2^n + 2^n$' in '$2\cdot 2^n = 2^{n+1}$'. In example IV.i two such replacements are required.

Let's take still another example of this.

1. Suppose that $2 < 2 + 2$.
2. Further, suppose that $1 + 1 = 2$.
3. Then $1 + 1 < 2 + 2$.

$$(lvi)$$

To translate this argument into formal notation, let *Puvw* stand for '$n < m + k$', *a* for '2', and *b* for '$1 + 1$'. We then obtain the following derivation.

1	*Paaa*
2	$b=a$
3	*Pbaa*

$$(lvii)$$

Evidently, we want to provide in the rule of identity elimination not only for cases in which *all* occurrences of a term are replaced by occurrences of another, but for cases in which only *some* of these occurrences are replaced. This is what happens in example lvii, where only one occurrence of *a* in *Paaa* is replaced by an occurrence of *b*.

In order to do this, we will need a notion of replacement of one term by another. Let's say that a formula *B* is a result $A\,{}^{s}\!/\!/t$ of replacing *t* by *s* in *A* if *B* can be obtained from *A* by replacing any number (even none) of the occurrences of *t* in *A* by occurrences of *s*. For example, *Pbaa* and *Pabb* are results of replacing *a* by *b* in *Paaa*. Also $(x)(Pxax \supset (\exists y)\sim u=y)$ and $(x)(Pxux \supset (\exists y)\sim a=y)$ are results of replacing *u* by *a* in $(x)(Pxux \supset (\exists y)\sim u=y)$, and $(y)Qyuuuu$, $(y)Qyaauu$, and $(y)Qyuuau$ are results of replacing *a* by *u* in $(y)Qyaaau$.

We can now present the rule of identity elimination. Since we'll permit either $s=t$ or $t=s$ as a premiss of the rule and will allow the premisses to occur in either order, there are four schematic forms of this rule.

$$
\begin{array}{c|c|c|c}
\vdots & \vdots & \vdots & \vdots \\
s=t & B & t=s & B \\
\vdots & \vdots & \vdots & \vdots \\
B & s=t & B & t=s \\
\vdots & \vdots & \vdots & \vdots \\
B^{\,s}\!/\!/t & B^{\,s}\!/\!/t & B^{\,s}\!/\!/t & B^{\,s}\!/\!/t
\end{array}
$$

A step $B^{\,s}\!/\!/t$ in a derivation is justified by the rule of identity elimination (id elim), if $s=t$ and $B^{\,s}\!/\!/t$ or $t=s$ and $B^{\,s}\!/\!/t$ occur as previous steps in the derivation.

The following are examples of ways in which the rule of identity elimination may be used. In each case, the third step follows from the first two by identity elimination.

$$
\begin{array}{c|c|c|c}
Puu \lor (x)Qx & Puvv \supset (x)Qxv & a=b & Pa \\
u=a & u=v & b=c & a=a \\
\hline
Puu \lor (x)Qx & Puvu \supset (x)Qxu & c=b & Pa
\end{array}
$$

12. When the introduction and elimination rules for identity are added to $\mathbf{S_p}$, a system we will call $\mathbf{S_{p=}}$ is obtained. Besides the rules for sentence connectives there are six other rules in $\mathbf{S_{p=}}$; examples of derivations using these rules in various combinations are given below. Filling in reasons for the steps in these examples is again left as an exercise.

$$
\begin{array}{ll}
\underline{(y)(\exists x)Pxy} & Pa \\
\quad u \mid (y)(\exists x)Pxy & \underline{(\exists y)(y=a \land y=b)} \\
\qquad (\exists x)Pxu & \quad u \mid u=a \land u=b \\
\qquad\quad v \mid Pvu & \qquad u=a \\
\qquad\qquad v=v & \qquad Pa \\
\qquad\qquad v=v \land Pvu & \qquad Pu \\
\qquad\qquad (\exists x)(x=x \land Pxu) & \qquad u=b \\
\qquad\quad (\exists x)(x=x \land Pxu) & \qquad Pb \\
\quad (y)(\exists x)(x=x \land Pxy) & Pb
\end{array}
$$

$$
\begin{array}{cc}
(lviii) & (lix)
\end{array}
$$

$(\exists x)(y)(Py \equiv x=y)$
Pa
Pb
$\quad u \mid (y)(Py \equiv u=y)$
$\qquad Pa \equiv u=a$
$\qquad Pa$
$\qquad u=a$
$\qquad Pb \equiv u=b$
$\qquad Pb$
$\qquad u=b$
$\qquad a=b$
$\quad a=b$

(lx)

$(\exists x)(y)x=y$
$u \mid \quad Pu$
$\quad\quad v \mid (\exists x)(y)x=y$
$\quad\quad\quad . \; w \mid (y)w=y$
$\quad\quad\quad\quad\quad Pu$
$\quad\quad\quad\quad\quad w=u$
$\quad\quad\quad\quad\quad w=v$
$\quad\quad\quad\quad\quad v=u$
$\quad\quad\quad\quad\quad Pv$
$\quad\quad\quad\quad Pv$
$\quad\quad\quad (y)Py$
$\quad\quad Pu \supset (y)Py$
$(z)(Pz \supset (y)Py)$

(lxi)

13. We've already indicated that finding derivations in $S_{p=}$ is a much more complicated matter than finding derivations in S_s. However, if the problem you are given is one that can in fact be solved, it's usually possible to find the desired derivation, as long as you search systematically for it and are mindful of the various restrictions on the rules for quantifiers. In this section we'll give some rules of thumb which should help to make such tasks easier.

First, all of the suggestions we gave in IV.15 still apply. For instance, when the goal is to obtain a formula $A \supset B$, the thing to do is to set up a subordinate derivation with hypothesis A and try to get B in that derivation.

A similar rule applies to universally quantified formulas; if you want to derive $(x)A\ ^x/u$, set up a barrier with regard to the parameter u, and try to derive A within that barrier. In practice, however, this leaves a good deal of leeway in choosing a parameter. Suppose, for instance, that the problem is to derive $(x)Px$ from certain premises. Now, $(x)Px$ is $(x)Pu\ ^x/u$, and so we can begin an attempt to get uq int in the following way.

$$u \mid \quad \vdots$$
$$\quad\quad Pu$$
$$(x)Px$$

On the other hand, $(x)Px$ is also $(x)Pv\ ^x/v$, so that we could just as well use the parameter v to derive $(x)Px$ by uq int, as follows.

$$v \mid \quad \vdots$$
$$\quad\quad Pv$$
$$(x)Px$$

There are cases in which it will make a difference which individual parameter we choose to use for universal quantifier introduction. Take as an example the problem of deriving $(x)Pxa$ from $(y)(Qu \lor Pya)$ and $\sim Qu$. If we set up our barrier using the parameter u, as follows,

$$
\begin{array}{|l}
(y)(Qu \lor Pya) \\
\sim Qu \\
\quad\begin{array}{|l}
u \\
\quad\begin{array}{|l}
Pua
\end{array}
\end{array} \\
(x)Pxa
\end{array}
$$

$$(lxii)$$

we're in for trouble. We can't reiterate either of the hypotheses through this barrier, since they both contain an occurrence of the parameter u. On the other hand, if we work on the hypotheses before reiterating, we can obtain $Qu \lor Pva$ by uq elim and then get to Pva by using rules for disjunction and negation. But although we can reiterate Pva past the barrier, we can't get from Pva to Pua.

The thing to do here is to use a parameter not occurring in the hypotheses, say v. Once this has been done it's easy to obtain $(x)Pxa$ by uq int; the finished derivation is as follows.

1	$(y)(Qu \lor Pya)$	hyp
2	$\sim Qu$	hyp
3	v $(y)(Qu \lor Pya)$	1, reit
4	$Qu \lor Pva$	3, uq elim
5	Qu	hyp
6	$\sim Pva$	hyp
7	Qu	5, reit
8	$\sim Qu$	2, reit
9	$\sim\sim Pva$	6–8, neg int
10	Pva	9, neg elim
11	Pva	hyp
12	Pva	4, 5–10, 11, dis elim
13	$(x)Pxa$	12, uq int

$$(lxiii)$$

The general rule of thumb for deriving a formula $(x)A$ $^{x}/u$ is then as follows. (Since we're adding to the rules of IV.4, we'll start numbering with '8'.)

8. When trying to derive a formula of the sort $(x)A$ $^{x}/u$, try to get it by uq int. If the parameter u does not occur in any formula that may need to be reiterated, do this by setting up a barrier for u and trying to get

A inside it. Otherwise choose another parameter *v* such that *A* $^x/u$ is the same expression as *B* $^x/v$, and such that *v* does not occur in any needed formula. Then set up a barrier for *v* and try to get *B* inside it.

The rule of existential quantifier elimination is very like disjunction elimination; you can never go wrong by using it. If you have a premiss $(\exists x)A$ $^x/u$ and want to get to a conclusion *B*, it always is a good idea to try eq elim. As in the case of uq int, however, you sometimes have to be careful to set up a barrier for the right parameter. To work successfully, this parameter must not occur in any needed formulas or in *B*. For instance, if we want to derive *Pu* ∨ *Pa* from $(y)(y=u \lor y=a)$ and $(\exists x)Px$, we should use eq elim on the hypothesis $(\exists x)Px$. But since the parameter *u* occurs in our desired conclusion and in our other hypothesis, we should use some other parameter, say *v*, in applying eq elim. We then will begin our derivation as follows.

$$(y)(y=u \lor y=a)$$
$$(\exists x)Px$$
$$v \mid Pv$$
$$?$$
$$Pu \lor Pa$$
$$Pu \lor Pa$$
$$(lxiv)$$

From here, finishing the derivation is just a matter of using uq elim, dis elim, and id elim.

$$(y)(y=u \lor y=a)$$
$$(\exists x)Px$$
$$v \mid Pv$$
$$(y)(y=u \lor y=a)$$
$$v=u \lor v=a$$
$$v=u$$
$$Pv$$
$$Pu$$
$$Pu \lor Pa$$

$$v=a$$
$$Pv$$
$$Pa$$
$$Pu \lor Pa$$
$$Pu \lor Pa$$
$$Pu \lor Pa$$
$$(lxv)$$

Put explicitly, our advice about eq elim is this.

9. When trying to derive B from a formula of the sort $(\exists x)A\,^x/u$, choose a parameter v such that $A\,^x/u$ is the same expression as $C\,^x/v$, and such that v does not occur in any needed formula or in B. Then try to use eq elim on $(\exists x)C\,^x/v$, employing v as the parameter in this application of the rule.

In discussing example xxxvii we said that existentially quantified formulas are like disjunctions in that it frequently is impossible to derive them by the appropriate introduction rule. This means that a problem with an existentially quantified conclusion will often call for an indirect argument. A good example is the problem of deriving $(\exists x)((\exists y)Py \supset Px)$ categorically in S_p. If we try to get this formula directly by the rule of eq int we will be led to attempt a categorical derivation of $(\exists y)Py \supset Pu$—a formula which, like $(\exists y)Py \supset (y)Py$, is not derivable categorically in S_p. The thing to do here is to use the rules for negation, and try to reduce $\sim(\exists x)((\exists y)Py \supset Px)$ to absurdity. After setting things up in this way, a derivation like the following one emerges.

$$
\begin{array}{l}
\quad\sim(\exists x)((\exists y)Py \supset Px) \\
\quad\ \ (\exists y)Py \\
\qquad\ \sim Pu \\
\qquad (\exists y)Py \\
\qquad\quad v\mid Pv \\
\qquad\qquad\qquad (\exists y)Py \\
\qquad\qquad\qquad Pv \\
\qquad\qquad (\exists y)Py \supset Pv \\
\qquad\qquad (\exists x)((\exists y)Py \supset Px) \\
\qquad\ \ (\exists x)((\exists y)Py \supset Px) \\
\qquad\ \ \sim(\exists x)((\exists y)Py \supset Px) \\
\qquad \sim\sim Pu \\
\qquad Pu \\
\quad\ (\exists y)Py \supset Pu \\
\quad\ (\exists x)((\exists y)Py \supset Px) \\
\sim\sim(\exists x)((\exists y)Py \supset Px) \\
(\exists x)((\exists y)Py \supset Px) \\
\end{array}
$$

$$(lxvi)$$

Our advice concerning existentially quantified conclusions is thus as follows.

10. When trying to derive a formula of the sort $(\exists x)A\,^x/u$, set up an indirect argument and try to obtain a contradiction from $\sim(\exists x)A\,^x/u$, unless there is some obvious way of deriving a premiss $A\,^t/u$ of eq int.

We have now discussed the cases in which we are required to reason to universally quantified conclusions, from existentially quantified premisses, and to existentially quantified conclusions. To be thoroughly systematic, we should also discuss the case in which the problem is to carry out a derivation from universally quantified premisses. Here, the procedure is straightforward; you never will be led into blind alleys by using the rule of uq elim on steps already established. Of course, any formula $(x)A\,^x/u$ will have infinitely many consequences by the rule of uq elim since there will be an instance $A\,^t/u$ of $(x)A\,^x/u$ for each term t. However, there will be only finitely many such terms occurring in the formulas we've already written down in trying to find a derivation, and it would be pointless to instantiate with any other terms. Our last rule, then, is this.

11. Use the rule of uq elim freely, instantiating with terms that occur in formulas already present in the attempted derivation.

You should also be mindful of opportunities to reiterate past barriers. The first thing to do, for instance, after setting up a barrier for the parameter u, would be to look for reiterable formulas not containing occurrences of u.

14. The restrictions on individual parameters in $S_{p=}$ aren't difficult to learn; they assert only that a formula containing an occurrence of the parameter u can't be moved through a barrier for u. Nevertheless, when people have difficulty in finding a derivation, they sometimes violate these restrictions in order to finish the problem. This usually happens only in cases where an indirect argument is required; a good example is the problem of deriving $P \lor (x)Qx$ from $(x)(P \lor Qx)$. (Here, P is a sentence parameter, and so of course contains no occurrences whatsoever of any individual parameter.)
We begin this problem by writing $(x)(P \lor Qx)$ above $P \lor (x)Qx$.

$$\lfloor (x)(P \lor Qx)$$

$$P \lor (x)Qx$$
(lxvii)

Anyone familiar with the difficulties that often come up in trying to derive disjunctions by dis int wouldn't be likely to attempt to complete lxvii by seeking to derive either P or $(x)Qx$ from $(x)(P \lor Qx)$. Besides, it's very implausible that either of these should be a logical consequence of $(x)(P \lor Qx)$.

The natural thing to do in this situation is to use uq elim on the hypothesis, instantiating with a parameter such as u. Having done this, you might want to use dis elim to get $P \lor (x)Qx$, as follows.

$$
\begin{array}{ll}
1 & (x)(P \lor Qx) \\
2 & P \lor Qu \\
3 & \quad P \\
4 & \quad P \lor (x)Qx \\
\\
5 & \quad Qu \\
6 & \quad (x)Qx \\
7 & \quad P \lor (x)Qx \\
8 & P \lor (x)Qx \\
& \textbf{\textit{(lxviii)}}
\end{array}
$$

But this doesn't work; step 6 is not justified by any rule of $\mathbf{S_{p=}}$, since Pu has not been obtained behind a barrier for u. No matter how you try to fix this by juggling with lxviii, you won't be able to make it come out right. The trouble is that once uq elim has been used on $(x)(P \lor Qx)$, there is no way to universalize instantiations such as Pu to obtain $Q \lor (x)Px$.

The thing to do, of course, is to try an indirect argument and seek to derive a contradiction from $\sim(P \lor (x)Qx)$. We thus will begin like this.

$$
\begin{array}{l}
(x)(P \lor Qx) \\
\quad \sim(P \lor (x)Qx) \\
\\
\textbf{\textit{(lxix)}}
\end{array}
$$

This gives us something to work with. From our experience with sentence logic, we know that from $\sim(P \lor (x)Qx)$ we can get $\sim P$. Since we can obtain $P \lor Qu$ from $(x)(P \lor Qx)$, we can derive Qu from these hypotheses. But if we do only this, we'll be stuck just as we were before, since we can't get directly from Qu to $(x)Qx$.

The insight needed to crack this problem is that from the hypotheses of lxviii we can derive $\sim(x)Qx$. To get a contradiction, then, it will suffice to obtain $(x)Qx$. We can do this by setting up a barrier for u and getting to Qu *within this barrier*. The following derivation then emerges.

1	$(x)(P \vee Qx)$	hyp
2	$\sim(P \vee (x)Qx)$	hyp
3	P	hyp
4	$P \vee (x)Qx$	3, dis int
5	$\sim(P \vee (x)Qx)$	2, reit
6	$\sim P$	3–5, neg int
7	u $(x)(P \vee Qx)$	1, reit
8	$P \vee Qu$	7, uq elim
9	P	hyp
10	$\sim Qu$	hyp
11	P	9, reit
12	$\sim P$	6, reit
13	$\sim\sim Qu$	10–12, neg int
14	Qu	13, neg elim
15	Qu	hyp
16	Qu	8, 9–14, 15, dis elim
17	$(x)Qx$	16, uq int
18	$P \vee (x)Qx$	17, dis int
19	$\sim\sim(P \vee (x)Qx)$	1–18, neg int
20	$P \vee (x)Qx$	19, neg elim

$$(lxx)$$

The trick to lxx is that things are done in the right order: uq elim is used on $(x)(P \vee Qx)$ only after this formula has been reiterated past a barrier. But we arrived at this derivation only after experimenting with several false attempts and successfully resisting the temptation to violate the restrictions on uq elim.

15. As in S_s, familiarity with various basic argument patterns is essential in acquiring skill at finding derivations in $S_{p=}$. In this concluding section some of the most important such patterns are listed, in incomplete form. Filling in the missing steps is left as an exercise.

$(x)A\,^x/u$	$\sim(\exists x)\sim A\,^x/u$	$\sim(x)A\,^x/u$	$(\exists x)\sim A\,^x/u$
$\vdots$	$\vdots$	$\vdots$	$\vdots$
$\sim(\exists x)\sim A\,^x/u$	$(x)A\,^x/u$	$(\exists x)\sim A\,^x/u$	$\sim(x)A\,^x/u$

$$\vdash \begin{array}{l} \sim(\exists x)A\,^x/u \\ \vdots \\ (x)\sim A\,^x/u \end{array} \quad \vdash \begin{array}{l} (x)\sim A\,^x/u \\ \vdots \\ \sim(\exists x)A\,^x/u \end{array} \quad \vdash \begin{array}{l} (x)(A\,^x/u \wedge B\,^x/u) \\ \vdots \\ (x)A\,^x/u \wedge (x)B\,^x/u \end{array} \quad \vdash \begin{array}{l} (x)A\,^x/u \wedge (x)B\,^x/u \\ \vdots \\ (x)(A\,^x/u \wedge B\,^x/u) \end{array}$$

$$\vdash \begin{array}{l} (\exists x)(A\,^x/u \vee B\,^x/u) \\ \vdots \\ (\exists x)A\,^x/u \vee (\exists x)B\,^x/u \end{array} \quad \vdash \begin{array}{l} (\exists x)A\,^x/u \vee (\exists x)B\,^x/u \\ \vdots \\ (\exists x)(A\,^x/u \vee B\,^x/u) \end{array}$$

$$\vdash \begin{array}{l} (x)(y)A\,^y/u\,^x/v \\ \vdots \\ (y)(x)A\,^y/u\,^x/v \end{array} \quad \vdash \begin{array}{l} (\exists x)(\exists y)A\,^y/v\,^x/u \\ \vdots \\ (\exists y)(\exists x)A\,^y/v\,^x/u \end{array}$$

$$\vdash \begin{array}{l} (\exists x)(y)A\,^y/v\,^x/u \\ \vdots \\ (y)(\exists x)A\,^y/v\,^x/u \end{array} \quad \vdash \begin{array}{l} (x)(A\,^x/u \supset B\,^x/u) \\ \vdots \\ (x)A\,^x/u \supset (x)B\,^x/u \end{array} \quad \vdash \begin{array}{l} r=s \\ s=t \\ \vdots \\ r=t \end{array} \quad \vdash \begin{array}{l} s=t \\ \vdots \\ t=s \end{array}$$

The derivability of the following argument patterns depends on the fact that, since C is a formula, there are no occurrences of any individual variable, and in particular no occurrences of x in C. If we replaced 'C' by '$C\,^x/u$' below, the resulting patterns would not in general be derivable in $S_{p=}$.

$$\vdash \begin{array}{l} (x)(C \vee B\,^x/u) \\ \vdots \\ C \vee (x)B\,^x/u \end{array} \quad \vdash \begin{array}{l} C \vee (x)B\,^x/u \\ \vdots \\ (x)(C \vee B\,^x/u) \end{array} \quad \vdash \begin{array}{l} (\exists x)(C \wedge B\,^x/u) \\ \vdots \\ C \wedge (\exists x)B\,^x/u \end{array} \quad \vdash \begin{array}{l} C \wedge (\exists x)B\,^x/u \\ \vdots \\ (\exists x)(C \wedge B\,^x/u) \end{array}$$

$$\vdash \begin{array}{l} (\exists x)B\,^x/u \supset C \\ \vdots \\ (x)(B\,^x/u \supset C) \end{array} \quad \vdash \begin{array}{l} (x)(B\,^x/u \supset C) \\ \vdots \\ (\exists x)B\,^x/u \supset C \end{array} \quad \vdash \begin{array}{l} C \\ \vdots \\ (x)C \end{array} \quad \vdash \begin{array}{l} (\exists x)C \\ \vdots \\ C \end{array}$$

Exercises

1. Answer the following questions.
   (a) Is $(x)(y)Pxy$ a universal quantification of $(y)Puy$?
   (b) Is $(x)(y)Pxy$ a universal quantification of $(y)Pvy$?
   (c) Is $(x)(y)Pxy$ a universal quantification of $(y)Pay$?
   (d) Is $(x)(y)Pxy$ a universal quantification of $(z)Puz$?
   (e) Is $(x)(Pax \supset. Qx \vee Ru)$ a universal quantification of $Pau \supset. Qu \vee Ru$?
   (f) Is $(y)(Pay \supset. Qy \vee Ry)$ a universal quantification of $Pau \supset. Qu \vee Ru$?
   (g) Is $(x)(Pxx \supset (z)Qzx)$ a universal quantification of $Puu \supset (z)Qzu$?

(h) Is $(x)(Pxx \supset (x)Qxx)$ a universal quantification of $Puu \supset (x)Qxu$?

(i) Is $(y)(Pyy \supset (x)Qxy)$ a universal quantification of $Puu \supset (x)Qxu$?

(j) Is Puv an instance of $(x)Pxx$?

(k) Is Paa an instance of $(x)Pxx$?

(l) Is $Pac \supset (y)(y=a \supset Pyc)$ an instance of $(x)(Pxc \supset (y)(y=x \supset Pyc))$?

(m) Is $Pac \supset (y)(y=a \supset Pyc)$ an instance of $(z)(Pzc \supset (y)(y=z \supset Pyc))$?

(n) Is $Pac \supset (y)(y=a \supset Pyc)$ an instance of $(y)(Pyc \supset (y)(y=y \supset Pyc))$?

(o) Is $(x)Pax$ an instance of $(x)(y)Pyx$?

(p) Is $(\exists x)(Pvx \supset Qax)$ an existential quantification of $Pvu \supset Qau$?

(q) Is $(\exists x)(Pvx \supset Qax)$ an existential quantification of $Pvw \supset Qaw$?

(r) Is $(\exists x)(Pvx \supset Qax)$ an existential quantification of $Puv \supset Qav$?

2. Derive the following in $S_{p=}$, supplying reasons for all steps.

(a) $(x)Px \land (x)Qx$ from $(x)(Px \land Qx)$

(b) $(x)(Px \land Qx)$ from $(x)Px \land (x)Qx$

(c) $(y)(x)Pxy$ from $(x)(y)Pxy$

(d) $(y)(\exists x)Pxy$ from $(\exists x)(y)Pxy$

(e) $(\exists x)(Px \supset Qx)$ from $(x)\sim Px$

(f) $(x)Px \supset (y)Qy$ from $(\exists x)(y)(Px \supset Qy)$

(g) $(\exists x)(y)(Px \supset Qy)$ from $(x)Px \supset (y)Py$

(h) $(\exists x)Px \supset (\exists y)Qy$ from $(x)(\exists y)(Px \supset Qy)$

(i) $(\exists x)Px \lor (\exists x)Qx$ from $(\exists x)(Px \lor Qx)$

(j) $(\exists x)(Px \lor Qx)$ from $(\exists x)Px \lor (\exists x)Qx$

(k) $(x)Px \equiv (\exists x)Px$ from $(x)Px \lor (x)\sim Px$

(l) $(x)(\exists y)(Px \supset Qy)$ from $(\exists x)Px \supset (\exists y)Qy$

(m) $b=a$ from $a=b$

(n) $(x)Px \lor (\exists x)Qx$ from $(x)(Px \lor Qx)$

(o) $(\exists x)Pa$ from Pa

(p) $(\exists x)(x=a \land Px)$ from Pa

(q) $(x)Px$ from $(\exists x)(\exists y)(z)(z=x \lor z=y)$, $Pa \land Pb$, and $\sim a=b$

(r) $(\exists x)(y)(Py \equiv x=y)$ from Pa and $(\exists x)(y)x=y$

(s) Pa from $(x)(Px \equiv x=a)$

(t) $(\exists x)(Px \land (Qx \supset (x)Qx))$ from $(x)Px$

(u) $(\exists x)Px \land (\exists x)Qx$ from $(\exists x)(Px \land Qx)$

(v) $(\exists x)(\exists y)Pxy$ from $(\exists x)(\exists y)(Pxy \lor Pyx)$

3. Find categorical derivations in $S_{p=}$ of the following. Give a reason for each step.

(a) $\sim(\exists x)Px \supset (x)(Px \supset Qx)$

(b) $(x)Px \lor (\exists x)\sim Px$

(c) $(x)(\exists y)Pxy \lor (\exists x)(y)\sim Pxy$

(d) $(\exists x)(Px \supset (x)Px)$

(e) $(\exists x)(\exists y)x=y$

(f) $(x)(Px \equiv (\exists y)(x=y \land Py))$

(g) $(\exists x)(\exists y)(Pxy \supset (x)(y)Pxy)$

(h) $(x)(Px \equiv (\exists y)(x = y \land Py))$
(i) $Pa \equiv (x)(x = a \supset Px)$
(j) $(\exists x)(y)(\sim Pay \lor Pax)$
(k) $(y)(\exists x)((z)Pyyz \supset (z)Pyxz)$
(l) $a = a \supset (\exists x)x = a$
(m) $(\exists x)(y)(z)((\sim Py \lor Qz) \supset \sim(Px \land \sim Qx))$

4. Translate the following arguments into $S_{p=}$, specifying the English correlates of individual constants, predicate parameters and sentence parameters used in the translation, and the domain of the individual variables. Then derive the conclusion of the argument from the premises.

(a) There is a line connecting any two distinct points.
   P is a point.
   Therefore if any point is distinct from P there is a line connecting it with P.

(b) Everyone is interested in himself.
   Therefore everyone is interested in someone.

(c) All cars are useful.
   Therefore everyone who has a car has something useful.

(d) Someone took something from the shelf.
   Anyone who took anything from the shelf was in the room last night.
   Therefore someone was in the room last night.

(e) Zero is less than every other number.
   Therefore zero is less than or equal to every number.

(f) Pegasus is Pegasus.
   Therefore Pegasus is something.

(g) Every number is the sum of two squares.
   The only numbers whose sum is one are zero and one.
   Therefore zero and one are squares.

(h) Only one person left the room during the talk.
   The man in the brown hat left the room during the talk.
   The man who passed out leaflets left the room during the talk.
   Therefore the man in the brown hat is the man who passed out leaflets.

(i) Boston is larger than Philadelphia or Philadelphia is larger than Boston.
   Therefore Boston is larger than Philadelphia or Philadelphia is larger than something.

(j) Amsterdam or The Hague is the capital of The Netherlands.
   Therefore there is a capital of The Netherlands.

(k) Anyone who composes plays some instrument.
   Therefore no one who composes plays no instrument.

(l) Nothing is prior to itself.
   Any cause is prior to any of its effects.
   Therefore nothing causes itself.

(m) Any cause of itself is a cause of anything else.
   Therefore any cause of itself is a cause of everything.

5. Suppose that existential quantification had been defined in S_p in terms of universal quantification and negation, as follows:

$$'(\exists x)A\,{}^x\!/u' =_{df} '\sim(x)\sim A\,{}^x\!/u'.$$

Show that the rules of S_p for the existential quantifier would then be derived rules.

6. Show in $S_{p=}$ that examples VIII.lx and VIII.lxi are equivalent. Do the same for $(x)(Px \supset Qx)$ and VIII.xl, and for VIII.cvii and VIII.cviii.

Problems

1. Let $(\exists! x)$ stand for unique existential quantification, so that, e.g., $(\exists! x)x = a$ stands for 'There is one and only one n such that $n = 3$', if a represents '3'. Define this kind of quantification in S_s and devise introduction and elimination rules for it. What about 'there are exactly 2', 'there are exactly 3', and, in general, 'there are exactly n'?

2. The locution 'for some but not all' corresponds to a quantifier. Define universal quantification in terms of this quantifier and sentence connectives.

X Predicate Logic with Identity: Syntax

1. Continuing with the program we followed in developing sentence logic, our next task will be a revision of $S_{p=}$ along the lines of the system H_s we discussed in Chapter V. This new system, $H_{p=}$, will be formulated using axiom-schemes and the rule *modus ponens*. Since we will want to prove meta-theorems about $H_{p=}$ we'll take care to set up this system more precisely than $S_{p=}$, beginning with definitions of *morphology* for $H_{p=}$ and of *formula of a morphology* for $H_{p=}$.

D1. A morphology M for $H_{p=}$ is a structure consisting of the following parts:
1. *An infinite set V_M of individual variables.*
2. *An infinite set IP_M of individual parameters.*
3. *A set C_M of individual constants.*
4. *For each $i \geq 0$, a set $P_M{}^i$ of i-ary predicate parameters.*

A morphology **M** for $H_{p=}$ determines which objects are to count as members of the various grammatical categories appropriate for $H_{p=}$; it provides materials for constructing formulas. Once we are given a morphology for $H_{p=}$, we can tell what things are individual variables, individual parameters, individual constants, 0-ary predicate parameters, 1-ary predicate parameters, and so forth.

We will require that the various grammatical categories of any morphology must always be disjoint; that is, no object can be both an individual constant and an individual variable, or both an individual variable and a 0-ary predicate parameter, or both a 2-ary predicate parameter and a 5-ary predicate parameter, and so on. But we won't demand that any of the categories except the class of individual variables and the class of individual parameters must be nonempty. For instance, a morphology M for $H_{p=}$ might have no 0-ary predicate parameters, and no i-ary predicate parameters for $i > 1$. In that case, we would have $P_M{}^0 = \varnothing$, and $P_M{}^i = \varnothing$ for all $i > 1$.

The notion of a 0-ary predicate parameter calls for explanation; we didn't discuss such things in Chapter IX. If we think of an n-ary predicate parameter as standing for some result of putting n different kinds of blanks for terms in an English sentence, a 0-ary predicate parameter will stand for an English sentence that contains no blanks at all. 0-ary predicate parameters, then, turn out to be familiar items under a new name; they are simply sentence parameters. In fact, we will retain our old way of talking and will speak of 0-ary predicate parameters of a morphology M for $H_{p=}$ as sentence parameters of M.

In this and the following chapters, we will be dealing almost exclusively with morphologies for $H_{p=}$. For short, then, we will speak simply of "morphologies" rather than of "morphologies for $H_{p=}$". When we want to talk about other kinds of morphologies (e.g., morphologies for H_s), we will be specific.

Given a morphology, we want to talk about its *terms* and *formulas*. A term of a morphology M for $H_{p=}$ is simply any individual parameter or individual constant of M; the formulas of M are characterized inductively.

D2. The set T_M of terms of a morphology M is $IP_M \cup C_M$.

D3. The set F_M of formulas of a morphology M for $H_{p=}$ is determined by the following rules.

  1. *If $s, t \in T_M$ then $s = t \in F_M$.*
  2. *If $P \in P_M{}^0$ then $P \in F_M$.*
  3. *If $P \in P_M{}^n$, where $n > 0$, and $t_1, \ldots, t_n \in T_M$, then $P t_1 \cdots t_n \in F_M$.*
  4. *If $A \in F_M$ then $\sim A \in F_M$.*

5. *If A, $B \in F_M$ then $(A \supset B) \in F_M$.*
6. *If $A \in F_M$, $x \in V_M$, and $u \in IP_M$ then $(x)A \; {}^x/u \in F_M$.*

The *symbols* of a morphology M consist of the members of V_M, C_M, and of the sets $P_M{}^i$, as well as the logical symbols $\sim$, $\supset$, and $=$, the parentheses $)$ and $($, and the comma , . (These last eight symbols of M must be distinct from one another and from the terms and predicate parameters of M.) An *expression* of M is any string of symbols of M. An expression of M is a formula of M only if it can be built up by successive applications of clauses 1 to 6. A formula A of M is said to be *atomic* if it is a formula of M by virtue of clauses 1, 2, or 3 of D3. A formula is atomic, then, if it contains no occurrences of sentence connectives or quantifiers.

Notice, by the way, that there is no clause in D3 for existential quantification. We have omitted such a clause because existential quantification can be defined in terms of negation and universal quantification. As in Chapter V, we are now concerned to formulate our system as economically as possible.

We'll continue to follow our practice of using 'P', 'Q', 'R', and 'S' to speak of predicate parameters; 'x', 'y', and 'z' to speak of individual variables; 'u', 'v', and 'w' to speak of individual parameters; 'a', 'b', and 'c' to speak of individual constants; 'r', 's', and 't' to speak of terms; and 'A', 'B', 'C', 'D', and 'E' to speak of formulas. Outermost parentheses will be omitted as usual in referring to formulas, and the other abbreviative conventions of V.6 will also be followed.

The simplest kind of morphology for $H_{p=}$ would be one having no individual constants or predicate parameters at all. That is, suppose that $C_M = \varnothing$ and that for all i, $P_M{}^i = \varnothing$. M must have infinitely many individual variables and infinitely many individual parameters: say these are x_1, x_2, ... and u_1, u_2, ... Then the following are formulas of M.

$u_1 = u_1$
$u_1 = u_2 \supset. \sim u_1 = u_3 \supset u_4 = u_4$
$(x_1) \sim (x_2)(x_1 = x_2 \supset \sim x_2 = x_1)$

$\sim (u_1 = u_3 \supset (x_3)u_1 = u_2)$
$\sim (x_2) \sim \sim (x_3) \sim x_2 = x_3$
$\sim (x_1) \sim \sim \sim (x_1)x_1 = x_1$

It should be clear from this example that each morphology has infinitely many formulas.

Suppose that we expand this morphology M a bit; let $V_{M'} = V_M$ and $IP_{M'} = IP_M$, but let $C_{M'} = \{a, b\}$, $P_{M'}{}^0 = \{P\}$, and $P_{M'}{}^3 = \{Q\}$. Let $P_{M'}{}^1 = \varnothing$ and $P_{M'}{}^2 = \varnothing$, and $P_{M'}{}^i = \varnothing$ for all $i > 3$. M' will have all the above formulas, of course, as well as formulas such as the following.

$(x_1)(P \supset \sim (x_2) \sim Qx_1ax_2)$
$\sim (x_1) \sim (x_3)P$

$(x_3)(x_3 = a \supset Qbbb)$
$\sim (P \supset. (u_1 = u_1 \supset. Qu_1ab \supset P))$

2. In order to formulate an axiomatic system we need first to characterize fundamental syntactic notions such as substitution of a term for an individual parameter in an expression of **M**.

D4. Let X be an expression of **M**, *and let s and t be any terms of* **M**. *The result* X^s/t *of substituting s for t in X is the formula obtained by putting an occurrence of s for every occurrence of t in X. Furthermore, let x be any individual variable of* **M**. *The result* X^x/t *of substituting x for t in X is the expression obtained by putting an occurrence of x for every occurrence of t in X.*

It is not required in D4 that t must occur in X; in case it doesn't, X^s/t and X^x/t will of course be the same expression as A. X^x/t will generally not be a formula of **M**. Specifically, X^x/t will be a formula if and only if X is a formula of **M** and t has no occurrences in X.

D5. Let $A \in F_M$ *and* $s, t \in T_M$. *A formula B of* **M** *is a result* $A^s/\!\!/t$ *of replacing t by s in A if B differs from A only in exhibiting occurrences of s at zero or more places where A exhibits occurrences of t.*

We also need to characterize the process of universal quantification. First, it is evident from D3 that any occurrence of a universal quantifier (x) in a formula A must be followed immediately in A by an expression having the form B^x/u. We will call this expression the *scope* of this occurrence of (x) in A. The notion of scope figures in defining the conditions under which an individual parameter is free for an individual variable in a formula.

D6. Let $A \in F_M$, $u \in IP_M$, *and* $x \in V_M$. *Then u is free for x in A if no occurrence of u in A falls within the scope of any occurrence of a universal quantifier (x) in A.*

D7. Let $A \in F_M$. *Then B is a universal quantification of A if, for some* $u \in IP_M$ *and* $x \in V_M$ *such that u is free for x in A, B is the formula* $(x)A^x/u$.

Just as in the last chapter, we will only use notation such as 'A^x/u' when u is free for x in A.

In axiomatizing $H_{p=}$ we'll also need a notion of *universalization*. A universalization of a formula A is any result of universally quantifying A a number of times. We will define this notion inductively: A is a universalization of A, and any universal quantification of a universal quantification of A is a universalization of A.

D8. Let $A \in F_M$. The universalizations of A are defined according to the following rules:

1. *A is a universalization of A.*
2. *If B is a universalization of A, then $(x)B\,^x/u$ is a universalization of A, where $u \in IP_M$, $x \in V_M$, and u is free for x in B.*

A formula C of M is a universalization of A only if it qualifies as such by virtue of clauses 1 and 2.

According to D6, $(x)A\,^x/u$ is a universalization of A if u is free for x in A; $(y)(x)A\,^x/u\,^y/v$ is a universalization of A if v is free for y in $(x)A\,^x/u$; and so forth. In particular, suppose we start with the formula

(i) $u=w \supset . \ Puwv \supset Pwuv.$

$(x)(u=x \supset . \ Puxv \supset Pxuv)$ is a universalization of i. Universally quantifying this universalization of i, we obtain other universalizations of i; for instance, $(y)(x)(y=x \supset . \ Pyxv \supset Pxyv)$. However, $(x)(x)(x=x \supset . \ Pxxv \supset Pxxv)$ is *not* a universal quantification of i, because u is not free for x in $(x)(u=x \supset . \ Puxv \supset Pxuv)$.

Universally quantifying $(y)(x)(y=x \supset . \ Pyxv \supset Pxyv)$, we obtain more universalizations of i, e.g., $(z)(y)(x)(y=x \supset . \ Pyxz \supset Pxyz)$. Other universalizations of i are i itself and vacuous universal quantifications such as $(x)(u=w \supset . \ Puwv \supset Pwuv)$ and $(x)(y)(u=w \supset . \ Puwv \supset Pwuv)$.

3. We now can characterize the axioms of the system $H_{p=}$. Like H_s, this system has infinitely many axioms, among them all instances of the following schemes.

AS1. $A \supset . \ B \supset A$
AS2. $(A \supset . \ B \supset C) \supset . \ A \supset B \supset . \ A \supset C$
AS3. $\sim A \supset \ \sim B \supset . \ B \supset A$
AS4. $(x)(A \supset B\,^x/u) \supset . \ A \supset (x)B\,^x/u$
AS5. $(x)(A\,^x/u \supset B\,^x/u) \supset . \ (x)A\,^x/u \supset (x)B\,^x/u$
AS6. $(x)A\,^x/u \supset A\,^t/u$
AS7. $t=t$
AS8. $s=t \supset . \ A \supset A\,^s/\!/t$

It is important that in AS4, as usual, 'A' stands only for formulas. There are therefore no occurrences of x in A that are not bound by quantifiers.

The instances of AS1 to AS8 do not exhaust all the axioms of $H_{p=}$. Besides these, we will count any universalization of such an instance as an axiom. A formula A (of any morphology for $H_{p=}$) is an axiom of $H_{p=}$ if and only if it is a universalization of some instance of axiom-schemes 1 to 8.

For example, let's suppose that a morphology M includes the individual variables x, y, and z, the individual parameters u, v, and w, the individual constants a and b, the 0-ary predicate parameter (i.e., the sentence parameter) P, and the 3-ary predicate parameter Q. Then among the formulas of M which are axioms of $H_{p=}$ are the following.

$$P \supset. \; Qaaa \supset P$$
$$(x)(y)(P \supset. \; Qaxx \supset P)$$
$$(z)((P \supset. \; P \supset z=u) \supset. \; P \supset P \supset. \; P \supset z=u)$$
$$(x)(\sim P \supset \; \sim P \supset. \; P \supset P)$$
$$(x)(P \supset x=a) \supset. \; P \supset (x)x=a$$
$$(z)(y)((x)((x)x=x \supset Qyxa) \supset. \; (x)x=x \supset (x)Qyxa)$$
$$(x)Qxxa \supset Qbba$$
$$(x)x=x \supset u=u$$
$$(x)(x=a \supset (z)Qzzx) \supset. \; v=a \supset (z)Qzzv$$
$$(x)(y)((z)(Qxxz \supset y=a) \supset. \; Qxxa \supset y=a)$$
$$(x)P \supset P$$
$$u=u$$
$$a=a$$
$$(y)u=u$$
$$(x)(y)x=x$$
$$u=a \supset. \; Quaa \supset Quau$$
$$u=a \supset. \; a=a \supset (x)Qxaa \supset. \; a=u \supset (x)Qxuu$$
$$(x)(a=x \supset. \; x=x \supset a=x)$$

Owing to the fact that u must be free for x in a universal quantification $(x)A \; {}^x/u$ of A, formulas such as $(x)((x)Pxx \supset Pvx)$ are *not* axioms of $H_{p=}$, even though $(x)Pxu \supset Pvu$ is an axiom. But $(y)((x)Pxy \supset Pvy)$ is a universalization of $(x)Pxu \supset Pvu$, and so is an axiom of $H_{p=}$. Axiom-schemes such as AS6 are subject to the same restriction. For this reason $(x)\sim(x)Pxx \supset \sim(x)Pax$ is not an instance of AS6, since u is not free for x in $\sim(x)Pux$.

4. There will be no new primitive rules in $H_{p=}$; its only primitive rule of inference is the familiar *modus ponens*. As before, then, a proof will be an array of formulas in which any entry is either an axiom or a consequence of previous entries by *modus ponens*.

D9. *A proof in $H_{p=}$ is an array $A_1, \ldots, A_n$ of formulas (of any morphology* *for* $H_{p=}$*) such that for all* i, $1 \leq i \leq n$, A_i *is an axiom of* $H_{p=}$, *or there exist numbers* $j, k < i$ *such that* A_j *is* $A_k \supset A_i$.

D10. A formula of a morphology **M** *is provable in* $H_{p=}$ (*or a theorem of* $H_{p=}$) *in case there exists an array of formulas of* **M** *which is a proof of* A *in* $H_{p=}$. *We will use* '$\vdash_{H_{p=}} A$' *to say that* A *is a theorem of* $H_{p=}$; *in this and the next two chapters, we'll omit the subscript from this notation.*

The notation '$\vdash A$' suggests that provability is a property of formulas which is independent of morphology, and we will not have justified this notation until we have shown that if A is a formula of both **M** and **M'**, then there is a proof of A in $H_{p=}$ consisting only of formulas of **M** if and only if there is a proof in $H_{p=}$ of A consisting only of formulas of **M'**. We will eventually show this in Section 13.

Something you will have noticed is that every axiom-scheme of H_s is an axiom-scheme of $H_{p=}$. Furthermore, we have the rule of *modus ponens* as a primitive rule of $H_{p=}$. This means that any array of formulas of $H_{p=}$ which has the form of a proof in H_s is a proof in $H_{p=}$. For instance, consider again the scheme V.vii. If we take the metavariable 'A' of this scheme to range over formulas of $H_{p=}$ rather than just over formulas of H_s as in Chapter V, any instance of the scheme is now a proof of $A \supset A$ in $H_{p=}$. When reconstrued in this more general way the scheme V.vii now shows that any formula of the kind $A \supset A$ is provable in $H_{p=}$. We thus have at once our first metatheorem about $H_{p=}$.

M1. $\vdash A \supset A$.

The methodological importance of this should be evident; it means that a good deal of the work of this chapter has already been done in Chapter V. In particular, wherever we have a *theorem-scheme* such as that of V.M1— i.e., a statement such as '$\vdash A \supset A$' or '$\vdash A \supset . \sim A \supset B$'—which has been established with respect to H_s, we also have the corresponding statement as a metatheorem of $H_{p=}$. We need only reinterpret the metavariables as ranging over formulas of $H_{p=}$. We will also be able to use many other results of $H_{p=}$ in this chapter.

5. Next, we want to define the notion of a *deduction* in $H_{p=}$. The definition is just like the one of Chapter V.

D11. Let Γ *be a set of formulas of* (*any morphology* **M** *for*) $H_{p=}$. *An array*

$A_1, \ldots, A_n$ of formulas of **M** is a deduction (of A_n) from hypotheses Γ in case for all i, $1 \le i \le n$, (1) A_i is an axiom of $\mathbf{H}_{p=}$, or (2) A_i is a member of Γ, or (3) for some $j, k < i$, A_j is $A_k \supset A_i$.

D12. A formula A is deducible in $\mathbf{H}_{p=}$ *from a set* Γ *of formulas of (any morphology* **M** *for)* $\mathbf{H}_{p=}$, *in case there exists an array of formulas of* **M** *which is a deduction of A from* Γ. *As usual, we write* '$\Gamma \vdash_{\mathbf{H}_{p=}} A$', *abbreviated* '$\Gamma \vdash A$', *to indicate that A is deducible from* Γ.

Again, we should note that deducibility must be shown independent of morphology; this will be established below, in Section 13.

Any deduction-scheme established in Chapter V for $\mathbf{H}_s$ can be construed as also determining deductions in $\mathbf{H}_{p=}$. Consider, for instance, the scheme V.ix. If we interpret the metavariables 'A' and 'B' of this scheme as standing for formulas of $\mathbf{H}_{p=}$, any instance of V.ix will be a deduction in $\mathbf{H}_{p=}$ of A from $\{\sim A \supset \sim B, B\}$. V.ix can thus be used to establish that for all formulas A and B of any morphology for $\mathbf{H}_{p=}$, $\sim A \supset \sim B, B \vdash A$.

This means that in general any *deducibility-scheme* established in Chapter V, such as '$\sim A, A \vdash B$' and '$\sim \sim A \vdash A$', holds also for the system $\mathbf{H}_{p=}$. If you think this over, you'll see that this shows that most of the results proved in Chapter V (e.g., V.M13) remain true even when reinterpreted more generally as referring to formulas of $\mathbf{H}_{p=}$.

6. In the same way as in Chapter V, we have at once the following results about deducibility in $\mathbf{H}_{p=}$; their proofs do not differ at all from the ones given in Chapter V.

M2. $\vdash A$ if and only if $\varnothing \vdash A$.

M3. $\Gamma \vdash A$ if and only if for some finite subset Δ of Γ, $\Delta \vdash A$.

M4. If $A \in \Gamma$ then $\Gamma \vdash A$.

M5. If $\Gamma \vdash A$ then $\Gamma \cup \Delta \vdash A$.

M6. If $\Gamma \vdash A$ and $\Delta \cup \{A\} \vdash B$, then $\Gamma \cup \Delta \vdash B$.

M7. If $\Gamma \vdash A \supset B$ then $\Gamma \cup \{A\} \vdash B$.

What about the deduction theorem? A little thought shows that there would be no point in going through the details of the proof of this result for $\mathbf{H}_{p=}$, since they would be exactly like the proof already given of V.M8. The only difference would be that the metavariables used in the demonstration of M8 would now be construed as standing for formulas of $\mathbf{H}_{p=}$, and that in case 1 of the demonstration, 'axiom' would mean 'axiom of $\mathbf{H}_{p=}$'. In other words, the same procedure is used in $\mathbf{H}_{p=}$ to construct a deduction of $A \supset B$ from Γ out of a deduction of B from $\Gamma \cup \{A\}$. Axioms of $\mathbf{H}_{p=}$ are treated just as axioms of $\mathbf{H}_s$ were in the previous procedure. We thus have the deduction theorem for $\mathbf{H}_{p=}$.

M8. If $\Gamma \cup \{A\} \vdash B$, then $\Gamma \vdash A \supset B$.

We could go on in the same way through M9 to M28 of Chapter V and point out that they all hold when generalized to $\mathbf{H}_{p=}$, but this would be tedious and repetitive. Let's simply say that all of these results do hold for $\mathbf{H}_{p=}$, and that in fact the proofs given of them in Chapter V can be regarded as proofs of their generalizations. We will therefore admit these metatheorems into this chapter in a body, and will begin numbering our next result with '29'.

Since some of the metatheorems in this group have to do with defined notions such as disjunction, we must also be careful to generalize the appropriate definitions from Chapter V. Like the metatheorems we have been discussing, these definitions look just like their sentential counterparts. The difference is again that their metavariables are construed more generally. At the same time we are repeating these, we can introduce a definition of existential quantification.

D13. '$A \lor B$' $=_{df}$ '$A \supset B \supset B$'.

D14. '$A \land B$' $=_{df}$ '$\sim(A \supset \sim B)$'.

D15. '$A \equiv B$' $=_{df}$ '$(A \supset B) \land (B \supset A)$'.

D16. '$(\exists x)A$' $=_{df}$ '$\sim(x)\sim A$'.

7. In order to advance our study of deducibility in $\mathbf{H}_{p=}$, we must investigate the distinctive features of $\mathbf{H}_{p=}$ which have to do with quantification and identity; so far, we have only examined the sentential structure of $\mathbf{H}_{p=}$. We will begin this study with a series of metatheorems designed to establish for $\mathbf{H}_{p=}$ analogues of the rules of $\mathbf{S}_{p=}$ for the quantifiers and for identity.

M29. If $\Gamma \vdash (x)A^{x}/u$ *then* $\Gamma \vdash A^{t}/u.$

    PROOF. 1. $\Gamma \vdash (x)A^{x}/u$ assumption

            2. $\vdash (x)A^{x}/u \supset A^{t}/u$ AS4

            3. $\Gamma \vdash A^{t}/u$ 1, 2, M11

M30. If $\vdash A$ *then* $\vdash (x)A^{x}/u$, *provided that u is free for x in A.*

    PROOF. Induce on the length of proof of A in $\mathbf{H}_{p=}$, showing that for all individual variables y and individual parameters u (of a given morphology $\mathbf{M}$) $\vdash (y)A^{y}/u$ if u is free for y in A. If A is an axiom of $\mathbf{H}_{p=}$ then $(y)A^{y}/u$ is a universalization of A if u is free for y in A, and hence is itself an axiom of $\mathbf{H}_{p=}$. This completes the basis step. Assume as inductive hypothesis that for all proofs of any formula B with fewer than k steps, there is for all individual variables y and individual parameters u a proof of $(y) B^{y}/u$, provided that u is free for y in B. Then suppose that there is a proof of A with k steps, and that v is free for z in A. We want to show that $\vdash (z)A^{z}/v$. We can assume that A isn't an axiom of $\mathbf{H}_{p=}$, so that there are steps C and $C \supset A$ in this proof of A, which both have proofs of fewer than k steps. Here, we must be careful in applying the hypothesis of induction, since we don't know whether v is free for z in C. Let x be an individual variable having no occurrences whatsoever in A or in C. (We know there is such an x, since any morphology has infinitely many individual variables.) This ensures that v is free for x in C and in $C \supset A$. Therefore, by the hypothesis of induction, $\vdash (x)C^{x}/v$ and $\vdash (x)(C^{x}/v \supset A^{x}/v)$. Since $(x)(C^{x}/v \supset A^{x}/v) \supset. (x)C^{x}/v \supset (x)A^{x}/v$ is an instance of AS5, we have $\vdash (x)A^{x}/v$. Now, $(x)A^{x}/v \supset A$ is an instance of AS6, and since v is free for z in A, $(z)((x)A^{x}/v \supset A^{x}/v)$ is a universalization of this axiom and hence is itself an axiom. But in view of AS4, $\vdash (z)((x)A^{x}/v \supset A^{z}/v) \supset. (x)A^{x}/v \supset (z)A^{z}/v$. Using *modus ponens* twice, we obtain $(z)A^{z}/v$; thus $\vdash (z)A^{z}/v$, as desired. This completes the induction, and the proof of M30.

    M30 shows that a rule of *universal generalization* is admissible in $\mathbf{H}_{p=}$, as follows.

$$\frac{A}{(x)A^{x}/u} \text{ where } u \text{ is free for } x \text{ in } A$$

The addition of this rule to $\mathbf{H}_{p=}$ as a primitive rule of inference would not yield any new theorems. There are many reasons, however, why we wouldn't want this to be a derived rule of $\mathbf{H}_{p=}$. For one thing, if it were true for all formulas A that $A \vdash (x)A^{x}/u$, $(x)x=u$ would then be derivable from $v=u$ and it would follow that $\vdash v=u \supset (x)x=u$. But this clearly is invalid; although $2 + 2$ equals 4, it isn't the case that every number equals 4.

The rule of universal generalization is therefore like the rule of substitution for sentence parameters which we discussed in V.14: it is an admissible but not a derived rule of $H_{p=}$. Although we would expect any universal quantification of a theorem of logic also to be a theorem of logic, there is no reason to believe that any universal quantification of a hypothesis should follow logically from that hypothesis. Indeed, this is why in Chapter IX we had to impose restrictions on the rule of uq int, using barriers that block certain reiterations.

Although M30 has to do with provability, it can easily be generalized to obtain results applying to deducibility.

M31. If $B_1, \ldots, B_n \vdash A$ and the parameter u is free for x in A and has no occurrences in any one of $B_1, \ldots, B_n$, then $B_1, \ldots, B_n \vdash (x)A\ ^x/u$.

PROOF. We will induce on n. M30 furnishes the basis step of this induction; suppose as hypothesis of induction that for all $C_1, \ldots, C_k$, and D, if $C_1, \ldots, C_k \vdash D$ and u is free for x in D and has no occurrences in any one of $C_1, \ldots, C_k$, then $C_1, \ldots, C_k \vdash (x)D\ ^x/u$. Furthermore, suppose that u is free for x in A and has no occurrences in any one of $B_1, \ldots, B_k, B_{k+1}$, and that $B_1, \ldots, B_k, B_{k+1} \vdash A$; we want to show that $B_1, \ldots, B_k, B_{k+1} \vdash (x)A\ ^x/u$. By M8, $B_1, \ldots, B_k \vdash B_{k+1} \supset A$, and by the hypothesis of induction, $B_1, \ldots, B_k \vdash (x)(B_{k+1}\ ^x/u \supset A\ ^x/u)$. Since u has no occurrences in B_{k+1}, $B_{k+1}\ ^x/u$ is B_{k+1}; therefore $B_1, \ldots, B_k \vdash (x)(B_{k+1} \supset A\ ^z/u)$. In view of AS4, $\vdash (x)(B_{k+1} \supset A\ ^x/u) \supset . B_{k+1} \supset (x)A\ ^x/u$, so by M11, $B_1, \ldots, B_k \vdash B_{k+1} \supset (x)A\ ^x/u$. And by M7, $B_1, \ldots, B_k, B_{k+1} \vdash (x)A\ ^x/u$. This completes the induction.

M32. If $\Gamma \vdash A$ and the parameter u is free for x in A and has no occurrences in any member of Γ, then $\Gamma \vdash (x)A\ ^x/u$.

PROOF. Suppose that $\Gamma \vdash A$; then by M3, for some $\{B_1, \ldots, B_n\}$ such that $\{B_1, \ldots, B_n\} \subseteq \Gamma$, it is the case that $B_1, \ldots, B_n \vdash A$. M31 then shows that $B_1, \ldots, B_n \vdash (x)A\ ^x/u$, and so by M5, $\Gamma \vdash (x)A\ ^x/u$.

8. Our next group of metatheorems has to do with substitution of terms for terms. We want in particular to show that if $\vdash A$ then $\vdash A\ ^s/t$, and to draw corollaries from this. To prove this result we need to look more closely at substitution itself: specifically, we will state and prove some metatheorems just about substitution of terms for terms. Some of you may see immediately that these metatheorems are true; if so, you may feel that proofs are unnecessary. But since not everyone sees such things directly, we will give short

proofs. It is possible to prove these metatheorems more rigorously, using inductive arguments; these, however, are rather long and tedious.

M33. If s differs from u and u differs from t then $A^x/u\,^s/t$ is the same expression as $A^s/t\,^x/u$. Similarly, if s differs from u, t differs from r and u differs from t then $A^r/u\,^s/t$ is the same formula as $A^s/t\,^r/u$.

PROOF. It must be the case that x differs from t, since x is an individual variable and t a term. Therefore, since t differs from u, t occurs in A^x/u at those and only those places where t occurs in A. $A^x/u\,^s/t$ is thus the result of putting occurrences of x for all occurrences of u in A, and putting occurrences of s for all occurrences of t in A. Similarly, since s differs from u and u differs from t, $A^s/t\,^x/u$ is the result of putting occurrences of s for all occurrences of t in A and occurrences of x for all occurrences of u in A. $A^x/u\,^s/t$ and $A^s/t\,^x/u$ are therefore the same expression. The same reasoning, replacing 'x' by 'r', establishes the second part of the metatheorem.

M34. $A^r/s\,^t/r$ is the same formula as $A^t/r\,^t/s$, and $A^r/s\,^x/r$ the same as $A^x/r\,^x/s$.

PROOF. $A^r/s\,^t/r$ is the result of putting occurrences of t for all occurrences of r in A^r/s. But r occurs in A^r/s at those places where r occurs in A or s occurs in A. Therefore $A^r/s\,^t/r$ is the same as $A^t/r\,^t/s$. A similar argument establishes the second part of the theorem.

Turning our attention now to the eight axiom-schemes of $\mathbf{H}_{p=}$, we will show that the result of substituting s for t in any instance of one of these schemes is an instance of the same scheme.

M35. Let A be an instance of one of AS1 to AS8. Then A^s/t is also an instance of the same axiom-scheme.

PROOF. We will consider three representative examples of these eight cases, leaving the remaining ones as exercises. First, suppose that A is an instance of AS1; then A is $B \supset . C \supset B$ and A^s/t is $B^s/t \supset . C^s/t \supset B^s/t$, which also is an instance of AS1.

Second, suppose that A is an instance of AS4; then A is $(x)(B \supset C^x/u) \supset . B \supset (x)C^x/u$. Let v be an individual parameter differing from s and t and not occurring in A; then C^x/u will be the same expression as $C^v/u\,^x/v$, so that A is $(x)(B \supset C^v/u\,^x/v) \supset . B \supset (x)C^v/u\,^x/v$. A^s/t is therefore $(x)(B^s/t \supset C^v/u\,^x/v\,^s/t) \supset . B^s/t \supset (x)C^v/u\,^x/t\,^s/t$. By M33, $C^v/u\,^x/v\,^s/t$ is $C^v/u\,^s/t\,^x/v$; hence, A^s/t is $(x)(B^s/t \supset D^x/v) \supset . B^s/t \supset (x)D^x/v$, where D is $C^v/u\,^s/t$. This shows A^s/t to be an instance of AS4.

As a final example, suppose that A is an instance of AS6; then A is $(x)B^x/u \supset B^r/u$. Again, let v be an individual parameter differing from r, s, and t, and not occurring in B. B^x/u is then the same expression as $B^v/u^x/v$, and B^r/u the same formula as $B^v/u^r/v$. By M33, $B^v/u^s/t^x/v$ is the same expression as $B^v/u^x/v^s/t$, and so is the same as $B^x/u^s/t$.

Now, suppose that t differs from r. Then by M33, $B^v/u^s/t^r/v$ is the same formula as $B^v/u^r/v^s/t$, and so is the same as $B^r/u^s/t$. A^s/t is therefore $(x)C^x/v \supset C^r/v$, where C is $B^v/u^s/t$, and thus is an instance of AS6.

Suppose on the other hand that t is the same term as r, so that A^s/t is $(x)B^x/u^s/t \supset B^t/u^s/t$. Again, $B^x/u^s/t$ is $B^v/u^s/t^x/v$, and $B^t/u^s/t$ is $B^v/u^t/v^s/t$, which by M34 is the same as $B^v/u^s/t^s/v$. Therefore A^s/t is $(x)C^x/v \supset C^s/v$, where C is $B^v/u^s/t$; and A^s/t is again an instance of AS6.

We want eventually to show that A^s/t is a theorem of $\mathbf{H}_{p=}$ if A is. The next step in doing this is to prove that if A is an axiom of $\mathbf{H}_{p=}$ then so is A^s/t.

M36. If A is an axiom of $\mathbf{H}_{p=}$ then A^s/t is an axiom of $\mathbf{H}_{p=}$.

PROOF. Let the *rank* of an axiom A be the number of universal quantifications of an instance of an axiom-scheme required to produce A; we will prove the metatheorem by an induction on rank. If A has rank 0, then A is itself an instance of one of AS1 to AS8 and M35 shows that A^s/t is an axiom of $\mathbf{H}_{p=}$. For the inductive step let A be $(x)B^x/u$, where u is free for x in B, and suppose as inductive hypothesis that for all axioms C having rank less than A, C^r/r' is an axiom of $\mathbf{H}_{p=}$ for all terms r and r'. Now, let v be an individual parameter differing from s and t and not occurring in A; then B^x/u is the same expression as $B^v/u^x/v$, and A^s/t is $(x)B^v/u^x/v^s/t$. But by M33, $B^v/u^x/v^s/t$ is the same expression as $B^v/u^s/t^x/v$, so that A^s/t is $(x)B^v/u^s/t^x/v$. But B is an axiom having rank less than that of A, so by the hypothesis of induction B^v/u is an axiom. Since the rank of B^v/u is still less than that of A, $B^v/u^s/t$ is also an axiom. Because A^s/t is a universal quantification $(x)B^v/u^s/t^x/v$ of $B^v/u^s/t$, it too is an axiom of $\mathbf{H}_{p=}$. This completes the induction.

Using M36, it's easy to show that $\vdash A^s/t$ if $\vdash A$.

M37. If $\vdash A$ then $\vdash A^s/t$.

PROOF. Since we know by M36 that if A is an axiom of $\mathbf{H}_{p=}$ then $\vdash A^s/t$, we need only show that if $\vdash (B \supset A)^s/t$ and $\vdash B^s/t$, then $\vdash A^s/t$. But this is immediate; since $(B \supset A)\,{}^S/t$ is $B\,{}^S/t \supset A\,{}^S/t$, $A\,{}^S/t$ follows from $B\,{}^S/t$ and $(B \supset A)\,{}^S/t$ by *modus ponens*.

There is another way of looking at the proof of this metatheorem. If we take a proof $B_1, \ldots, B_n$ of A, $B_1\,{}^S/t, \ldots, B_n\,{}^S/t$ will be a proof of $A\,{}^S/t$, since substitution of s for t transforms axioms into axioms and does not affect applications of *modus ponens*. This shows in a more perspicuous way why $A\,{}^S/t$ is provable if A is.

Using M37, we are now able to show that we can universally generalize theorems of $\mathbf{H}_{p=}$ not only with respect to individual parameters, but also with respect to individual constants. That is, if $\vdash A$, then $\vdash (x)A\,{}^x/t$ for any term t free for x in A.

M38. If $\vdash A$ and t is free for x in A, then $\vdash (x)A\,{}^x/t$.

PROOF. Suppose that t is free for x in A and that $\vdash A$. Let u be any individual parameter not occurring in A; then $(x)A\,{}^x/t$ is $(x)A\,{}^u/t\,{}^x/u$ and u is free for x in $A\,{}^u/t$. By M37, $\vdash A\,{}^u/t$, and by M30 $\vdash (x)A\,{}^u/t\,{}^x/u$. Therefore, $\vdash (x)A\,{}^x/t$.

M38 can be generalized in the same way as M30.

M39. If $B_1, \ldots, B_n \vdash A$ and t is free for x in A and has no occurrences in any one of $B_1, \ldots, B_n$, then $B_1, \ldots, B_n \vdash (x)A\,{}^x/t$.

PROOF. Induce on n. If $n = 0$, then $\vdash (x)A\,{}^x/t$ by M38. Suppose as hypothesis of induction that for all formulas $C_1, \ldots, C_k$, and D, if $C_1, \ldots, C_k \vdash D$ and t is free for x in D and has no occurrences in any one of $C_1, \ldots, C_k$, then $C_1, \ldots, C_k \vdash (x)D\,{}^x/t$. Suppose also that $B_1, \ldots, B_k, B_{k+1} \vdash A$ and that t is free for x in A and has no occurrences in any one of $B_1, \ldots, B_k, B_{k+1}$. By M8, $B_1, \ldots, B_k \vdash B_{k+1} \supset A$, and by the hypothesis of induction $B_1, \ldots, B_k \vdash (x)(B_{k+1}\,{}^x/t \supset A\,{}^x/t)$. Since t has no occurrences in B_{k+1}, $B_{k+1}\,{}^x/t$ is B_{k+1}; therefore $B_1, \ldots, B_k \vdash (x)(B_{k+1} \supset A\,{}^x/t)$. In view of AS4 and M7, $(x)(B_{k+1} \supset A\,{}^x/t), B_{k+1} \vdash (x)A\,{}^x/t$. M6 then shows that $B_1, \ldots, B_k, B_{k+1} \vdash (x)A\,{}^x/t$. This completes the induction.

M40. If $\Gamma \vdash A$ and t is free for x in A and has no occurrences in any member of Γ, then $\Gamma \vdash (x)A\,{}^x/t$.

PROOF. Suppose that $\Gamma \vdash A$; then by M3, for some $\{B_1, \ldots, B_n\}$ such that $\{B_1, \ldots, B_n\} \subseteq \Gamma$, it is the case that $B_1, \ldots, B_n \vdash A$. M39 then shows that $B_1, \ldots, B_n \vdash (x)A\,{}^x/t$, and so by M5, $\Gamma \vdash (x)A\,{}^x/t$.

9. The above metatheorems develop the more important properties of universal quantification. With this sequence of results completed, we can now prove some results about identity. We want to establish analogues for $\mathbf{H_{p=}}$ of the introduction and elimination rules for identity of $\mathbf{S_{p=}}$. Also, looking forward to the task of showing $\mathbf{H_{p=}}$ semantically complete, we want to show that the relation $s \simeq t$, where $s \simeq t$ if and only if $\Gamma \vdash s=t$, is an *equivalence relation*. That is, we want to prove the following three things for all terms r, s, and t: $s \simeq s$; if $s \simeq t$ then $t \simeq s$; and if $r \simeq s$ and $s \simeq t$ then $r \simeq t$. This is done in M45 to M47.

In the proofs below, we will use the notation '$\mathbf{H_s}$' to justify any step that depends only on M1 to M28; that is, which depends only on sentential considerations.

M41. If $\Gamma \cup \{s=t\} \vdash A$ then $\Gamma \cup \{s=t\} \vdash A\,^S\!/\!/t$.
   PROOF. 1. $\Gamma \cup \{s=t\} \vdash A$ assumption
        2. $\vdash s=t \supset. A \supset A\,^S\!/\!/t$ AS8
        3. $\Gamma \cup \{s=t\} \vdash A\,^S\!/\!/t$ 1, 2, $\mathbf{H_s}$

M42. $s-t, A\,^S\!/\!/t \vdash A$.
   PROOF. 1. $s=t, \sim A \vdash \sim A$ M4
        2. $s=t, \sim A \vdash \sim A\,^S\!/\!/t$ 1, M41
        3. $s=t, A\,^S\!/\!/t \vdash A$ 2, M12

M43. $s=t \vdash A \equiv A\,^S\!/\!/t$.

M44. If $\Gamma \vdash s=t$ then $\Gamma \vdash A$ if and only if $\Gamma \vdash A\,^S\!/\!/t$.

M45. $\Gamma \vdash t=t$.

M46. If $\Gamma \vdash s=t$ then $\Gamma \vdash t=s$.
   PROOF. 1. $\Gamma \vdash s=t$ assumption
        2. $\Gamma \cup \{s=t\} \vdash t=t$ M45
        3. $\Gamma \cup \{s=t\} \vdash t=s$ 2, M41
        4. $\Gamma \vdash t=s$ 1, 3, M6

M47. If $\Gamma \vdash r=s$ and $\Gamma \vdash s=t$ then $\Gamma \vdash r=t$.

The proof of M47 is left as an exercise; M43 follows easily from M41 and M42, and M44 is a corollary of M43.

10. We would now like to develop some properties of the existential quantifier, as defined in D16. As usual, we want to obtain analogues of the introduction and elimination rules of $S_{p=}$ for the existential quantifier. Using M29, it's easy to get an analogue of eq int; its proof is left as an exercise.

M48. If $\Gamma \vdash A \, {}^t/u$ then $\Gamma \vdash (\exists x)A \, {}^x/u$.

The following metatheorem corresponds to eq elim.

M49. If $\Gamma \vdash (\exists x)A \, {}^x/u$ and $\Gamma \cup \{A\} \vdash B$, where u is free for x in A and has no free occurrences in B or in any member of Γ, then $\Gamma \vdash B$.

PROOF.
1. $\Gamma \vdash (\exists x)A \, {}^x/u$ assumption
2. $\Gamma \vdash \sim(x)\sim A \, {}^x/u$ 1, D16
3. $\Gamma \cup \{A\} \vdash B$ assumption
4. $\Gamma \cup \{\sim B\} \vdash \sim A$ 3, H_s
5. $\Gamma \cup \{\sim B\} \vdash (x)\sim A \, {}^x/u$ 4, M32
6. $\Gamma \vdash \sim\sim B$ 2, 5, H_s
7. $\Gamma \vdash B$ 6, M19

We now will begin a series of metatheorems which will be required in our proof of the semantic completeness of $H_{p=}$; the most important of these results are M52 and its corollary, M58, which is proved in Section 11.

M50. If $\Gamma \cup \{A\} \vdash B$ and u is free for x in A and has no occurrences in B or in any member of Γ, then $\Gamma \cup \{(\exists x)A \, {}^x/u\} \vdash B$.

PROOF.
1. $\Gamma \cup \{A\} \vdash B$ assumption
2. $\Gamma \cup \{\sim B\} \vdash \sim A$ 1, H_s
3. $\Gamma \cup \{\sim B\} \vdash (x)\sim A \, {}^x/u$ 2, M32
4. $\Gamma \cup \{\sim(x)\sim A \, {}^x/u\} \vdash B$ 3, H_s
5. $\Gamma \cup \{(\exists x)A \, {}^x/u\} \vdash B$ 4, D16

M51. $\vdash (\exists y)((\exists x)A \, {}^x/u \supset A \, {}^y/u)$, provided that u is free for x and for y in A.

PROOF.
1. $\sim((\exists x)A \, {}^x/u \supset A) \vdash (\exists x)A \, {}^x/u$ H_s
2. $\sim((\exists x)A \, {}^x/u \supset A) \vdash \sim A$ H_s
3. $\vdash (y)\sim((\exists x)A \, {}^x/u \supset A \, {}^y/u) \supset \sim((\exists x)A \, {}^x/u \supset A)$ AS6
4. $(y)\sim((\exists x)A \, {}^x/u \supset A \, {}^y/u) \vdash \sim A$ 2, 3, H_s
5. $(y)\sim((\exists x)A \, {}^x/u \supset A \, {}^y/u) \vdash (x)\sim A \, {}^x/u$ 4, M32
6. $(y)\sim((\exists x)A \, {}^x/u \supset A \, {}^y/u) \vdash (\exists x)A \, {}^x/u$ 1, 3, H_s
7. $(y)\sim((\exists x)A \, {}^x/u \supset A \, {}^y/u) \vdash \sim(x)\sim A \, {}^x/u$ 6, D16

8. $\vdash \sim(y)\sim((\exists x)A\,^x/u \supset A\,^y/u)$ 5, 7, M20
9. $\vdash (\exists y)((\exists x)A\,^x/u \supset A\,^y/u)$ 8, D16

M52. If $\Gamma \cup \{(\exists x)A\,^x/u \supset A\,^v/u\} \vdash B$ and u is free for x in A and v has no occurrences in A, B, or in any member of Γ, then $\Gamma \vdash B$.

PROOF. Let y be an individual variable not occurring in A. Then v is free for y in $(\exists x)A\,^x/u \supset A\,^v/u$; also $((\exists x)A\,^x/u \supset A\,^y/u)$ is the same expression as $((\exists x)A\,^x/u \supset A\,^v/u)\,^y/v$. The following argument then shows that $\Gamma \vdash B$.

1. $\Gamma \cup \{(\exists x)A\,^x/u \supset A\,^v/u\} \vdash B$ assumption
2. $\Gamma \cup \{(\exists y)((\exists x)A\,^x/u \supset A\,^y/u)\} \vdash B$ 1, M50
3. $\vdash (\exists y)((\exists x)A\,^x/u \supset A\,^y/u)$ M51
4. $\Gamma \vdash B$ 2, 3, M6

Among the corollaries of M49 is the following result. The proof of this metatheorem is left as an exercise.

M53. If $\Gamma \vdash (\exists x)A\,^x/u$, where u is free for x in A, and $\Gamma \vdash (x)(A^x/u \supset B)$ then $\Gamma \vdash B$.

11. In V.15 we discussed the notion of consistency and decided to say that a set Γ of formulas is consistent in case some formula cannot be deduced from it. The resulting definition, however, referred to deducibility in $\mathbf{H_s}$, and now that we have revised our underlying logic we should also revise our definition of consistency to accord with deducibility in $\mathbf{H_{p=}}$. Our new definition has the same form as V.D11.

D17. A set Γ of formulas of $\mathbf{H_{p=}}$ is consistent (in $\mathbf{H_{p=}}$) if there is some formula A of $\mathbf{H_{p=}}$ such that not $\Gamma \vdash A$. A set of formulas is said to be inconsistent if it is not consistent.

But though it is like V.D11 in form, D17 is much more probing in allowing us to seek out inconsistencies. The sets $\{\sim a = a\}$ and $\{(x)Px, (x)(Px \supset Qx), \sim(x)Qx\}$, are consistent in $\mathbf{H_s}$, since there is no way to deduce a contradiction from either of these sets using only AS1 and AS3 together with *modus ponens*. Both sets, however, are inconsistent in $\mathbf{H_{p=}}$.

Just as V.M1 to V.M28 hold when reconstrued as statements about $\mathbf{H_{p=}}$, so do V.M32 to V.M35. We reproduce these below as M54 to M57. As we remarked above, M58 is a corollary of M52; its proof is left as an exercise.

M54. A set Γ of formulas of $\mathbf{H_{p=}}$ is inconsistent if and only if for some formula A of $\mathbf{H_{p=}}$, $\Gamma \vdash A$ and $\Gamma \vdash \sim A$.

M55. A set Γ of formulas of $\mathbf{H}_{p=}$ *is consistent if and only if every finite subset of* Γ *is consistent.*

M56. Γ ⊢ *A if and only if* Γ ∪ {∼ *A} is inconsistent.*

M57. If Γ *is consistent then for all formulas A of* $\mathbf{H}_{p=}$, *either* Γ ∪ {*A} is consistent or* Γ ∪ {∼ *A} is inconsistent.*

M58. If Γ *is consistent in* $\mathbf{H}_{p=}$, *u is free for x in A and v has no occurrences in A or in any member of* Γ, *then* Γ ∪ {(∃x)A $^x/u$ ⊃ A $^v/u$} *is consistent in* $\mathbf{H}_{p=}$.

12. V.M29 differs from previous metatheorems of Chapter V in that its proof doesn't carry over immediately to $\mathbf{H}_{p=}$. The proof uses induction on the complexity of formulas of $\mathbf{H}_s$. In this induction three cases are considered: the formula may be a sentence parameter, an implication, or a negation. To prove that it also holds for $\mathbf{H}_{p=}$, we must take into consideration the case in which the formula is a universal quantification; furthermore, we must take into account the fact that in $\mathbf{H}_{p=}$ atomic formulas need not be sentence parameters. To begin with, we will generalize V.D9 to obtain a definition of replacement for $\mathbf{H}_{p=}$.

D18. 1. *If A is (the same formula as) C, then both C and B are results of replacing A by B in C.*
   2. *If A is not (the same formula as) C ⊃ D, then if C' is a result of replacing A by B in C, and D' a result of replacing A by B in D, then C' ⊃ D' is a result of replacing A by B in C ⊃ D.*
   3. *If A is not (the same formula as) ∼ C, then if C' is a result of replacing A by B in C, then ∼ C' is a result of replacing A by B in ∼ C.*
   4. *If A is not (the same formula as) (x)C $^x/u$, then if D is a result of replacing A by B in C $^v/u$, where v is an individual parameter not occurring in A, B, or C, then (x)D $^x/v$ is a result of replacing A by B in C.*
   5. *If A is not (the same formula as) C and C is atomic, then C is a result of replacing A by B in C.*

The function of the parameter *v* in clause 4 of D18 is to mark those places in *C* where *u* occurs, so that we will know where to put occurrences of *x* in universally quantifying a result of replacing *A* by *B* in *C*. We must require that *v* not occur in *B* or *C* so that it will record only those places corresponding to occurrences of *u* in *C* and not places arising, e.g., from replacing *A* by *B*. It is convenient to require also that *v* does not occur in *A*.

In proving M60, our main metatheorem about replacement, we will need the following result, whose proof is left as an exercise.

M59. $(x)(A\,^x/u \equiv B\,^x/u) \vdash (x)A\,^x/u \equiv (x)B\,^x/u.$

M60. If C' is a result of replacing A by B in C then $A \equiv B \vdash C \equiv C'$.

PROOF. As in the proof of V.M29, we induce on the complexity of C. If C is atomic then by D18 either (1) C' is C or (2) A is C and C' is B. In case 1, $\vdash C \equiv C'$ by M4 and M25, and so by M5, $A \equiv B \vdash C \equiv C'$. In case 2, by M4, $A \equiv B \vdash C \equiv C'$. This completes the basis step of the induction.

Assume now as hypothesis of induction that $A \equiv B \vdash C_1 \equiv C_1'$ for all formulas C_1 shorter than C, where C_1' is any result of replacing A by B in C_1. Either (1) C is an implication $D \supset E$, (2) C is a negation $\sim D$, or (3) C is a universal quantification $(x)D\,^x/u$. Cases 1 and 2 are just like cases 1 and 2 of the proof of V.M29. In case 3, D18 guarantees that either (3.1) C' is C; or (3.2) A is C and C' is B; or (3.3) C' is $(x)E\,^x/v$, where E is a result of replacing A by B in $D\,^v/u$ and v does not occur in A, B, or D. Cases 3.1 and 3.2 are just like cases 1 and 2 of the basis step. In case 3.3, $D\,^v/u$ is less complex than $(x)D\,^x/u$ and so the hypothesis of induction ensures that $A \equiv B \vdash D\,^v/u \equiv E$. M32 then shows that $A \equiv B \vdash (x)(D\,^v/u\,^x/v \equiv E\,^x/v)$, and M59 that $A \equiv B \vdash (x)D\,^v/u\,^x/v \equiv (x)E\,^x/v$. But since v doesn't occur in D, $(x)D\,^v/u\,^x/v$ is $(x)D\,^x/u$; i.e., is C. Therefore $A \equiv B \vdash C \equiv C'$. This completes the inductive step and the proof of M60.

M60 has the following corollaries; their proof is left as an exercise.

M61. If $\vdash A \equiv B$ and C' is a result of replacing A by B in C then $\vdash C \equiv C'$.

M62. If $\vdash A \equiv B$ and C' is a result of replacing A by B in C, then $\Gamma \vdash C$ if and only if $\Gamma \vdash C'$.

Although these metatheorems are perhaps the most straightforward generalizations of the results of Chapter V concerning replacement, there are ways in which they are deficient. For instance, M62 does not permit us to infer that $\vdash (x)(\sim\sim Px \lor \sim Px)$ from the fact that $\vdash (x)(Px \lor \sim Px)$. The trouble here is that according to D18 we can't speak of $(x)(\sim\sim Px \lor \sim Px)$ as a result of replacing Px by $\sim\sim Px$ in $(x)(Px \lor \sim Px)$, because Px is *not a formula*. This expression doesn't fall under the scope of D19 because it contains an occurrence of an individual variable not bound by a quantifier.

These limitations can be overcome by generalizing D19; for details, see E8, below.

13. We observed in Section 4 that provability was defined relative to a morphology; this holds true of other important syntactic notions such as *derivability* and *consistency*. In spite of this we have chosen to speak of these notions without regard to any morphology; e.g., we spoke simply of *provability* rather than of *provability with respect to* **M**. We will now legitimatize this way of speaking by showing that it really doesn't matter which morphology we have in mind when we think of provability, derivability, and consistency. In this sense, these notions are absolute.

M63. Let **M** *and* **M′** *be morphologies for* $H_{p=}$, *and A be a formula of both* **M** *and* **M′**. *If there exists an array* $B_1, \ldots, B_n$ *of formulas of* **M** *which is a proof of A in* $H_{p=}$, *then there exists an array of formulas of* **M′** *which also is a proof of A in* $H_{p=}$.

PROOF. The strategy of our argument depends on the fact that the terms and predicate parameters occurring in $B_1, \ldots, B_n$ which do not appear in A are "redundant" and can be eliminated from the proof in favor of terms and predicate parameters of **M′** in such a way that the result is still a proof in $H_{p=}$.

We want to operate on $B_1, \ldots, B_n$, putting symbols of **M′** for symbols of **M**. Below, we do this in three stages: first individual variables, then individual terms, then predicate parameters.

First, then, let $x_1, \ldots, x_m$ be all those individual variables of **M** which have occurrences in any one of the steps $B_1, \ldots, B_n$, and which are not individual variables of **M′**. Let $y_1, \ldots, y_m$ be distinct individual variables of **M′** which do not occur in any step B_i of the given proof, and let B_j' be the result of exchanging each occurrence of x_1 in B_j for an occurrence of y_1, then each occurrence of x_2 in B_j for an occurrence of y_2, and so on. It's evident that $B_1', \ldots, B_n'$ is still a proof, since if B_i is an axiom of $H_{p=}$ then so is B_i', and if B_i follows from B_j and B_k by *modus ponens*, then B_i follows from B_j' and B_k' by *modus ponens*.

Second, let $t_1, \ldots, t_h$ be all those individual terms that have occurrences in any one of the steps $B_1', \ldots, B_n'$, and which are not individual terms of **M′**. Let u be an individual parameter of **M′** which does not occur in any of $B_1', \ldots, B_n'$, and let B_i'' be the result of putting occurrences of u for all occurrences in B_i' of any of $t_1, \ldots, t_h$. Again, the array $B_1'', \ldots, B_n''$ is still a proof, and for the same reason; this transformation takes axioms of $H_{p=}$ into axioms of $H_{p=}$, and applications of *modus ponens* into applications of *modus ponens*.

Third, where $e_1, \ldots, e_k$ are arbitrary terms or individual variables of $\mathbf{M}'$, let the expression $E_{e_1 \ldots e_k}$ be $e_1 = e_1 \wedge \cdots \wedge e_k = e_k$. (We have chosen $E_{e_1 \ldots e_k}$ as a simple example of an expression that contains free occurrences of each of the terms and individual variables $e_1, \ldots, e_k$, and which contains occurrences of no other terms or individual variables. Note also that if each of $e_1, \ldots, e_k$ is a term or individual variable of $\mathbf{M}'$, then $E_{e_1 \ldots e_k}$ is an expression of $\mathbf{M}'$.) Then, let C_i be the result of putting occurrences of $E_{e_1 \ldots e_k}$ for each occurrence of $Pe_1 \cdots e_k$ in B_i'', for every k-ary predicate parameter P of $\mathbf{M}$ but not of $\mathbf{M}'$ ($k > 0$), and of putting an occurrence of $(z)z = z$ for each occurrence in B_i'' of every 0-ary predicate parameter which does not belong to $\mathbf{M}'$, where z is an individual variable of $\mathbf{M}'$. The formula C_i will be a formula of $\mathbf{M}'$, and again it is easy to verify that $C_1, \ldots, C_n$ is a proof.

But, since A is a formula of $\mathbf{M}'$, it is unchanged by the transformation described above; C_n is A. Therefore, $C_1, \ldots, C_n$ is a proof of A involving only formulas of $\mathbf{M}'$, and M62 is proved.

This metatheorem guarantees not only that provability is independent of what morphology a formula is conceived of as belonging to, but also shows the same thing of derivability and consistency. For, using M3, M7, and M8, we can reduce derivability to provability. ($\Gamma \vdash A$ if and only if for some finite subset $\{B_1, \ldots, B_n\}$ of Γ, $\vdash B_1 \supset. \cdots \supset. B_n \supset A$.) And, of course, we know that consistency reduces to derivability. The proof of M62 shows us the basic reason why these notions are absolute; the axioms of $\mathbf{H}_{p=}$ were chosen in such a way that they are invariant under the transformations used in the proof of M62. This would not have been the case, for instance, if we had allowed morphologies possessing only finitely many individual parameters. In that case, there would be formulas that would be provable when regarded as belonging to one morphology, but not provable when regarded as formulas of another morphology.

14. There are many more things that can be done with the syntax of $\mathbf{H}_{p=}$, but we will leave it to the exercises and problems at the end of this chapter to provide an indication of these. In this concluding section we will turn to the problem of relating $\mathbf{H}_{p=}$ to natural deduction systems, and show how the procedure of V.16 can be generalized to yield a proof of the equivalence of $\mathbf{H}_{p=}$ and $\mathbf{S}_{\supset \sim \mathbf{v}=}$. (By '$\mathbf{S}_{\supset \sim \mathbf{v}=}$', we understand the fragment of $\mathbf{S}_{p=}$ consisting just of formulas of $\mathbf{H}_{p=}$, and involving only the introduction and elimination rules for implication, negation, universal quantification, and identity. Since we will have to speak of this system often and the name '$\mathbf{S}_{\supset \sim \mathbf{v}=}$' is long, we'll coin '$\mathbf{S}_k$' as a nickname of it for use in this section.)

As in the case of sentence logic, it's a simple matter to show that if a formula is provable in $H_{p=}$, it is derivable categorically in S_k. M64 is an analogue of V.M36.

M64. If $\vdash B$ then $\vdash_{S_k} B$.

PROOF. Essentially, all that needs to be done here is to verify that any instance of AS1 to AS8 is derivable categorically in S_k. This is easily accomplished. Having done this, we can see that any axiom of $H_{p=}$ is derivable categorically in S_k, since if a formula A can be derived categorically in S_k, then $(x)A$ $^x/u$ can be derived categorically in S_k by means of uq int.

And just as in the case of H_s, we know that if A and $A \supset C$ are derivable categorically in $H_{p=}$, then so is C. M64 follows by induction on the length of proof of B in $H_{p=}$.

Using M64, we can get a corresponding result for arguments. M65 is proved in the same way as V.M37.

M65. If $A_1, \ldots, A_n \vdash B$ then $A_1, \ldots, A_n \vdash_{S_k} B$.

As in the sentential case, the converse of M65 requires a more searching examination of the natural deduction system. As in Chapter V we will use the notion of an augmented derivation to carry out our argument. Let's say that an array is an *augmented derivation* (in S_k) if it is like a derivation in S_k, except that any axiom of $H_{p=}$ may be introduced anywhere in it. The following array, then, is an augmented derivation in S_k.

$$
\begin{array}{l}
\lfloor (y)(x)(Px \supset Qyx) \\
\quad \lfloor (x)Px \\
\qquad u \mid (x)Px \\
\qquad \quad (y)(x)(Px \supset Qyx) \\
\qquad \quad (x)(Px \supset Qux) \\
\qquad \quad (x)(Px \supset Qux) \supset . (x)Px \supset (x)Qux \\
\qquad \quad (x)Px \supset (x)Qux \\
\qquad \quad (x)Qux \\
\qquad (y)(x)Qyx \\
\quad (x)Px \supset (y)(x)Qyx
\end{array}
$$

Retracing the route we traversed in Chapter V, we want to show by systematically removing subordinated derivations from augmented derivations in S_k that if there exists a derivation in S_k of B from $A_1, \ldots, A_n$, there is a deduction in $H_{p=}$ of B from $A_1, \ldots, A_n$. Let's state this as a metatheorem.

M66. If there is an augmented derivation in $\mathbf{S}_k$ *of B from* $A_1, \ldots, A_n$ *then there is a deduction in* $\mathbf{H}_{p=}$ *of B from* $A_1, \ldots, A_n$.

PROOF. As in the proof of V.M38, we want to systematically eliminate from augmented derivations all applications of the rules of neg int and imp int. Since the rationale of the argument is to remove all subordinated derivations from the augmented derivations, we also want to eliminate all applications of uq int; this rule also involves something like subordination. In this part of the proof, the elimination of subordinated derivations involving hypotheses (i.e., subordinated derivations such as the one pictured in V.xiv) is carried out as described in the proof of V.M38.

This leaves us with the task of eliminating innermost subordinations involving barriers for variables, such as the following one.

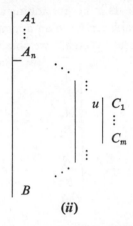

(*ii*)

The first step in getting rid of the barrier for u is to erase it and replace each step C_i to the right of this barrier by $(x)C_i \, {}^x/u$. This gives the following array.

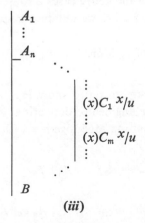

(*iii*)

Now, iii is easily transformed into an augmented derivation by inserting steps that use only *modus ponens* and axioms of $H_{p=}$. Specifically, besides *modus ponens*, there are just six cases regarding a step C_i; either it is (1) an axiom of $H_{p=}$, (2) a reiteration, (3) a consequence by neg elim of some previous C_k, (4) a consequence by uq elimination of some previous C_k, (5) a consequence by id elim of some previous formulas C_j and C_k, or (6) a consequence $t = t$ by id int. In case 1, $(x)C_i {}^x/u$ is still an axiom and we don't have to do anything. In case 2, u has no occurrences in C_i, and $(x)C_i {}^x/u$ can be obtained from C_i by axioms of $H_{p=}$ and *modus ponens* (see E8(n) below). Cases 3 to 5 are similar to case 2. And case 6 is just a special case of 1.

Finally, if below $(x)C_m {}^x/u$ in iii there is some consequence of a step C_i of ii by the rule of uq int, this consequence will be $(x)C_i {}^x/u$ and it can simply be erased, since it already appears in iii. So, adding steps to iii in the way suggested by the above paragraph results in an augmented derivation.

If we repeat these procedures, eventually we obtain an augmented derivation

$$
\begin{array}{|l}
A_1 \\
\vdots \\
A_n \\
\hline
D_1 \\
\vdots \\
D_k \\
B
\end{array}
$$

(*iv*)

of B from $A_1, \ldots, A_n$, in which no subordinated derivations or barriers occur. Every step of iii which is not an axiom of $H_{p=}$ or justified by *modus ponens*, then, will fall under one of the above cases 2 to 6. Hence, by adding appropriate steps to iv in cases 2 to 6, we obtain a deduction in $H_{p=}$ of B from $A_1, \ldots, A_n$.

This completes the proof of M66.

Using M66, we can easily go on to show $H_{p=}$ and S_k equivalent. Since every derivation in S_k is an augmented derivation, we have M67 immediately and M68 is obtained by putting M65 together with M67.

M67. *If* $A_1, \ldots, A_n \vdash_{S_k} B$ *then* $A_1, \ldots, A_n \vdash B$.

M68. $A_1, \ldots, A_n \vdash B$ *if and only if* $A_1, \ldots, A_n \vdash_{S_k} B$.

Exercises

1. Let $V_M = \{x, y, z, x_1, y_1, z_1, \ldots\}$, $IP_M = \{u, v, w, u_1, v_1, w_1, \ldots\}$, $C_M = \{a, b\}$, $P_M{}^0 = \{P\}$, $P_M{}^1 = \{Q\}$, and $P_M{}^3 = \{R\}$. Find arrays of formulas of M which are proofs in $H_{p=}$ of the following formulas.

  (a) $(x)(Qx \supset (y)(y = x \supset Qx))$
  (b) $(x)(Rxxx \supset. Qx \supset x = a) \supset. (x)Rxxx \supset (x)(Qx \supset x = a)$
  (c) $(x) \sim Qx \supset. (\exists x)Qx \supset Qa$
  (d) $P \supset (x)P$
  (e) $(x)(P \supset (x)P)$
  (f) $(x)(y)(x = y \supset y = x)$
  (g) $(x)Qx \supset (y)Qy$

2. Let M be as in E1, and find arrays of formulas of M which are deductions establishing the following statements.

  (a) $(x)(y)Rxay \vdash Raaa$
  (b) $(\exists x)Qx \supset (y)Ryya \vdash (y)((\exists x)Qx \supset Ryya)$
  (c) $(x)(y)(x = y \supset Rxyy) \vdash Raaa$
  (d) $(x)(P \supset. x = x \supset Qx), P \vdash (x)Qx$
  (e) $(x)(x = a \supset Px), (x)(Px \supset x = b) \vdash Pb$

3. Using any metatheorems of this chapter except those of Section 14, establish the following statements.

  (a) $Qa \vdash (x)(\sim Qx \supset \sim x = a)$
  (b) $\vdash (\exists x)(Qx \supset (x)Qx)$
  (c) $(\exists x)(y)(z)Rxyz \vdash (y)(z)(\exists x)Rxyz$
  (d) $(\exists x)Raxx, (y)(Rayy \supset Qy) \vdash (\exists z)Qz$
  (e) $a = b, (\exists x)Rabx \vdash (\exists y)(\exists x)Ryyx$
  (f) $(x)(P \vee Qx), \sim P \vdash (x)Qx$
  (g) $(x)(Qx \vee x = b) \vdash (\exists x)Qx \vee (x)x = b$

4. Using any metatheorems of this chapter, establish the following results.

  (a) $\sim (\exists x) \sim A\,{}^x/u \vdash (x)A\,{}^x/u$
  (b) $(x)(A\,{}^x/u \supset B) \vdash (\exists x)A\,{}^x/u \supset B$
  (c) If $A \vdash B$ then $(x)A\,{}^x/u \vdash (x)B\,{}^x/u$
  (d) If $A \vdash B$ then $(\exists x)A\,{}^x/u \vdash (\exists x)B\,{}^x/u$
  (e) $(x)A\,{}^x/u \vdash (\exists x)A\,{}^x/u$
  (f) $A \supset (x)B\,{}^x/u \vdash (x)(A \supset B\,{}^x/u)$
  (g) $(x)(A \supset B\,{}^x/u), A \vdash (x)B\,{}^x/u$
  (h) $A \supset (\exists x)B\,{}^x/u \vdash (\exists x)(A \supset B\,{}^x/u)$
  (i) $(\exists x)(A \supset B\,{}^x/u), A \vdash (\exists x)B\,{}^x/u$
  (j) $(x)A\,{}^x/u \supset B \vdash (\exists x)(A\,{}^x/u \supset B)$
  (k) $(\exists x)(A\,{}^x/u \supset B) \vdash (x)A\,{}^x/u \supset B$
  (l) $(\exists x)A\,{}^x/u \supset B \vdash (x)(A\,{}^x/u \supset B)$

(m) $(x)(A^x/u \supset B), (\exists x)A^x/u \vdash B$

(n) $A \vdash (x)A$

(o) $(y)(x)A^x/u^y/v \vdash (z)A^z/u^z/v$, where u is free for x in A, v is free for y in $(x)A^x/u$, and u and v are free for z in A.

5. Prove the following metatheorems. Feel free to use any metatheorems listed before them.

    (a) M43   (b) M44   (c) M45   (d) M47

    (e) M48   (f) M53   (g) M58   (h) M59

    (i) M61   (j) M62

6. Let $\mathbf{H}^1_{p=}$ have as axioms all instance of AS1, AS2, AS3, AS6, AS7, and AS8 (but *not* their universalizations). Let the rules of inference of $\mathbf{H}^1_{p=}$ be *modus ponens* and the following rule of *conditional generalization*:

$$\frac{A \supset B}{A \supset (x)B^x/u},$$

where u is free for x in B and does not occur in A. Show that $\mathbf{H}_{p=}$ and $\mathbf{H}^1_{p=}$ have the same theorems.

7. Define the notion of a *relettering* A' of a formula A inductively, as follows.
1. A is a relettering of A.
2. If A' is a relettering of A and B' a relettering of B, then $A' \supset B'$ is a relettering of $A \supset B$.
3. If A' is a relettering of A then $\sim A'$ is a relettering of $\sim A$.
4. If A' is a relettering of A and u is free for y in A' then $(y)A'^y/u$ is a relettering of $(x)A^x/u$.

A formula is a relettering of A only if it can be shown to be such by virtue of clauses 1 to 4.

    Show that if A' is a relettering of A then $\vdash A \equiv A'$.

8. By a *semiformula* of a morphology $\mathbf{M}$ for $\mathbf{H}_{p=}$ we mean any result of substituting individual variables of $\mathbf{M}$ for individual parameters of $\mathbf{M}$ in a formula of $\mathbf{M}$. (We can define this notion inductively by stipulating that if A is a formula of $\mathbf{M}$ then A is a semiformula of $\mathbf{M}$, and that if F is a semiformula of $\mathbf{M}$, u an individual parameter of $\mathbf{M}$, x an individual variable in $\mathbf{M}$, and u is free for x in F, then F^x/u is a semiformula of $\mathbf{M}$.) We will use 'F', 'G', and 'H' to stand for semiformulas. Where F is a semiformula of $\mathbf{M}$, a *universal closure* $(\ )F$ of F is any formula of $\mathbf{M}$ obtained by prefixing universal quantifiers to F. Thus $(x)(y)Pxy$, $(y)(x)Pxy$, and $(z)(y)(x)(x)Pxy$ are universal closures of Pxy.
    (a) Give an inductive definition along the lines of D18 of *a result of replacing F by G in H*.
    (b) Show that if H' is a result of replacing F by G in H then $(\ )(F \equiv G) \vdash (\ )(H \equiv H')$.

Problems

1. Show that if a formula contains no occurrences of individual variables and is a
   theorem of $H_{p=}$, then it can be proved using only instances of AS1 to AS3 and
   of AS7 and AS8 (and no universalizations of such instances), and *modus
   ponens*. Go on to show that if a theorem of $H_{p=}$ contains no occurrences of $=$
   and no occurrences of individual variables, then it can be proved using only
   instances of AS1 to AS3 and *modus ponens*. Use the latter result to prove that
   $H_{p=}$ is consistent; i.e., that some formula is not a theorem of $H_{p=}$.

2. A formula is said to be in *prenex normal form* if it is the result of successively
   universally and existentially quantifying a quantifier-free formula, with no
   quantifiers in the same variable and no vacuous quantifications. More precisely, A is in prenex normal form if A has the form $(U_1x_1) \cdots$
   $(U_nx_n)B^{x_n}/u_n \cdots x_1/u_1$, where B contains no quantifiers, x_i differs from x_j
   and u_i from u_j if $i \neq j$, each u_i occurs in B and is free for x_i in $(U_{i+1}x_{i+1}) \cdots$
   $(U_nx_n)B^{x_n}/u_n \cdots B^{x_{i+1}}/u_{i+1}$, and each expression (U_ix_i) is either (x_i) or $(\exists x_i)$.
   Show that for every formula A of $H_{p=}$, there is a formula B of $H_{p=}$ such that
   B is in prenex normal form and $\vdash A \equiv B$.

3. Define *deduction* for the system $H^1_{p=}$ of E6 in such a way that deducibility in
   $H^1_{p=}$ is equivalent to deducibility in H_{p-}.

4. Try to define a notion of *substitution* for formulas of $H_{p=}$ which is an appropriate generalization of V.D10. You should be able to establish an analogue
   of V.M31 for $H_{p=}$. (*Warning:* This is a very complicated matter; many
   restrictions are needed.)

5. Let $H^2_{p=}$ have as axioms all universalizations of instances of AS1, AS2, AS3,
   AS4, AS5, AS8, and the following scheme:

$$(\exists x)x = t.$$

   The only rule of inference of $H^2_{p=}$ is *modus ponens*. Show that the theorems of
   $H^2_{p=}$ are the same as the theorems of $H_{p=}$.

XI Predicate Logic with Identity: Semantics

1. Since our work in previous chapters provides a good idea of what we are now about to do, there is little need to indulge in preliminaries. Chapter VI has given us a semantic theory and Chapters VIII to X have developed various aspects of predicate logic with identity. We now want to formulate a semantic theory of this logic. The sentence connectives $\supset$ and $\sim$ of $\mathbf{H_s}$ are contained in the language of $\mathbf{H_{p=}}$, and in accounting for them we can adopt the theory of Chapter VI wholesale. Our task, then, is to find a good generalization of the semantics of sentence logic, a generalization which will deal with universal quantification and identity as well as implication and negation.

We pointed out in Chapter VIII that quantifications cannot be interpreted until a *domain* has been specified for the individual variables. What we said there also indicates how individual constants and predicate parameters should be interpreted, once a domain has been chosen. Individual constants should be assigned members of D; these will be the things named by, or *referents* of these constants. And predicate letters should be assigned properties and relations on the domain D.

What about individual parameters? In VIII.6, we said that these symbols represent arbitrary members of the domain. Now, there are various ways of construing this semantically. We could say, for instance, that individual parameters are to be assigned no values whatsoever; their referents would then be semantically indeterminate. But this would mean that we couldn't assign truth-values to formulas containing parameters. It's much better to say that in interpreting a morphology, we must arbitrarily assign members of the domain to individual parameters. This means that individual parameters will behave semantically just like individual constants.

Let's see how this works by looking at some examples. First, we need a morphology: let $V_M = \{x, y, z, x_1, y_1, z_1, \ldots\}$, $IP_M = \{u_1, u_2, \ldots\}$, $C_M = \{a, b, c\}$, $P_M^0 = \{P\}$, $P_M^1 = \{Q\}$, $P_M^2 = \{R\}$, and for all $i > 2$, $P_M^i = \varnothing$. The morphology M thus has three individual constants and just one sentence parameter. It has one 1-ary predicate parameter and one 2-ary predicate parameter.

It will be simpler to use a small domain in interpreting the individual variables of M: let's choose the set $D = \{1, 2\}$, consisting of the numbers 1 and 2, for this purpose. To complete our interpretation of M we must assign values to a, b, c, P, Q, and R; we should also choose values for the individual parameters $u_1, u_2, \ldots$. Since we want to give individual constants values in the domain $\{1, 2\}$, let's assign 1 to a and b, and 2 to c. The constants a and b will then be different names of the same thing, the number 1.

Although we've not yet finished specifying our valuation of M, we have enough information to determine the truth-values of many formulas. For instance $a = c$ is false because a and c name different members of D, and $a = b$ is true because a and b name the same member of D. $(\exists x)x = a$ is true, since there is a member of D (namely, 1) which equals 1, and likewise $(y)(\exists x)x = y$ is true, since for any member of D there is a member of D (i.e., the same one) which equals it. But $(x)x = a$ is false, since not every member of D equals 1, and likewise $(y)(x)x = y$ is false, since not every member of D is equal to every other member. A more complicated formula is $(\exists x)(\exists y)(z)(x = z \lor y = z)$. This formula is true. Since D has only two members, there exist members of D (namely, 1 and 2) such that every member of D is equal to one or the other of them.

Just as in Chapter VI, the sentence parameter P should be assigned a truth-value; let's give it the value F. We want to assign a property pertaining to members of D to the predicate parameter Q. Many such properties come to mind: for instance *being even*, which holds of 2 and doesn't hold of 1, and *being odd*, which holds of 1 and doesn't hold of 2. We'll give the property of *being even* to the predicate parameter Q. Among the two-term relations that pertain to members of D are *being less than, being greater than,* and *being less than or equal to.* We'll give the relation of *being less than* to the predicate parameter R.

Finally, we need to give values in D to the individual parameters $u_1, u_2, \ldots$ of **M**. We can do this any way we like; assign 1 to u_i if i is even, and 2 to u_i if i is odd. This finishes our valuation of **M**.

This valuation of **M** will make every atomic formula of **M** true or false. For example, take the following atomic formulas of **M**.

(*i*) $u_1 = u_3$ (*ii*) $a = u_3$

(*iii*) Qa (*iv*) Qc

(*v*) Rac (*vi*) Rcu_2

Since u_1 and u_3 are both assigned the value 2, i is true, but a takes the value 1, so that ii is false. Formula iii says that 1 has the property of being even, and so is false; iv says that 2 is even, and so is true. Formula v says that 1 is less than 2, and so is true; vi says that 2 is less than 1, and so is false.

Now let's look at some complex formulas of **M**, such as the following ones.

(*vii*) $\sim b = c$ (*viii*) $Rac \supset P$

(*ix*) $(x)Rax$ (*x*) $(x)(Rax \lor a = x)$

(*xi*) $(x)(Rxu_3 \supset (y)\sim Ryx)$ (*xii*) $(x)(\exists y)Rxy$

Examples vii and viii pose no problems that are new. Their truth-values are computed in the usual way, given the truth-values of their atomic components. Thus, since $b = c$ is false, $\sim b = c$ is true; since Rac is true and P is false, viii is false. The universal quantifier figures in ix; what this formula says is that 1 is less than all members of D. Since D = {1, 2}, this amounts to saying that 1 is less than 1 and 1 is less than 2, which is false. Example x, on the other hand, says that every member of D is either greater than 1 or equal to 1, which is true. Example xi says that for every member of D, if it is less than 2 then no member of D is less than it. Since the only member of D less than 2 is 1 and no member of D is less than 1, xi is true. Finally, example xii says that for every member of D there is a member of D greater than it, which is false; there is no member of D greater than 2.

In this interpretation we used a domain consisting of mathematical objects; the members of D are numbers. Although domains made up of numbers are useful for many purposes, there is no reason why other domains can't be used to build valuations. For instance, we can use a domain consisting of the New England states to interpret the morphology **M**, as follows. Let E = {Connecticut, Massachusetts, Rhode Island, New Hampshire, Vermont,

Maine}. We only have enough individual constants to name three of these; let a name Connecticut, b name Maine, and c name Massachusetts. Assign New Hampshire to u_1, Rhode Island to u_2, and Vermont to u_i for all $i > 2$. Let P take the value T, and assign Q the property of *being inland* and R the relation of *bordering on*. (Here, we will understand 'bordering on' in such a way that a state does not border on itself.) The formulas of **M** now take on wholly different meanings under this valuation. Formula xii, for instance, which before said that every number in D is less than some number in D, now says that every New England state borders on some New England state, which is true.

Here are some other formulas which take on interesting meanings with respect to this valuation.

(xiii) $(x)(Px \supset x = u_3)$ **(xiv)** $(\exists x)(\exists y)(\sim x = y \wedge \sim Rxy)$

(xv) $(\exists x)(y)(\sim y = x \supset Ryx)$ **(xvi)** $(x)(y)(Rxy \supset Ryx)$

Formula xiii says that every inland New England state is identical to Vermont; i.e., Vermont is the only inland New England state. This is true; if you look at a map you'll see that all the other New England states have coastlines. Example xiv says that there are two (different) New England states not bordering one another. This is true; Connecticut and Maine are such states. Formula xv says that there is a New England state bordering on every other New England state. To see that this is false, you can take a map and go through these states systematically, showing that in each case another New England state can be found not bordering on it. (Massachusetts, for instance, doesn't border on Maine, New Hampshire doesn't border on Rhode Island, and so on.) Finally, xvi clearly is true; the bordering relation doesn't depend on the order in which states are taken.

2. Now that we're well acquainted with the notion of a valuation of a morphology, we are ready to give a rigorous definition of this concept, so that we can prove metatheorems about it. The outlines of this definition should already be apparent: a valuation of **M** on a domain D should assign each individual constant and individual parameter of **M** a member of D, each sentence parameter of **M** a truth-value T or F, and each i-ary predicate parameter of **M** (where $i \geq 1$) an i-termed relation pertaining to members of D.

But before we can make this definition, something should be cleared up: what do we mean by 'an i-termed relation pertaining to members of D'? Unless we clarify this point the notion of a valuation on a domain D will be vague in many respects; for instance, we won't be able to tell whether two valuations V and V' of **M** on D are the same, since without criteria of sameness for relations we will be unable to tell whether V and V' assign predicate parameters of **M** the same relations.

This problem can be overcome by reflecting on the work we expect relations to do in our semantic theory. For instance, we want 1-termed relations (i.e., properties) on a domain D to enable us to tell the truth-values of formulas such as *Pt*. For this we need to know which members of D have the property. The simplest way of defining 'property' so that this will work out is to identify a property pertaining to members of D with a set of members of D: those members of D having the property. We will therefore say that a 1-termed relation on D is just a subset of D. More generally, an *i*-termed relation on D is a set of *i*-tuples of members of D; i.e., a subset of the Cartesian power D^i. (See XIII.10 and XIII.11 for an account of *i*-tuples and Cartesian powers.) For example, let D consist of all the nonnegative integers; $D = \{0, 1, 2, \ldots\}$. By the property of being an even member of D, we will understand the set $\{0, 2, 4, \ldots\}$ of even members of D. By the 2-termed relation on members of D of *being less than*, we will understand the set $\{\langle m, n\rangle / m, n \in D \text{ and } m < n\}$ of those ordered pairs of nonnegative integers whose first members are less than their second members.

D1. Where $i > 1$, an i-termed relation on a domain D is a subset of the Cartesian power D^i.

With this understood, we can go on to define what is meant by 'a valuation of **M** on D'.

*D2. Let D be a nonempty set. A valuation of a morphology **M** for $H_{p=}$ on the domain D is a function that assigns:*

1. *Each individual constant c of **M** a unique value V(c) in D.*
2. *Each individual parameter u of **M** a unique value V(u) in D.*
3. *Each 0-ary predicate parameter P of **M** a unique truth-value V(P) which is either T or F.*
4. *Each i-ary predicate parameter Q of **M** (where $i \geq 1$) a subset V(Q) of the Cartesian power D^i.*

Some of the commitments of these definitions should be made explicit. First, D2 presupposes that the domain D is nonempty. This assumption is required because we have to assign individual parameters values in D, and if there were nothing in the domain, we couldn't do this. (A deeper reason is that formulas such as $(\exists x)(\exists y)x = y$ are theorems of $H_{p=}$, but these would be invalid in an empty domain.) Second, D1 commits us to a thesis called the *principle of extensionality*, which says that *i*-termed relations on D which hold of exactly the same members of D are identical. For instance, on the domain {Illinois, Tennessee, California} the properties of *being east of the Mississippi* and *being inland* are identical, since they are both identified with the set {Illinois, Tennessee}. There are various intuitive objections to the principle of extensionality; it's very plausible that there is more to a relation than the things of which it holds. But these objections have little bearing on the use we will make of the principle, since in the semantics of $H_{p=}$ we are concerned only with the truth-values given to formulas of $H_{p=}$ by valuations. To determine these truth-values, all we need to know about a relation is the set of things of which it holds.

Given the notion of a valuation of a morphology **M**, we want to determine which formulas of **M** are made true by a valuation and which are made false. Here the main problem is to formulate the conditions under which a universal formula $(x)A \, ^x/u$ is made true by a valuation V on a domain D. As usual, we suppose that u is free for x in A.

What we will do here is to say that $V((x)A \, ^x/u) = T$ in case V would make A true no matter what value in D it were to assign u. This means that for any member d of D, if V is changed so that it assigns u the value d, it still will make A true. In order to say this concisely it will be useful to coin a notation for the result of changing V so that it assigns u the value d. Since this is a kind of substitution of d for the value given by V to u, we will use the notation 'V $^d/u$'.

D3. Let V be a valuation of a morphology **M** *for* $H_{p=}$ *on a domain* D, *and let* $u \in IP_M$ *and* $d \in D$. *The result* V $^d/u$ *of semantically substituting* d *for the value given by* V *to* u *is the valuation of* **M** *which assigns to every symbol of* **M** *other than* u *the same value given to it by* V, *and which gives* u *the value* d. *That is,* V $^d/u$ *is just like* V, *except that* V $^d/u(u) = $ d.

With this notation defined we can proceed to determine how valuations give truth-values to formulas. We will break this definition up into two parts: D4 is for atomic formulas and D5 for complex formulas. Notice that the method of definition is inductive, with D4 giving the basis clause and D5 the inductive clause.

D4. Let V be a valuation of a morphology **M** *for* $H_{p=}$ *on a domain* D *and let* A *be an atomic formula of* **M**. *In case* A *is a* 0-*ary predicate parameter P, the* *truth-value* V(A) *of A is already given by* D2. *Otherwise,* V(A) *is determined as follows:*

1. $V(Pt_1 \cdots t_n) = T$ *if* $\langle V(t_1), \ldots, V(t_n) \rangle \in V(P)$, *and* $V(Pt_1 \cdots t_n) = F$ *otherwise.*
2. $V(s=t) = T$ *if* $V(s)$ *is the same as* $V(t)$, *and* $V(s=t) = F$ *otherwise.*

D5. *Let* V *be a valuation of a morphology* **M** *for* $H_{p=}$ *on a domain* D. *The truth-value* V(A) *of a complex formula A of* **M** *is determined according to the following rules.*

1. *If A is* $B \supset C$, *then* $V(A) = T$ *if* $V(B) = F$ *or* $V(C) = T$, *and* $V(A) = F$ *otherwise.*
2. *If A is* $\sim B$, *then* $V(A) = T$ *if* $V(B) = F$, *and* $V(A) = F$ *otherwise.*
3. *If A is* $(x)B\,^x/u$ *where u is free for x in B, then* $V(A) = T$ *if for all* $d \in D$, $V^{\,d}/u(B) = T$, *and* $V(A) = F$ *otherwise.*

3. To see how D4 and D5 work, let's go back to our first example of a valuation, which was given in Section 1. Recall that here the morphology **M** had individual parameters $u_1, u_2, \ldots$, and three individual constants, a, b, and c. **M** also had one 0-ary predicate parameter P, one 1-ary predicate parameter Q, and one 2-ary predicate parameter R. We discussed informally a valuation V of **M** on the domain $\{1, 2\}$; we let $V(a) = 1$, $V(b) = 1$, $V(c) = 2$, and $V(u_i) = 1$ if i is even and $V(u_i) = 2$ if i is odd. Also, we let $V(P) = F$. The parameter Q was assigned the property of *being even* and R the relation of *being less than*; now, we would say that $V(Q) = \{2\}$ and $V(R) = \{\langle 1, 2 \rangle\}$.

We can now apply D4 and D5 to some of the formulas we discussed in Section 1 to see whether these definitions give the same results we obtained using just common sense. First, consider $\sim a = c$; by D5, $V(\sim a = c) = T$ if $V(a=c) = F$; and by D4, $V(a=c) = F$ if $V(a)$ differs from $V(c)$. But $V(a) = 1$ and $V(c) = 2$, and 1 differs from 2; so $V(\sim a = c) = T$. The formula $(x)Rax$ is a little more complicated since it involves a universal quantifier. According to D5, $V((x)Rax) = F$ if it is not the case that for all $d \in \{1, 2\}$, $V^{\,d}/u_1(Rau_1) = T$. Therefore $V((x)Rax) = F$ if $V^{\,1}/u_1(Rau_1) = F$ or $V^{\,2}/u_1(Rau_1) = F$. Now, $V^{\,1}/u_1(a) = 1$ and $V^{\,1}/u_1(u_1) = 1$, and it isn't the case that 1 is less than 1: $\langle 1, 1 \rangle \notin \{\langle 1, 2 \rangle\}$. Thus, $V((x)Rax) = F$.

The formula $(x)(Rax \lor a=x)$ by definition is $(x)(Rax \supset a=x \supset a=x)$. By D5, $V((x)(Rax \supset a=x \supset a=x)) = T$ if for all $d \in D$, $V^{\,d}/u_1(Rau_1 \supset a=u_1 \supset a=u_1) = T$; i.e., if $V^{\,1}/u_1(Rau_1 \supset a=u_1 \supset a=u_1) = T$ and $V^{\,2}/u_1(Rau_1 \supset a=u_1 \supset a=u_1) = T$. But $V^{\,1}/u_1(u_1) = 1$ and $V^{\,1}/u_1(a) = 1$, so by D4, $V^{\,1}/u_1(a=u_1) = T$. Also, it's easy to see that $V^{\,2}/u_1(Rau_1) = T$ and

$V^2/u_1(a=u_1) = F$, so by D5, $V^2/u_1(Rau_1 \supset a=u_1) = F$ and $V^2/u_1(Rau_1 \supset a=u_1 \supset a=u_1) = T$. Therefore $V((x)(Rax \lor a=x)) = T$.

Finally, let's take $(x)(\exists y)Rxy$. By D5, $V((x)(\exists y)Rxy) = F$ if it is not the case that for all $d \in \{1, 2\}$, $V^d/u_1((\exists y)Ru_1 y) = T$. Consider V^2/u_1; does $V^2/u_1((\exists y)Ru_1 y) = T$? By definition, $(\exists y)Ru_1 y$ is $\sim(y)\sim Ru_1 y$, and $V^2/u_1(\sim(y)\sim Ru_1 y) = F$ if $V^2/u_1((y)\sim Ru_1 y) = T$. We have to use D5 again here: $V^2/u_1((y)\sim Ru_1 y) = T$ if for all $d \in \{1, 2\}$, $V^2/u_1{}^d/u_2(\sim Ru_1 u_2) = T$; i.e., if $V^2/u_1{}^1/u_2(\sim Ru_1 u_2) = T$ and $V^2/u_1{}^2/u_2(\sim Ru_1 u_2) = T$. This amounts to saying that $\langle 2, 1\rangle \notin \{\langle 1, 2\rangle\}$ and $\langle 2, 2\rangle \notin \{\langle 1, 2\rangle\}$ which is the case. It follows that $V^2/u_1((\exists y)Ru_1 y) = F$, and hence $V((x)(\exists y)Rxy) = F$.

The calculations we have used in this example are tedious, but there is no necessity for going to such lengths in using D4 and D5; we can be much more direct and brief. For one thing, we can assume that $V((x)A^x/u) = F$ if for some $d \in D$, $V^d/u(A) = F$; this follows from M1, below. In view of M1 and M2, we can also suppose that $V((\exists x)A^x/u) = T$ if for some $d \in D$, $V^d/u(A) = T$, and $V((\exists x)A^x/u) = F$ if for all $d \in D$, $V^d/u(A) = F$. Finally, we can use the results of Chapter VII and work on defined sentence connectives directly; for instance, we can assume that $V(A \lor B) = T$ if $V(A) = T$ or $V(B) = T$.

Bearing all this in mind let's consider another example, in which the domain is infinite. Let M' have only one predicate parameter P, which is 2-ary, and let $C_{M'} = \{a\}$. We needn't bother to specify what the individual variables and individual parameters of M' are, but will suppose that x, y, and z are among the individual variables and u, v, and w among the individual parameters. Let $D = \{0, 1, 2, \ldots\}$ and let $U(a) = 0$ and $U(P) = \{\langle m, n\rangle \mid m, n \in D$ and $m < n\}$. It doesn't matter for the examples we will consider what values U gives to individual parameters; all we'll need to know is that U makes a a name of 0 and assigns P the relation of *being less than*.

First, let's use D4 and D5 on $(x)(Pax \lor x=a)$. $U((x)(Pax \lor x=a)) = T$ if $U^n/u(Pau \lor u=a) = T$ for all $n \in D$; i.e., if for all $n \in D$, $0 < n$ or $n = 0$. This amounts to saying that 0 is less than or equal to every $n \in D$, which is true. Therefore $U((x)(Pax \lor x=a)) = T$. Another example is $(x)(\exists y)Pxy$. $U((x)(\exists y)Pxy) = T$ if for all $n \in D$, $U^n/u((\exists y)Puy) = T$, and this if for all $n \in D$ there is an $m \in D$ such that $U^n/u{}^m/v(Puv) = T$. Now, $U^n/u{}^m/v(Puv) = T$ if and only if $n < m$; so $U((x)(\exists y)Pxy) = T$ if for all $n \in D$ there is an $m \in D$ such that $n < m$. Since this is the case (for instance, let $m = n + 1$), $U((x)(\exists y)Pxy) = T$. Last, consider $(x)(y)(Pxy \supset (\exists z)(Pxz \land Pzy))$. $U((x)(y)(Pxy \supset (\exists z)(Pxz \land Pzy))) = T$ if and only if for all $m, n \in D$, $U^m/u{}^n/v(Puv \supset (\exists z)(Puz \land Pzv)) = T$; and this if and only if for all $m, n \in D$, if $m < n$ then $U^m/u{}^n/v((\exists z)(Puz \land Pzv)) = T$. Finally, this is the case if and only if for all $m, n \in D$ if $m < n$ then for some $k \in D$, $m < k$ and $k < n$; i.e., k is between m and n. But this isn't so; for instance $1 < 2$, but there are no members of D between 1 and 2. Therefore $U((x)(y)(Pxy \supset (\exists z)(Pxz \wedge Pzy))) = F$.

Practice with examples such as these will make it easy to use D4 and D5 in seeking to determine the truth-value given to a formula by a valuation. But even so, problems of this kind are much more complex than they were in Chapter VII. This complexity doesn't arise from any obscurity in our definitions and notation, but from the fact that once these definitions have been used on a formula we may not know enough about the domain to be able to tell whether or not the formula is true. For example, let's enlarge the morphology **M′** of the above example by adding a 1-ary predicate parameter Q, and another 2-ary predicate R; call the resulting morphology **M″**. Let D be the set of nonnegative integers, as before, and define a valuation W on **M″** so that W assigns the same values as U to symbols of **M′**, and $W(Q) = \{n \mid n \in D$ and n is prime$\}$ and $W(R) = \{\langle m, n \rangle \mid m, n \in D$ and $n = m + 2\}$. (A number n is said to be *prime* if it differs from 1 and is evenly divisible by no integers other than itself and 1; the first five prime numbers are 2, 3, 5, 7, and 11.)

Now consider the formula

(xvii) $(x)(\exists y)(\exists z)(Pxy \wedge Qy \wedge Qz \wedge Ryz)$.

Using D4 and D5, it's easy to see that W makes xvii true if and only if there are arbitrarily large pairs of prime numbers m and n such that $m = n + 2$. Once we've done this, D4 and D5 can be of no further help to us. In order to tell whether W makes xvii true we have to verify or refute this general statement about prime numbers. But this is something which no one has been able to do; this is an unsolved mathematical problem.

The source of this increased complexity in the calculation of truth-values is the presence of infinite domains in predicate logic. When working with truth-tables, and with valuations for predicate logic on finite domains, it is always possible to compute the truth-value of any formula mechanically in a finite number of steps. But this is no longer possible where the domain is infinite. Here, to establish that a universal formula is true we must show that infinitely many things possess some property, and in general there is no guarantee that a finite procedure will succeed in settling such a problem.

This means only that we have sacrificed the mechanical feature of truth-tables in passing to the semantics of predicate logic; it doesn't entail that we will not be able to establish general results about valuations, just as we did in Chapter VI. Indeed, the rest of this chapter will be devoted to this task.

4. First, we should make explicit the fact that every valuation on a domain gives each formula a unique truth-value.

M1. Let **M** *be a morphology for* $\mathbf{H}_{\mathrm{p}=}$, D *be a nonempty domain, and* V *be a valuation of* **M** *on* D. *Then every formula A of* **M** *is given a unique truth-value* T *or* F *by* V.

PROOF. Just as in the proof of VI.M1, we induce on the complexity of A. Now, however, our hypothesis of induction is that for *all* valuations U of **M** on D, U assigns all formulas of **M** less complex than A a unique truth-value T or F. Using D4, it's easy to see that any such valuation assigns any atomic formula of **M** a unique truth-value; this furnishes the basis step of the induction. The cases of the inductive step in which A is an implication or a negation are just like the corresponding cases of the proof of VI.M1. In case A is a universal formula $(x)B^{x}/u$ (where u is free for x in B) the hypothesis of induction guarantees that for all $d \in D$, $V^{d}/u(B)$ takes a unique truth-value T or F, for any valuation V of **M** on D. But then, in view of clause 3 of D4, A is given a unique truth-value T or F by V.

In the examples of Section 3 we made use of the fact that an existential formula $(\exists x)A^{x}/u$ is made true by a valuation V on a domain D if and only if for some $d \in D$, $V^{d}/u(A) = T$. This is our next metatheorem; its proof is left as an exercise.

M2. Let V *be a valuation of* **M** *on* D, *and* $(\exists x)A^{x}/u$ *be a formula of* **M**. *Then* $V((\exists x)A^{x}/u) = T$ *if and only if for some* $d \in D$, $V^{d}/u(A) = T$.

As in Chapter VI, we wish to generate from D4 and D5, the definitions of satisfaction, characterizations of the notions *satisfiability* and *validity*. These definitions look just like their sentential analogues.

D6. A formula A of **M** *is satisfiable if there exists a nonempty domain* D *and a valuation* V *of* **M** *on* D *such that* $V(A) = T$.

D7. A formula A of **M** *is valid if for all nonempty domains* D *and all valuations* V *of* **M** *on* D, $V(A) = T$.

For instance, consider the formula $(\exists x)(y)Pxy$ of the morphology **M'** that we discussed in Section 3. If we let $D = \{0, 1\}$ and $V(P) = \{\langle 0, 0 \rangle, \langle 0, 1 \rangle\}$, we will make $V((\exists x)(y)Pxy) = T$, because $V^{0}/u((y)Puy) = T$. Thus, $(\exists x)(y)Pxy$ is satisfiable, and by the same token, $\sim(\exists x)(y)Pxy$ is invalid.

Now, consider the formula $(x)(y) \sim Pxy$. The valuation V doesn't satisfy this formula, so to show it satisfiable we need to try another valuation. Since $(x)(y) \sim Pxy$ says that nothing stands in the relation, let U assign P the subset $\varnothing$ of $\{0, 1\}$. Then for all $n, m \in D$, $U^{n}/u\,^{m}/v(Puv) = F$, so that $U((x)(y) \sim Pxy) = T$. Therefore $(x)(y) \sim Pxy$ is satisfiable.

A slightly more complicated formula is $\sim((x)Pxx \supset (x)(y)(Pxy \supset Pyx))$. To satisfy this formula we must make $(x)Pxx$ true and $(x)(y)(Pxy \supset Pyx)$ false; the relation assigned to P must therefore contain every pair of the sort $\langle d, d \rangle$, where $d \in D$, and must contain some pair $\langle d, e \rangle$ and not contain $\langle e, d \rangle$. So, still using the domain $\{0, 1\}$, let $W(P) = \{\langle 0, 0 \rangle, \langle 1, 1 \rangle, \langle 0, 1 \rangle\}$. It's easy to see that W satisfies $\sim((x)Pxx \supset (x)(y)(Pxy \supset Pyx))$, so this formula is satisfiable.

We show formulas to be satisfiable (or to be invalid) by finding domains and valuations which make them true (or false). How do we show formulas to be valid? As an example, let's take a formula of the same morphology, say $(\exists x)(y)Pxy \supset (x)(\exists y)Pxy$. To establish the validity of this formula we must produce an argument showing that for any nonempty domain D, any valuation V of $\mathbf{M'}$ on D satisfies the formula. So, let D be an arbitrary nonempty domain and V be a valuation of $\mathbf{M'}$ on D. Suppose that $V((\exists x)(y)Pxy) = T$; we must show that $V((y)(\exists x)Pxy) = T$. By assumption, there is a member d of D such that $V^{d}/u((y)Puy) = T$, hence such that for all $e \in D$, $V^{d}/u\,^{e}/v(Puv) = T$. Since u differs from v, $V^{d}/u\,^{e}/v$ is the same valuation as $V^{e}/v\,^{d}/u$, so that for all $e \in D$, $V^{e}/v\,^{d}/u(Puv) = T$. But then $V^{e}/v((\exists x)Pxv) = T$ for all $e \in D$, and therefore $V((y)(\exists x)Pxy) = T$. This argument shows that $V((\exists x)(y)Pxy \supset (y)(\exists x)Pxy) = T$ for any valuation V of $\mathbf{M'}$ on any nonempty domain D, and thus this formula is valid.

Arguments of this sort are, of course, more complicated and difficult than the mechanical computations which sufficed to show formulas of $\mathbf{H_s}$ valid. But again, there is no avoiding it; predicate logic is more complex than sentence logic.

An example of another kind is $(\exists x)(y)x = y$. This formula is satisfiable. For instance, let $D = \{1\}$ and V be any valuation on D; V will satisfy $(\exists x)(y)x = y$. A little reflection shows, more generally, that any valuation V on a domain D satisfies this formula if and only if there is exactly one thing in D. Whether $(\exists x)(y)x = y$ is true or not depends only on the size of the domain; this formula says, in effect, that D contains just one member. We would like to say in this case that $(\exists x)(y)x = y$ is *valid in any domain containing just one element* and is not *satisfiable in any domain containing more than one element*. When we say such things we are using 'validity' and 'satisfiability' in relative senses, which are defined as follows.

D8. A formula A of **M** *is satisfiable in* D, *where* D *is a nonempty domain, if there exists a valuation* V *of* **M** *on* D *such that* V(A) = T.

D9. A formula A of **M** *is valid in* D, *where* D *is a nonempty domain, if for every valuation* V *of* **M** *on* D, V(A) = T.

Satisfiability and *validity* in the unqualified sense can be defined in terms of the relative notions of D8 and D9; a formula is satisfiable if it is satisfiable in *some* nonempty domain, and is valid if it is valid in *all* nonempty domains. Thus, $(\exists x)(y)x=y$ is satisfiable in $\{1\}$, but not satisfiable in $\{1, 2\}$, and $\sim(\exists x)(y)x=y$ is valid in $\{1, 2\}$, but isn't valid. Another example is $(\exists x)(\exists y)(z)(\sim x=y \wedge (z=x \vee z=y))$. This formula is valid in $\{1, 2\}$, but its negation is valid in $\{1\}$ and in $\{1, 2, 3\}$.

As you might expect, whether or not a formula is satisfiable (or valid) in a given domain depends only on the size of that domain, and not on particular properties of the elements that constitute the domain. We will prove this as a metatheorem in Section 7, below. Once this has been shown, one can ask, given a formula, what cardinalities (i.e., sizes) are cardinalities of domains in which the formula is satisfiable. Such questions are instances of a general kind of problem called the *spectrum* problem; in this and the next chapter we will discuss various aspects of this question. A typical result from the theory of spectra, which we will not be able to establish until we have proved semantic completeness in Chapter XII, is the following form of *Löwenheim's theorem*: if a formula A is satisfiable in any infinite domain, then it is satisfiable in the domain $\{0, 1, 2, \ldots\}$ of nonnegative integers.

5. In this section we'll unfold some of the basic metatheorems concerning satisfiability and validity (in both the relative and the unqualified senses). First, in view of M1, we have the expected relationships between satisfiability and validity; their proofs are left as exercises.

M3. A is valid in D *if and only if* ~A *is not satisfiable in* D.

M4. A is satisfiable in D *if and only if* ~A *is not valid in* D.

M5. A is valid if and only if ~A *is not satisfiable.*

M6. A is satisfiable if and only if ~A *is not valid.*

As in Chapter VI, we also need to establish that satisfiability and validity are independent of morphology. We'll not use quite the same strategy we employed in Chapter VI in accomplishing this. We need a slightly more complicated argument for predicate logic.

*M7. Let **M** and **M'** be morphologies for* $H_{p=}$*, V be a valuation of **M** on D, and V' a valuation of **M'** on D. Let A be a formula of both **M** and **M'**, such that V and V' agree on A. (By this, we mean that V and V' give the same values to all terms and predicate parameters occurring in A. That is, for all terms t having occurrences in A, V(t) = V'(t), and for all predicate parameters P occurring in A, V(P) = V'(P).) Then V(A) = V'(A).*

PROOF. We induce on the complexity of formulas A of both **M** and **M'** showing that *all* valuations U of **M** and U' of **M** which agree on A assign the same value to A. In case A is atomic, we have $U(A) = U'(A)$ for all such U and U', in view of D4. For instance, if A is $s=t$, we have $U(s) = U'(s)$ and $U(t) = U'(t)$ by assumption, so that $U(s) = U(t)$ if and only if $U'(s) = U'(t)$; thus, by D4, $U(s=t) = U'(s=t)$. As inductive hypothesis, assume that for all formulas B is less complex than A, and all valuations U of **M** and U' of **M'** on D which agree on B, $U(B) = U'(B)$. The cases in which A is an implication or negation are straightforward. In case A is $(x)B^x/u$ (where u is free for x in B), let U and U' be valuations on D agreeing on A. Our inductive hypothesis ensures that for all $d \in D$, $U'^{\,d}/u(B) = U^{\,d}/u(B)$. Then by D5, $U'(A) = U(A)$. This completes the induction.

*M8. Let **M** and **M'** be morphologies for* $H_{p=}$*, and A be a formula of both **M** and **M'**. Let D be a nonempty domain. Then there is a valuation of **M** on D that satisfies A if and only if there is a valuation of **M'** on D that satisfies A.*

PROOF. Given M7, this is easy. Suppose that V is a valuation of **M** on D which satisfies A, and let V' give the same values as V to the terms that occur in A, and to the predicate parameters that occur in A, and give arbitrarily chosen values to the other terms and parameters of **M'**. By M7, $V'(A) = V(A)$, so V' satisfies A, and hence there is a valuation of **M'** on D which satisfies A. If there is a valuation V' of **M'** on D which satisfies A, the same argument shows that there is a valuation of **M** on D which satisfies A.

Our next metatheorem shows that validity is independent of morphology. We'll omit its proof, which uses M7 in the same way as the above proof of M8.

*M9. Let **M** and **M'** be morphologies for* $H_{p=}$ *and A be a formula of both **M*** *and* **M'**. *Let* D *be a nonempty domain. Then every valuation of* **M** *on* D *satisfies* A *if and only if every valuation of* **M'** *on* D *satisfies* A.

6. Let's begin now to investigate the line of thought we began when we discussed the notions of satisfiability and validity in a given domain. What we said there suggested that satisfiability in D and validity in D will depend only on the size of D. In developing a proof of this, the key notion turns out to be a concept of *isomorphism* for valuations. We want to say that two valuations of a morphology **M** are isomorphic if the valuations are alike in form, although they may involve different domains and relations on these domains. It's often helpful to think of valuations of **M** in a way stressing their role as structures in which **M** is interpreted, and deemphasizing their character as ways of construing **M**. When regarded in this way as language-dependent, valuations are often called *relational structures*; a relational structure V is said to be *of type* **M** if it is a valuation of **M**. To clarify the notion of isomorphic relational structures, let's consider an example of two different relational structures which are alike in all essential respects: for instance, the positive integers, ordered by *being less than*, and the negative integers, ordered by *being greater than*.

To make this example precise, let's choose a specific morphology **M** for $H_{p=}$. Let **M** have individual variables $x_1, x_2, x_3, \ldots$, individual parameters $u_1, u_2, u_3, \ldots$, only one individual constant a, and just one predicate parameter P, where P is binary. Corresponding to the positive integers ordered by *being less than*, take a relational structure V of type **M** on the domain D, where $D = \{1, 2, 3, \ldots\}$. Let $V(U_i) = i$ for all individual parameters u_i of **M**. Let $V(a) = 1$ and $V(P) = \{\langle m, n \rangle \mid m, n \in D \text{ and } m < n\}$. For a relational structure V' corresponding to the negative integers ordered by *being greater than*, take $D' = \{-1, -2, -3, \ldots\}$, and let $V'(u_i) = -i$ for all individual parameters u_i of **M**, $V'(a) = -1$, and $V'(P) = \{\langle m, n \rangle \mid m, n \in D \text{ and } m > n\}$.

It isn't difficult to see that V and V' operate in the same way on formulas. For instance $V(Pu_iu_j) = T$ if and only if $V'(Pu_iu_j) = T$, since $i < j$ if and only if $-i > -j$. In the same way, we have $V(A) = T$ if and only if $V'(A) = T$ for all atomic formulas A of **M**; and this can be generalized to all formulas of **M** by an inductive argument. Whatever is true about the nonnegative integers, using 'less than', is true about the nonpositive integers, using 'greater than'.

The reason why V and V' have the same structure is that there is a correlation of the domains D and D' which turns the structure V into the structure V'. This correlation can be pictured geometrically; if the negative integers are flipped over, one obtains a structure that looks just like the positive integers. We used this fact in the paragraph above, where we said that $i < j$

if and only if $-i > -j$. Of course, it is not in general the case that relational structures can be correlated in this way; for instance, if V″ is a relational structure on the integers (positive and nonpositive), ordered by *being less than*, no such correlation with V can be found, because the one structure has a first element, whereas the other does not.

The definition below of *isomorphism* among valuations (or relational structures) generalizes this idea. The point of this definition is that two relational structures are alike in structure if there exists a one-one correlation of their domains (i.e., a one-one function from the domain of the one onto the domain of the other), which transforms relations of the first structure into relations of the other. In defining the conditions under which relational structures are isomorphic, we must also stipulate that in case the morphology **M** of these relational structures has sentence parameters, the structures must assign these parameters the same truth-values.

D10. Let V *be a relational structure of type* **M** *on* D *and* V′ *a relational structure of type* **M** *on* D′*, where* **M** *is a morphology for* $H_{p=}$ *and* D *and* D′ *are nonempty domains. A function* φ *taking members of* D *into members of* D′ *is said to be isomorphism of* V *and* V′ *if* (1) φ *is a one-one function from* D *onto* D′*;* (2) *for all terms t of* **M**, $\varphi(V(t)) = V'(t)$; *and* (3) *for all n-ary predicate letters P of* **M** (*where* $n > 0$) *and* $d_1, \ldots, d_n$ *in* D, $\langle d_1, \ldots, d_n \rangle \in V(P)$ *if and only if* $\langle \varphi(d_1), \ldots, \varphi(d_n) \rangle \in V'(P)$. V *is said to be isomorphic to* V′ *if for all* $P \in P_M^0$, $V(P) = V'(P)$, *and there exists an isomorphism of* V *and* V′.

Now that we have our definition of isomorphism, we can use it to develop some results about satisfiability and validity in particular domains. The first thing we need to do is to check that isomorphic valuations satisfy the same formulas.

M10. Let **M** *be a morphology and* V *and* V′ *be isomorphic relational structures of type* **M**, *with domains* D *and* D′, *respectively. Then for all formulas A of* **M**, $V(A) = V'(A)$.

PROOF. Induce on the complexity of A. If A is $Pt_1 \cdots t_n$, D4 and D10 guarantee immediately that $V(A) = V'(A)$, since $\langle V(t_1), \ldots, V(t_n) \rangle \in V(P)$ if and only if $\langle V'(t_1), \ldots, V'(t_n) \rangle \in V'(P)$. Similarly, if A is $s = t$, $\varphi(V(s)) = V'(s)$ and $\varphi(V(t)) = V'(t)$. Therefore, since φ is a one-one function, $V(s) = V(t)$ if and only if $V'(s) = V'(t)$; hence, $V(A) = V'(A)$, by D4. If A is a sentence parameter, $V(A) = V'(A)$, by D10. This completes the basis step, showing that for all isomorphic relational structures U and U′ with domains D and D′, respectively, $V(A) = V'(A)$ where A is an atomic formula.

As inductive hypothesis, suppose that for all isomorphic relational structures U and U' on domains D and D', respectively, $U(B) = U'(B)$ for all formulas B of **M** less complex than A. Here, the cases of the inductive step in which A is an implication or a negation are straightforward. If A is a universal formula $(x)C^x/u$, let V and V' be isomorphic valuations on D and D', respectively. Let φ be an isomorphism of V and V'. Comparing D3 and D10, it's easy to see that for all $d \in D$, φ is also an isomorphism of V^d/u and $V'^{\varphi(d)}/u$; hence, by the hypothesis of induction, $V^d/u(B) = V'^{\varphi(d)}/u(B)$ for all $d \in D$. Since every member of D' is a correlate under φ of some member of D, we have $V^d/u(B) = T$ for all $d \in D$ if and only if $V'^{d'}/u(B) = T$ for all $d' \in D'$; so by D5, $V(A) = V'(A)$.

As a corollary of M10 we know at once that if D and D' have the same cardinality (or size), then a formula A is satisfiable in D if and only if A is satisfiable in D', and valid in D if and only if A is valid in D'.

M11. If D *and* D' *are nonempty domains of the same cardinality, then* A *is satisfiable in* D *if and only if* A *is satisfiable in* D'.

PROOF. Let A be a formula of **M**, and let φ be a one-one function from D onto D'. (The hypothesis that D and D' have the same cardinality ensures that there is such a function; see XIII.15.) Let V be a valuation of **M** on D such that $V(A) = T$. (The hypothesis that A is satisfiable in D ensures the existence of such a valuation.) Then define a valuation V' of **M** on D' by letting $V'(t) = \varphi(V(t))$ for all terms t of **M** and $V'(P) = V(P)$ for all sentence parameters P of **M**, and letting $\langle d_1', \ldots, d_n' \rangle \in V'(Q)$ if and only if $\langle d_1, \ldots, d_n \rangle \in V(Q)$, for all n-ary predicate parameters Q of **M**, where $\varphi(d_1) = d_1', \ldots, \varphi(d_n) = d_n'$. Now, V' has been constructed so that it is isomorphic to V; so by M10, $V'(A) = T$, and A is therefore satisfiable in D'. A similar argument shows that A is satisfiable in D if A is satisfiable in D'.

M12. If D *and* D' *are nonempty domains of the same cardinality, then* A *is valid in* D *if and only if* A *is valid in* D'.

The proof of M12 is left as an exercise.

The results of this section show that for logical purposes the particular individuals that constitute a domain do not matter a great deal. As in sentence logic where the only important aspect of situations was the truth-values assumed by sentences in these situations, in predicate logic we are concerned only with the size of domains, and the extensions of relations on these domains. These are the only features of situations (i.e., of relational structures) which matter. As far as satisfiability and validity go, the domain {California, Ohio, New Jersey} is just as good as the domain {1, 2, 3}. Corresponding to any relation (e.g., *being less than*) on the latter domain there is a relation (e.g., *being to the east of*) on the former domain which does the same work as regards satisfaction. (Really, this is all there is to the trick that is used in proving M11 and M12.)

This circumstance is enough to justify our habitual use of numbers in constructing examples of relational structures; we lose no generality in doing so, and we gain in convenience, since we have at our disposal a systematic notation for talking about numbers.

7. As in Chapter VI, we want to generalize the notion of satisfaction to sets of formulas. The definition of simultaneous satisfaction is carried out just as in sentence logic.

D11. Let Γ be a set of formulas of a morphology $\mathbf{M}$ for $\mathbf{H}_{p=}$ and let V be a valuation of $\mathbf{M}$. The valuation V simultaneously satisfies Γ if V satisfies every formula in Γ.

When we think of V as a relational structure, we may also say that V is *a model of* Γ, meaning that V simultaneously satisfies Γ. This terminology gives us a convenient way of discussing mathematical theories and their realizations. As a simple example, let's take the theory of partial orderings. The morphology $\mathbf{M}$ of this theory has no individual constants and only one predicate parameter P, which is binary; its individual parameters are, say, $u_1, u_2, u_3, \ldots$ There are two postulates for partial orderings:

$$(x)(y)(z)(Pxy \supset . Pyz \supset Pxz) \qquad \text{and} \qquad (x)(y)(Pxy \supset \sim Pyx).$$

(Here, of course, x, y, and z are individual variables of $\mathbf{M}$.)

Now, any model of the set $\Gamma = \{(x)(y)(z)(Pxy \supset . Pyz \supset Pxz), (x)(y)(Pxy \supset \sim Pyx)\}$ of postulates of this theory will be a structure patterned according to these postulates; that is, it will be a realization of the theory. In particular, the models of Γ will be *partial orderings*. The models of the postulates of a theory, then, are the structures that the theory is about; and by looking at the various models of these postulates we can obtain an idea of their content.

The set Γ of postulates for partial orderings has a variety of models. Perhaps the first of these that comes to mind is the positive integers, ordered by the relation of *being less than*. The domain D of this valuation is $\{1, 2, \ldots\}$, and it assigns P the relation $\{\langle m, n \rangle \mid m, n \in D \text{ and } m < n\}$. This relational structure V_1 is a model of Γ, because for all positive integers i, j, and k, if $i < j$ and $j < k$, then $i < k$; and if $i < j$ then it is not the case that $j < i$.

But there are many other relations on the positive integers that also give models of Γ; for instance, *being a proper divisor of*. (A positive integer i is a proper divisor of a positive integer j if there is a positive integer k different from 1 such that $i \cdot k = j$.) This model V_2 of Γ will have the same domain D as the previous model, V_1; but its relation will be the set $\{\langle m, n \rangle \mid m, n \in D$ and m is a proper divisor of $n\}$. These models are *not* isomorphic. There are many positive integers (e.g., 2 and 3) which are *incomparable* with regard to proper divisibility; i.e., 2 is not a proper divisor of 3, and 3 is not a proper divisor of 2. This shows that V_2 is a model of $\Gamma \cup \{\sim(x)(y)(Pxy \vee Pyx \vee x=y)\}$, whereas V_1 is a model of $\Gamma \cup \{(x)(y)(Pxy \vee Pyx \vee x=y)\}$. Thus, by M10, we know that V_1 and V_2 are not isomorphic.

The integers (positive and nonpositive), ordered by *being less than*, constitute another model, V_3, of Γ. This model shows us that the postulates for partial orderings do not commit us to the existence of a least element; though both V_1 and V_2 satisfy $(\exists x)(y)(\sim y = x \supset Pxy)$, V_3 does not satisfy this formula.

Still another model, V_4, of Γ has a domain consisting of just one element, say 1, and correlates the *null relation* $\varnothing$ to P: $V_4((\exists x)(\exists y)Pxy) = F$. This structure is rather strange, but it's easy to show that it satisfies both postulates in Γ, and so is a model of Γ. V_4 shows that the formulas in Γ do not commit us to the existence of more than one thing; V_4 is a model of $\Gamma \cup \{(\exists x)(y)x=y\}$. Nor do these formulas warrant the conclusion that the ordering relation isn't vacuous, that anything stands in the relation corresponding to P. For, as we have already pointed out, V_4 is a model of $\Gamma \cup \{(x)(y)\sim Pxy\}$.

The theory of orderings given by the two postulates in Γ, then, is evidently very general; it admits a wide variety of models. By constructing different models of Γ such as V_1 to V_4, we can obtain a conception of the commitments made by this theory.

REMARK. Notice that in characterizing V_1 to V_4, we didn't bother to specify what individuals these valuations assign to individual parameters of M. This omission is justified by M7. Since both of the members of Γ contain no occurrences of parameters, we know by M7 that whether or not a valuation V of M satisfies these formulas—and hence, whether or not V is a model of Γ—does not depend at all on the values that V assigns to individual parameters of M. By the same token, since in our discussion of V_1 to V_4 we considered only formulas of M such as $(x)(y)(x=y \vee Pxy \vee Pxy)$ which contain no occurrences of individual parameters, we do not need to know what values V_1 to V_4 assign to individual parameters in order to tell whether or not V_1 to V_4 satisfy these formulas.

8. In the above example we discovered a number of claims to which the set Γ of postulate does *not* commit us; we showed, for instance, that a partial ordering need not have a least element. To what consequences *does* the set Γ commit us? These will be the formulas that are satisfied in *all* models of Γ. Recalling Chapter VI, you will recognize that we are now talking about the formulas that are *implied* by Γ.

D12. Let Δ be a set of formulas of a morphology $\mathbf{M}$ for $\mathbf{H}_{p=}$, and let A be a formula of $\mathbf{M}$. Δ (semantically) implies A, $\Delta \Vdash A$, if every valuation of $\mathbf{M}$ which simultaneously satisfies Δ also satisfies A.

Another way of stating the definition is to say that $\Delta \Vdash A$ if A is satisfied in every model of Δ. Thus, where Γ is still the set of postulates for partial orderings, $\Gamma \Vdash (x) \sim Pxx$, as is shown by the following argument. Suppose that V is a model of Γ on a domain D; then $V((x)(y)(Pxy \supset \sim Pyx)) = T$, so that for all d, e $\in$ D, $V^{d}/u\,^{e}/v(Puv) = F$ or $V^{d}/u\,^{e}/v(Pvu) = F$. Hence, in particular, $V^{d}/u\,^{d}/v(Puv) = F$ for all $d \in D$; but $V^{d}/u\,^{d}/v\,(Puv) = V^{d}/u(Puu)$, so that for all d $\in$ D, $V^{d}/u\,(Puu) = F$. Therefore $V((x) \sim Pxx) = T$.

In view of previous developments, we know pretty much what results are wanted concerning simultaneous satisfaction, simultaneous satisfiability, and semantic implication. Many of the following metatheorems are easily obtained and can be stated without proof. The following three, for instance, duplicate metatheorems of VI.12.

M13. Let $\{A_1, \ldots, A_n\}$ be a set of formulas of a morphology $\mathbf{M}$ for $\mathbf{H}_{p=}$, and V be a valuation of $\mathbf{M}$. Then V simultaneously satisfies $\{A_1, \ldots, A_n\}$ if and only if V satisfies $A_1 \wedge \cdots \wedge A_n$.

M14. Let Γ be a set of formulas of a morphology $\mathbf{M}$ for $\mathbf{H}_{p=}$, and let V be a valuation of $\mathbf{M}$. Then V simultaneously satisfies Γ if and only if for all finite subsets $\{A_1, \ldots, A_n\}$ of Γ, V satisfies $A_1 \wedge \cdots \wedge A_n$.

M15. Let Γ be a set of formulas of a morphology $\mathbf{M}$ for $\mathbf{H}_{p=}$, and let V be a valuation of $\mathbf{M}$. Then if V simultaneously satisfies Γ, V simultaneously satisfies every subset of Γ.

We have not yet given a definition of *simultaneous satisfiability*; a set is simultaneously satisfiable if it has at least one model.

D13. Let Γ *be a set of formulas of a morphology* **M** *for* $H_{p=}$. Γ *is said to be simultaneously satisfiable if there is a valuation of* **M** *which simultaneously satisfies* Γ.

To show that it is independent of morphology whether or not Γ is simultaneously satisfiable, we use M7. Let's say that V and V' *agree on* a set Γ of formulas if V and V' agree on all the formulas in Γ. Using M7 and D13, we have at once the following result.

M16. Let **M** *and* **M'** *be morphologies for* $H_{p=}$, V *be a valuation of* **M** *on* D, *and* V' *a valuation of* **M'** *on* D. *Let* Γ *be a set of formulas of* **M** *and* **M'** *(i.e.,* $\Gamma \subseteq F_{\mathbf{M}} \cap F_{\mathbf{M'}}$), *and suppose that* V *and* V' *agree on* Γ. *Then* V *simultaneously satisfies* Γ *if and only if* V' *simultaneously satisfies* Γ.

This metatheorem is then used as follows to establish the desired result about independence.

M17. Let **M** *and* **M'** *be morphologies for* $H_{p=}$, *and* Γ *be a set of formulas of both* **M** *and* **M'**. *Then there is a valuation of* **M** *which simultaneously satisfies* Γ *if and only if there is a valuation of* **M'** *which simultaneously satisfies* Γ.

PROOF. Suppose V is a valuation of **M** which simultaneously satisfies Γ. Where D is the domain of V, define a valuation V' of **M'** on D by letting V' give the same values as V to the terms and predicate parameters which are common to **M** and **M'**, and give arbitrary values to the other terms and predicate parameters of **M'**. By assumption, V' agrees with V on Γ, and so by M7, V' simultaneously satisfies Γ. The same argument can be used to establish the converse of this.

The following sequence of metatheorems duplicates VI.M13 to VI.M23.

M18. If a set Γ *of formulas is simultaneously satisfiable, then every subset of* Γ *is simultaneously satisfiable.*

M19. {A} *is simultaneously satisfiable if and only if A is satisfiable.*

M20. If Γ *is simultaneously satisfiable and A is valid, then* $\Gamma \cup \{A\}$ *is simultaneously satisfiable.*

M21. Let Γ *be a set of formulas of both* **M** *and* **M'**, *and let A be a formula of both* **M** *and* **M'**. *Then A is satisfied by every valuation of* **M** *which simultaneously* satisfies Γ if and only if A is satisfied by every valuation of $\mathbf{M}'$ which simultaneously satisfies Γ.

M22. $\Gamma \Vdash A$ if and only if $\Gamma \cup \{\sim A\}$ is not simultaneously satisfiable.

M23. $\varnothing \Vdash A$ if and only if A is valid.

M24. If $A \in \Gamma$, then $\Gamma \Vdash A$.

M25. If $\Gamma \Vdash A$, then $\Gamma \cup \Delta \Vdash A$.

M26. If $\Gamma \Vdash A$ and $\Delta \cup \{A\} \vdash B$, then $\Gamma \cup \Delta \Vdash B$.

M27. If $\Gamma \Vdash A \supset B$, then $\Gamma \cup \{A\} \Vdash B$.

M28. If $\Gamma \cup \{A\} \Vdash B$, then $\Gamma \Vdash A \supset B$.

Besides these familiar metatheorems, we'll record one more which has to do specifically with universal quantification, and thus has no analogue in Chapter VI. This metatheorem will be useful below in Chapter XII, when we turn to the task of showing that every theorem of $\mathbf{H}_{\mathrm{p}=}$ is valid.

M29. If $\Vdash A$, then $\Vdash (x)A\,{}^x/u$, where u is free for x in A.
    PROOF. Let A be a formula of $\mathbf{M}$ with u free for x in A, and suppose that $\Vdash A$. Let D be any nonempty domain, and V be any valuation of $\mathbf{M}$ on D; then, since $\Vdash A$, $V\,{}^d/u(A) = T$ for all $d \in D$, so that $V((x)A\,{}^x/u) = T$. Hence, for all nonempty domains D, for all valuations V of $\mathbf{M}$ on D, $V((x)A\,{}^x/u) = T$; i.e., $\Vdash (x)A\,{}^x/u$.

9. In Section 6 we spoke of satisfiability relative to a domain D. Similarly, we can talk about *simultaneous* satisfiability in a given domain D.

D14. Let D be a nonempty domain. A set Γ of formulas of $\mathbf{M}$ is simultaneously satisfiable in D if there exists a valuation V of $\mathbf{M}$ on D such that V simultaneously satisfies Γ.

In other words, Γ is simultaneously satisfiable in D if Γ possesses a model with domain D.

We can also define a notion of implication relative to a domain D.

D15. A set Γ of formulas of M (semantically) implies a formula A of M in a nonempty domain D if every valuation of M on D which simultaneously satisfies Γ also satisfies A.

For instance, the set $\{\sim a = b, (\exists x)(\sim x = a \wedge \sim x = b)\}$ is not simultaneously satisfiable in the domain $\{1, 2\}$. And in this domain the set $\{Pa, \sim Pb\}$ implies $(x)(x = a \vee x = b)$.

These relative notions of simultaneous satisfiability and implication have many of the structural characteristics of the absolute notions. For instance, given any nonempty domain D, M18 to M29 will also hold for simultaneous satisfiability and implication in D. Also, it's easy to show that simultaneous satisfaction and implication in D depend only on the size of D; we will state these as metatheorems, leaving their proofs as exercises.

M30. If D and D' are nonempty domains having the same cardinality, then Γ is simultaneously satisfiable in D if and only if Γ is simultaneously satisfiable in D'.

M31. If D and D' are nonempty domains having the same cardinality, then Γ implies A in D if and only if Γ implies A in D'.

10. In this concluding section, we will state and prove a metatheorem about valuations that we will need in our proof of semantic completeness. The point of the metatheorem is that semantic substitution has the same effect as syntactic substitution. In particular, suppose that A is a formula of M and V a valuation of M with $V(t) = d$. If we syntactically substitute t for u in the formula A, then we get the result A^t/u of putting a name of d for all occurrences u in A. But we can also *semantically* substitute by changing the meaning of u; i.e., by replacing V by the valuation V^d/u in which the parameter u is reconstrued as a name of d. Our metatheorem says that these operations have precisely the same effect, so that $V(A^t/u) = V^d/u(A)$.

M32. For all valuations V on any domain D, $V(A^t/u) = V^{V(t)}/u(A)$.

proof. Induce on the complexity of A. In case A is atomic, the metatheorem holds because of D4. This is most easily seen by considering an example; suppose, for instance, that A is $Pautu$; also, let $V(t) = d$. Then A^t/u is $Pattt$, and $V(A^t/u) = T$ if and only if $\langle V(a), d, d, d \rangle \in V(P)$. On the other hand, since $V^d/u(u) = d$, $V^d/u(A) = T$ if and only if $\langle V(a), d, d, d \rangle \in V(P)$. Therefore, $V(A^t/u) = V^d/u(A)$. It should be clear that this will hold generally, for all terms t and atomic formulas A.

As inductive hypothesis, suppose that for all formulas B less complex than A, $U(B\,{}^t/u) = U\,{}^{U(t)}/u(B)$ for all valuations U on D. Again, let $V(t) = d$; we want to show that $V(A\,{}^t/u) = V\,{}^d/u(A)$. As usual, there are three cases. If A is a negation $\sim C$, the hypotheses of induction tells us that $V(C\,{}^t/u) = V\,{}^d/u(C)$, where V is an arbitrary valuation on D. Thus, since $\sim C\,{}^t/u$ is $A\,{}^t/u$, $V(A\,{}^t/u) = V\,{}^d/u(A)$, by D5. The case in which A is $C \supset D$ is handled in the same way.

In case A is $(x)B\,{}^x/v$ (where v is free for x in B), we can assume without loss of generality that v differs from u and from t. (For if A is $(x)C\,{}^x/w$ and w is the same as u or t, let v be the first individual parameter not occurring in B and differing from u and t. Then, where B is $C\,{}^v/w$, A is $(x)B\,{}^x/v$.) Let e be an arbitrary member of D, and consider the valuation $V\,{}^e/v$; by the hypothesis of induction, $V\,{}^e/v(B\,{}^t/u) = V\,{}^e/v\,{}^d/u(B)$. Since u differs from v, $V\,{}^e/v\,{}^d/u$ is the same valuation as $V\,{}^d/u\,{}^e/v$, so that $V\,{}^e/v(B\,{}^t/u) = V\,{}^d/u\,{}^e/v(B)$. Therefore $V\,{}^e/v(B\,{}^t/u) = T$ for all $e \in D$ if and only if $V\,{}^d/u\,{}^e/v(B) = T$ for all $e \in D$; i.e., $V((x)B\,{}^t/u\,{}^x/v) = V\,{}^d/u((x)B\,{}^x/v)$. But by M33, $B\,{}^t/u\,{}^x/v$ is the same expression as $B\,{}^x/v\,{}^t/u$. Thus $V((x)B\,{}^x/v\,{}^t/u) = V\,{}^d/u((x)B)$; i.e., $V(A\,{}^t/u) = V\,{}^d/u(A)$.

This completes the induction and the proof of M32.

Exercises

1. Let **M** be the morphology and V be the valuation of **M** on $\{1, 2\}$ described in Section 1. Determine the truth-values given by V to the following formulas of **M**.
   (a) Rba
   (b) Rbc
   (c) $(x)(Qx \lor Rxa)$
   (d) $\sim Qu_2 \supset (\exists x)Rxx$
   (e) $(x)(y)(Rxy \supset Qy)$
   (f) $(\exists y)(x)(\sim x = y \supset Rxy)$

2. Let **M** be as in E1, and let U be the valuation on {Connecticut, Massachusetts, Rhode Island, New Hampshire, Vermont, Maine} described in Section 1. Determine the truth-values given by U to the following formulas of **M**.
   (a) $Rab \supset \sim Qc$
   (b) $(x)(\exists y)Rxy$
   (c) $(x)(\exists y)(Qy \land Rxy)$
   (d) $(\exists y)(x)(Rxy \supset Qy)$
   (e) $(x)(y)(Rxy \supset Ryx)$
   (f) $(\exists x)(y)(Ryx \supset Qa)$

3. Let **M'** have one individual constant a; individual variables $x, y, z, x_1, x_2, \ldots$; and just two predicate parameters P and Q, the former 2-ary and the latter 3-ary. Let $u_1, u_2, \ldots$ be the individual parameters of **M'**. Let $D = \{1, 2, 3, \ldots\}$ and $W(t) = 1$ for all terms t of W; also let $W(P) = \{\langle m, n \rangle \mid m, n \in D$ and

$m > n\}$ and $W(Q) = \{\langle k, m, n \rangle \mid k, m, n \in D$ and $k + m = n\}$. What truth-values does W give to the following formulas of **M′**?

(a) $u_1 = a$

(b) $(y)(Pay \lor a = y)$

(c) $(\exists x)(y)Qxyy$

(d) $(x)(y)(Qxya \supset Pxy)$

(e) $(x)(y)(\exists z)Qxzy$

(f) $(x)(y)(Pyx \supset (\exists z)Qxzy)$

(g) $(x)(y)(\exists z)(x_1)(Qxyz \equiv x_1 = z)$

(h) $(x)(y)(z)(x_1)(Qxz \supset . Qyxx_1 \supset z = x_1)$

4. By finding appropriate valuations, show the following formulas invalid and satisfiable.

(a) $(\exists x)(y)(Pxy \supset Pyx)$

(b) $(\exists x)(\exists y)(z)(z = x \lor z = y)$

(c) $Pu \supset (x)Px$

(d) $(x)(Px \supset (x)Px)$

(e) $((\exists x)Px \land (\exists x)Qx) \supset (\exists x)(Px \land Qx)$

(f) $(x)(y)(z)(Pxy \supset . Pyz \supset Pxz) \supset (x)Pxx$

(g) $(x)(Px \supset Q) \supset \sim(\exists x)Px$

(h) $((x)Px \supset (x)Qx) \supset (x)(Px \supset Qx)$

(i) $(\exists x)(y) \sim Pxy \supset (y) \sim (\exists x)Pxy$

5. Show that the following formulas are valid.

(a) $(x)(Px \supset Qx) \supset . (x)Px \supset (x)Qx$

(b) $(x)x = x$

(c) $(x)(a = x \supset . Px \supset Pa)$

(d) $(x)(\exists y)(Pxy \supset Pyx)$

(e) $(\exists x)(P \land Qx) \equiv (P \land (\exists x)Qx)$

(f) $(\exists x)(Px \supset (x)Px)$

(g) $Pa \equiv (x)(x = a \supset Px)$

(h) $(x)(\exists y)Py \equiv (\exists y)Py$

6. Show that the following formulas are not satisfiable.

(a) $(\exists x)(y)(z)(Pxyz \land \sim Pyxz)$

(b) $(x)((\exists x)Px \land \sim Px)$

7. Show that any formula having one of the following three forms is valid.

(a) $A \supset . B \supset A$

(b) $(A \supset . B \supset C) \supset . A \supset B \supset . A \supset C$

(c) $\sim A \supset \sim B \supset . B \supset A$

8. (a) Show that any formula of the kind $t = t$ is valid. (b) Show that any formula of the kind $(x)(A^x/u \supset B^x/u) \supset . (x)A^x/u \supset (x)B^x/u$ is valid. (c) Show that any formula of the kind $(x)(A \supset B^x/u) \supset . A \supset (x)B^x/u$ is valid.

9. Prove that if $V(s) = V(t)$ then $V(A) = V(A^{s}\!/\!/t)$. Use this to show that any formula of the kind $s = t \supset . A \supset A^{s}\!/\!/t$ is valid.

10. Prove the following metatheorems. You may use any metatheorems appearing before them.
    - (a) M2
    - (b) M3
    - (c) M4
    - (d) M5
    - (e) M6
    - (f) M9
    - (g) M12
    - (h) M16
    - (i) M30
    - (j) M31

11. List all the 1-ary relations on the domain $\{1, 2\}$. List all the 2-ary relations on this domain.

12. For each $n > 0$, find a formula A_n which is valid in any domain of cardinality n, but not satisfiable in a domain of any other cardinality.

13. Show that the formula
$$(x)(y)((\exists z)Pxz \wedge (z)(Pxy \supset . Pyz \supset Pxz)) \supset (\exists x)Pxx$$
is valid in every finite domain. Go on to show the formula invalid. In what domains, then, is its negation satisfiable?

14. Show that $(x)((x)(Px \wedge Qx) \supset Rx)$ does not imply $(x)(Px \wedge Qa) \supset Ra$.

Problems

1. Let Γ be a set of formulas of a morphology M for $H_{p=}$. Γ is said to be *categorical* if all the models V of Γ are isomorphic to some relational structure U. (a) Find an example of a categorical set of formulas. (b) Show that if a set Γ of formulas is categorical, then Γ is complete with respect to negation (i.e., for all formulas A of M, $A \in \Gamma$ or $\sim A \vdash \Gamma$), provided Γ is implicatively closed.

2. Let Γ be a set of formulas of a morphology M for $H_{p=}$, and suppose that no identity signs occur in any members of Γ. (a) Show that if Γ is simultaneously satisfiable in a domain D and D has cardinality less than or equal to E, then Γ is simultaneously satisfiable in E. (b) Find a counterexample to the converse of (a).

3. Let M have just one predicate parameter P, where P is 1-ary. Let A be a formula of M in which no identity sign occurs. Show that if A is satisfiable, then A is satisfiable in a domain containing just two elements.

4. According to our semantic theory $(a = b \wedge Pa) \supset Pb$ is valid. But suppose 'Jekyll is Hyde' and 'the police believe Hyde is a murderer' to be true; this does not seem to imply that 'The police believe Jekyll is a murderer' is true. Do examples such as this raise serious difficulties for our theory? If so, how can they be resolved?

XII Predicate Logic with Identity: Semantic Completeness

1. We now come to the problem of showing $\mathbf{H}_{p=}$ semantically complete with respect to the interpretation developed in the last chapter. With a few modifications, the method we used to show $\mathbf{H}_s$ complete will work also for $\mathbf{H}_{p=}$; this means that we'll be employing new concepts only at a few places in this chapter.

First, we want to establish that every theorem of $\mathbf{H}_{p=}$ is valid. Given the fact that every axiom of $\mathbf{H}_{p=}$ is valid, this should come as no surprise.

M1. If A is an instance of AS1 to AS8, then ⊩ A.

PROOF. Seven of these eight cases are assigned as exercises in Chapter XI (see XI.E7 to XI.E9). Here we will prove only the remaining case, in which A is a formula of $\mathbf{M}$ of the sort $(x)B\,^x/u \supset B\,^t/u$, where u is free for x in B. Suppose that $V((x)B\,^x/u) = T$, where V is an arbitrary valuation of $\mathbf{M}$; then for all $d \in D$, $V\,^d/u(B) = T$. In particular, $V\,^e/u(B) = T$, where $e = V(t)$. But by XI.M32, $V\,^e/u(B) = V(B\,^t/u)$; therefore $V(B\,^t/u) = T$.

This argument shows that $V(B^{t}/u) = T$ if $V((x)B^{x}/u) = T$, for any valuation V of **M** on any domain D. $(x)B^{x}/u \supset B^{t}/u$ is therefore valid.

From M1 and XI.M29, it follows at once that every axiom of $\mathbf{H}_{p=}$ is valid.

M2. If A is an axiom of $\mathbf{H}_{p=}$ then $\Vdash A$.

PROOF. If A is an axiom of $\mathbf{H}_{p=}$ then A is obtained from some instance B of AS1 to AS8 by successive universal quantifications. But $\Vdash B$ by M1, and by XI.M29 universal quantifications of valid formulas are valid. Therefore $\Vdash A$.

M3. If $\vdash A$ then $\Vdash A$.

PROOF. By M2, every axiom of $\mathbf{H}_{p=}$ is valid. Since the sole primitive rule of $\mathbf{H}_{p=}$ is *modus ponens*, to prove every theorem of $\mathbf{H}_{p=}$ valid it will suffice to show that if $\Vdash B$ and $\Vdash B \supset C$ then $\Vdash C$. An argument based only on sentential considerations will establish this: if for all valuations V of **M**, $V(B) = T$ and $V(B \supset C) = T$, then $U(C)$ can't be F for any valuation U of **M** since if $U(C) = F$ and $U(B) = T$ then $U(B \supset C) = F$. This shows that $U(C) = T$ for all valuations U of **M**; i.e., $\Vdash C$.

Putting M3 to work in precisely the same way that the corresponding metatheorem is used in Chapter VII, we get at once the following results.

M4. If $\Gamma \vdash A$ then $\Gamma \Vdash A$.

M5. If Γ is simultaneously satisfiable then Γ is consistent.

2. These three metatheorems have many applications in settling questions concerning $\mathbf{H}_{p=}$; M3 and M4 can be used to show that certain formulas are not provable in $\mathbf{H}_{p=}$ and certain inferences not deducible in $\mathbf{H}_{p=}$, and M5 to show that certain sets of postulates are consistent in $\mathbf{H}_{p=}$.

In IX.7, for instance, we showed that violations of the restrictions on the rule of eq elim would enable us to carry out various derivations that we found undesirable: of $(\exists x)Px \supset (x)Px$ categorically, of $(\exists x)(Px \wedge \sim Px)$ from $\{(\exists x)Px, (\exists x)\sim Px\}$, and of $(\exists x)\sim x = x$ from $\{(\exists y)(\exists x)\sim x = y\}$. Using M4, we can now establish that none of the corresponding deductions can be performed in $\mathbf{H}_{p=}$; to accomplish this, all we need to do is to check that $(\exists x)Px \supset (x)Px$ is invalid, that $\{(\exists x)Px, (\exists x)\sim Px\}$ does not imply $(\exists x)(Px \wedge \sim Px)$, and that $\{(\exists y)(\exists x)\sim x = y\}$ does not imply $(\exists x)\sim x = x$. But this is easily done. If, for instance, we take our domain to be $\{1, 2\}$ and let P correspond to the property of *being even*, so that $V(P) = \{2\}$, this valuation V will satisfy $(\exists x)Px$, $(\exists x)\sim Px$, and $(\exists y)(\exists x)\sim x=y$; but V will not satisfy $(x)Px$, $(\exists x)(Px \wedge \sim Px)$, or $(\exists x)\sim x=x$.

M5 furnishes a method of showing, in an absolute sense, that certain sets of formulas are consistent. For instance, it was thought not so long ago that if a two-termed relation R is transitive and symmetric, then it is reflexive. (The argument given in support of this went as follows. By symmetry, if $\langle d, e \rangle \in R$, then $\langle e, d \rangle \in R$ for any d, e in the domain of R. So by transitivity, $\langle d, d \rangle \in R$.) This argument, which is fallacious, purports to show that the set $\Gamma = \{(x)(y)(z)(Pxy \supset. Pyz \supset Pxz), (x)(y)(Pxy \supset Pyx), (\exists x)\sim Pxx\}$ is *inconsistent*.

This argument can be refuted by using M5 to show that Γ is consistent. If we let $D = \{1\}$, and assign P the null relation $\varnothing$, every formula in Γ is satisfied; hence, Γ is simultaneously satisfiable and so is consistent. This model of Γ also shows us what is wrong with the above argument; what it assumes is that *there is* an e such that $\langle d, e \rangle \in R$. Thus, if we add $(x)(\exists y)Pxy$ to Γ, the resultant set *is* inconsistent.

This method of showing a set Γ of formulas consistent by establishing the existence of a model of Γ is often very useful but it has its limitations. In order to be informative, a metatheoretic proof of the existence of a model of Γ should not involve assumptions less plausible than those posited in the theory corresponding to Γ. Situations of this sort often arise in the case of very strong theories; for instance, the only known way of proving the consistency of standard versions of set theory is by positing (directly or indirectly) the existence of sets so large that their existence cannot be established in these set theories. This means that in proving the consistency of strong theories, you often have to be rather self-conscious about your metatheory; but this only becomes a problem where models with infinite domains are concerned. In a proof of consistency such as the one we gave above, where the domain is finite, we needn't worry about what assumptions have been made in proving the existence of the model. Here, the model can be presented directly as a finite structure.

3. Now let's think ahead to our proof of completeness; this will remind us of the strategy of the argument and ensure that we will generalize the concepts of Chapter VII in the right way.

We want eventually to show that if a set Γ of formulas of $H_{p=}$ is consistent, it has a model. If we follow the line of thought we used in sentence logic, this will break down into two steps; showing that if Γ is consistent then Γ has an M-saturated extension, and that if Δ is M-saturated then Δ has a model.

If we analyze the proof we gave of VII.M7, we see that this argument, without any alteration, will work for $\mathbf{H}_{p=}$ as well as for $\mathbf{H}_s$. The proof of VII.M12, however, proceeds by an induction on the complexity of formulas, and it is by no means clear that it will generalize to $\mathbf{H}_{p=}$. Let's look at this more closely.

Suppose that Δ is a set of formulas of a morphology $\mathbf{M}$ for $\mathbf{H}_{p=}$, such that (1) Δ is consistent, and (2) for all formulas A of $\mathbf{M}$, $A \in \Delta$ or $\sim A \in \Delta$. We want somehow to define a valuation V of $\mathbf{M}$ so that Δ will be the set of formulas of $\mathbf{M}$ satisfied by V. To do this we first define V appropriately, and then show by an induction on the complexity of formulas of $\mathbf{M}$ that for all such formulas A, $V(A) = T$ if and only if $A \in \Delta$. Let's assume that we can generalize the definition of V given in the proof of VII.M12 so that the basis step of our argument works, as well as the cases of the inductive step in which A is an implication or a negation. What about the case in which A is $(x)B^x/u$? We have to show here that $V((x)B^x/u) = T$ if and only if $(x)B^x/u \in \Delta$. In this case our inductive hypothesis does guarantee that $V(B) = T$ if and only if $B \in \Delta$, but this isn't much help; $V(B)$ might very well be T while $V((x)B^x/u)$ is F.

But the hypothesis of induction also ensures that for all terms t of $\mathbf{M}$, $V(B^t/u) = T$ if and only if $B^t/u \in \Delta$. Can we use this fact to show that $V((x)B^x/u) = T$ if and only if $(x)B^x/u \in \Delta$? To do this we need to establish some connection between the way the instantiations B^t/u of $(x)B^x/u$ belong to Δ, and the membership of $(x)B^x/u$ itself in Δ. In other words, we need an analogue for universal quantification of the principle that $C \supset D \in \Delta$ if and only if $C \notin \Delta$ or $D \in \Delta$.

It is natural to conjecture here that $(x)B^x/u \in \Delta$ if and only if for all $t \in T_\mathbf{M}$, $B^t/u \in \Delta$: a universal formula is in a consistent and negation-complete set of formulas of $\mathbf{M}$ if and only if all instantiations of the formula with terms of $\mathbf{M}$ is in the set. Half of this claim is trivially true; since $(x)B^x/u \vdash B^t/u$, it follows that $B^t/u \in \Delta$ if $(x)B^x/u \in \Delta$, provided that Δ is negation-complete and consistent. But the converse of this isn't always true. It may sometimes happen that even though Δ is negation-complete and consistent, B^t/u is in Δ for every term t of $\mathbf{M}$, but $(x)B^x/u$ is *not* in Δ.

For instance, let $\mathbf{M}$ have no predicate parameters or individual constants, and individual parameters $u_1, u_2, u_3, \ldots$; also, let x be among the individual variables of $\mathbf{M}$. Let V be the valuation of $\mathbf{M}$ on the domain $\{0, 1\}$ such that $V(u_i) = 0$ for all individual parameters of $\mathbf{M}$, and let $\Gamma = \{A \mid A \in F_\mathbf{M}$ and $V(A) = T\}$. By M5 and XI.M1 we know that Γ is consistent and is negation-complete with respect to $\mathbf{M}$. But it's false that $(x)B^x/u_1 \in \Gamma$ whenever $B^t/u_1 \in \Gamma$ for all $t \in T_\mathbf{M}$. For example, let B be $u_1 = u_2$. We have $t = u_2 \in \Gamma$ for all $t \in T_\mathbf{M}$. But $V((x)x = u_2) = F$, since $V^1/u_1(u_1 = u_2) = F$.

Here, the crucial fact is that V doesn't give a name to the individual 1. Once we realize this, we can see why it can happen that $\Gamma \vdash \sim(x)B\,^x/u$, even though $\Gamma \vdash B\,^t/u$ for all terms t of the morphology. It may be that every model U of Γ fails to give names to all the members of its domain. And if all the members d of D such that $U\,^d/u(B) = F$ are given no names by U, it will turn out that $(x)B\,^x/u$ is false while $B\,^t/u$ is true for every term t. There is no reason why this sort of thing can't happen, since we never required that valuations should give a name to every member of the domain; V, for instance, is a perfectly good valuation.

4. To remedy this difficulty, we will understand by an **M**-*saturated set* a set of formulas of **M** having the structural properties of a set of formulas true in some situation *in which everything has a name*. Strictly speaking, we aren't changing our concept of an **M**-saturated set in doing this; we are just bringing to light a feature of the concept which wasn't needed in sentence logic.

As before, in defining **M**-saturation we require that every **M**-saturated set be negation-complete with respect to **M** and consistent. But also, we stipulate that if $A\,^t/u$ is in such a set for all terms t of **M**, then $(x)A\,^x/u$ must be in the set. This requirement is meant to express the intuitive idea that the set is a set of truths in a situation in which everything possesses a name.

*D1. Let Γ be a set of formulas of a morphology **M** for $\mathbf{H}_{p=}$. Γ is **M**-saturated if:*

1. *For all formulas A of **M**, $A \in \Gamma$ or $\sim A \in \Gamma$.*
2. *Γ is consistent.*
3. *For all formulas A, individual parameters u and individual variables x of **M**, if u is free for x in A and $A\,^t/u \in \Gamma$ for all $t \in T_\mathbf{M}$, then $(x)A\,^x/u \in \Gamma$.*

Using this definition, we will have no difficulty in carrying through a proof that every **M**-saturated set of formulas is the set of formulas satisfied by some valuation V of **M**. By augmenting the argument given in Chapter VII, we can also show that every consistent set of formulas can be extended to an **M**-saturated set for some morphology **M**. Putting these results together, we will have semantic completeness.

Before launching this argument, we will record as metatheorems some of the more important properties of **M**-saturated sets. The first five of these are analogues of VII.M1 to VII.M5 and are proved just as before. The proof of M11 is left as an exercise.

*M6. If Γ is **M**-saturated, $A \in F_\mathbf{M}$ and $\Gamma \vdash A$ then $A \in \Gamma$.*

M7. If Γ is M-saturated and $A \in F_M$, then $\Gamma \vdash A$ if and only if $A \in \Gamma$.

M8. If Γ is M-saturated and $A \in F_M$, then $A \in \Gamma$ if and only if $\sim A \notin \Gamma$.

M9. If Γ is M-saturated and $A, B \in F_M$, then $A \supset B \in \Gamma$ if and only if $A \notin \Gamma$ or $B \in \Gamma$.

M10. If Γ is M-saturated and $\Gamma \subseteq \Delta$, where Δ is a consistent set of formulas of **M**, *then $\Gamma = \Delta$.*

M11. If Γ is M-saturated, $A \in F_M$, $u \in IP_M$, $x \in V_M$, and u is free for x in A, then $(x)A \, {}^x/u \in \Gamma$ if and only if for all $t \in T_M$, $A \, {}^t/x \in \Gamma$.

M12. If (a) for all formulas A of **M**, $A \in \Gamma$ *or* $\sim A \in \Gamma$; (b) Γ *is consistent; and* (c) *for all formulas A, individual parameters u and individual variables x of* **M** *such that u is free for x in A, there is a term t of* **M** *such that $(\exists x)A \, {}^x/u \supset A \, {}^t/x \in \Gamma$, then Γ is M-saturated.*

PROOF. Since (a) and (b) correspond to clauses 1 and 2 of D1, we need only show that (a) to (c) imply that Γ conforms to clause 3 of D1. Suppose, then, that $A \, {}^t/u \in \Gamma$ for all $t \in T_M$, where u is free for x in A. By (c), there is a term s of **M** such that $(\exists x)\sim A \, {}^x/u \supset \sim A \, {}^s/u \in \Gamma$. Therefore, since $A \, {}^s/u \in \Gamma$, the set Γ would be inconsistent if $(\exists x)\sim A \, {}^x/u$ were in Γ, so that $(\exists x)\sim A^x/u$ is not in Γ. Therefore $\sim(\exists x)\sim A \, {}^x/u \in \Gamma$, and since $\sim(\exists x)\sim A \, {}^x/u \vdash (x)A \, {}^x/u$, it follows that $(x)A \, {}^x/u \in \Gamma$.

5. Let's turn now to the problem of showing that every consistent set has a saturated extension. This problem is more subtle for predicate than for sentence logic, because of clause 3 of the new definition of **M**-saturation. Our discussion in Section 3 has disclosed the fact that a set Γ of formulas of **M** may be consistent and yet have the property that for some formula A, $\Gamma \vdash A \, {}^t/u$ for all $t \in T_M$, even though $\Gamma \vdash \sim(x)A \, {}^x/u$. Under these circumstances, there can be no hope of obtaining an **M**-saturated extension of Γ. Any negation-complete and consistent set Δ of formulas of **M** which is an extension of Γ must contain $\sim(x)A \, {}^x/u$ as well as $A \, {}^t/u$ for all terms t of **M**, and so Δ will not be **M**-saturated.

To resolve this problem, let's look at it from a semantic standpoint. If $\Gamma \vdash A \, {}^t/u$ for all $t \in T_M$ and $\Gamma \vdash \sim(x)A \, {}^x/u$, this means that no model V of Γ can supply a name in **M** to each individual of its domain; there must always be members of the domain of V which have no names in **M**. But by simply adding enough new terms to **M** and enlarging V so that all these unnamed individuals become named, we can obtain a model of Γ in which every member of the domain has a name.

This suggests the following syntactic procedure. Where Γ is a consistent set of formulas of a morphology **M**, first add new individual parameters to **M**, obtaining in this way a larger morphology **M'**. Then extend Γ to an **M'**-saturated set.

How many individual parameters do we have to add to **M** to make this procedure work? For some consistent sets a finite number will suffice, but in general we must add as many individual parameters as there are formulas of **M**. As in Chapter VII, we will simplify our proof of completeness by assuming that this set is *always denumerable*, leaving it as a problem to generalize our results to morphologies of arbitrary infinite cardinality. This means that to obtain a morphology **M'** for which there is an **M'**-saturated extension of a consistent set of formulas of **M**, we need only add denumerably many individual parameters to **M**.

D2. Let **M** *be a morphology for* $H_{p=}$ *(where* F_M *is denumerable), and* $u_1, u_2, u_3, \ldots$ *be distinct symbols not occurring in any category of* **M**. *Let* **M'** *be like* **M** *except that* $C_{M'} = C_M \cup \{u_1, u_2, u_3, \ldots\}$. *Then* **M'** *is said to be an* S-*extension of* **M**.

We want to show that every consistent set Γ of formulas of a morphology **M** has an **M'**-saturated extension, where **M'** is an S-extension of **M**. We'll do this in two parts. First, we'll show that, where **M'** is an S-extension of **M**, there is a consistent set of Δ of formulas of **M'** such that $\Gamma \subseteq \Delta$ and for every formula $(x)A^{\,x}/u$ of **M'** there is a $t \in IP_{M'}$ such that $(\exists x)A^{\,x}/u \supset A^{\,t}/u \in \Delta$. We will also prove an analogue of VII.M11 which will guarantee that since Δ is consistent, it has an extension which is consistent and negation-complete with respect to **M'**. By M12, it will then follow that Δ is **M'**-saturated.

M13. Let Γ *be a consistent set of formulas of a morphology* **M** *for* $H_{p=}$ *and* **M'** *be any* S-*extension of* **M**. *Then there is a consistent set* Δ *of formulas of* **M'** *such that for all formulas A, individual parameters u and individual variables x of* **M'**, *if u is free for x in A then there is an individual parameter v of* **M'** *such that* $(\exists x)A^{\,x}/u \supset A^{\,v}/u \in \Delta$, *and* $\Gamma \subseteq \Delta$.

PROOF. Since F_M is denumerable, $F_{M'}$ is denumerable (see XIII.E12), and therefore the set of formulas of **M'** of the sort $v=v \wedge (x)A^{\,x}/v$ is denumerable. Let $v_1=v_1 \wedge (\exists x_1)A_1^{\,x_1}/v_1$, $v_2=v_2 \wedge (\exists x_2)A_2^{\,x_2}/v_2, \ldots$ be an enumeration of all the formulas of **M'** having the form $v=v \wedge (\exists x)A^{\,x}/v$, where v is free for x in A. Let S be the set of individual parameters of $\mathbf{M}'$ which are not individual parameters of $\mathbf{M}$; since $\mathbf{M}'$ is an S-extension of $\mathbf{M}$, S is denumerably infinite.

Now, define a sequence $u_1, u_2, \ldots$ of members of S inductively, as follows. Let u_1 be the first member of S not occurring in $(\exists x_1)A_1 \, {}^{x_1}/v_1$, and let u_{n+1} be the first member of S differing from each of $u_1, \ldots, u_n$ and not occurring in any of $(\exists x_1)A_1 \, {}^{x_1}/v_1, \ldots, (\exists x_n)A_n \, {}^{x_n}/v_n$. Our strategy now is to add every formula $(\exists x_n)A \, {}^{x_n}/v_n \supset A_n \, {}^{u_n}/v_n$ to Γ: let $\Delta = \Gamma \cup \{(\exists x_1)A_1 \, {}^{x_1}/v_1 \supset A_1 \, {}^{u_1}/v_1, (\exists x_2)A_2 \, {}^{x_2}/v_2 \supset A_2 \, {}^{u_2}/v_2, \ldots\}$.

By virtue of this construction, Δ is an extension of Γ such that for all formulas A, individual parameters v and individual variables x of $\mathbf{M}'$, if u is free for x in A then there is an individual parameter u of $\mathbf{M}'$ such that $(\exists x)A \, {}^{x}/v \supset A \, {}^{u}/v \in \Delta$. Thus, to complete the proof of M13 we need only show that Δ is consistent.

But if Δ were inconsistent, some finite subset of Δ would be inconsistent, and hence for some n the set $\Gamma \cup \{(\exists x_1)A_1 \, {}^{u_1}/v_1 \supset A_1 \, {}^{u_1}/v_1, \ldots, (\exists x_n)A_n \, {}^{x_n}/v_n \supset A_n \, {}^{u_n}/v_n\}$ would be inconsistent. However, it's easy to show inductively that for all n this set is consistent. For by X.M55, since u_1 has no occurrences in $(\exists x_1)A_1 \, {}^{x_1}/v_1$ or in any member of Γ, the set $\Gamma \cup \{(\exists x_1)A_1 \, {}^{x_1}/v_1 \supset A \, {}^{u_1}/v_1\}$ is consistent, since Γ is. And if we assume as inductive hypothesis that $\Gamma \cup \{(\exists x_1)A_1 \, {}^{u_1}/v_1 \supset A_1 \, {}^{u_1}/v_1, \ldots, (\exists x_n)A_n \, {}^{x_n}/v_n \supset A_n \, {}^{u_n}/v_n\}$ is consistent, then X.M55 again guarantees that $\Gamma \cup \{(\exists x_1)A \, {}^{x_1}/v_1 \supset A_1 \, {}^{u_1}/v_1, \ldots, (\exists x_{n+1})A_{n+1} \, {}^{x_{n+1}}/v_{n+1} \supset A_{n+1} \, {}^{u_{n+1}}/v_{n+1}\}$ is consistent. This argument shows that Δ is consistent, and so M13 is proved.

M14. Let Γ be a consistent set of formulas of a morphology $\mathbf{M}$ for $\mathbf{H}_{p=}$. Then there is a consistent set Δ of formulas of $\mathbf{M}$ such that $\Gamma \subseteq \Delta$, and for formulas A of $\mathbf{M}$ either $A \in \Delta$ or $\sim A \in \Delta$.

This metatheorem is proved in the same way as VII.M11. In fact, the proof given of VII.M11 can also be regarded as a proof of M14. Putting M13 and M14 together, we obtain the result that every consistent set Γ has an $\mathbf{M}'$-saturated extension, where $\mathbf{M}'$ is an S-extension of the morphology of Γ.

M15. Let Γ be a consistent set of formulas of a morphology $\mathbf{M}$ for $\mathbf{H}_{p=}$. Then for some morphology $\mathbf{M}'$, there is an $\mathbf{M}'$-saturated set Θ such that $\Gamma \subseteq \Theta$. (In particular, we can always assume that $\mathbf{M}'$ is an S-extension of $\mathbf{M}$.)

PROOF. Let Γ be a consistent set of formulas of $\mathbf{M}$ and let $\mathbf{M}'$ be an S-extension of $\mathbf{M}$. By M13 there is a consistent set Δ of formulas of $\mathbf{M}'$ such that $\Gamma \subseteq \Delta$ and for all formulas of $\mathbf{M}$ of the sort $(\exists x)A \, {}^{x}/v$ there is a $u \in \mathrm{IP}_{\mathbf{M}'}$ such that $(\exists x)A\ ^x/u \supset A\ ^u/v \in \Delta$, provided u is free for x in A. By M14 there is a consistent set Θ of formulas of $\mathbf{M'}$ such that $\Delta \subseteq \Theta$ and for all formulas B of $\mathbf{M'}$, $B \in \Theta$ or $\sim B \in \Theta$. By M12, Θ is $\mathbf{M'}$-saturated.

6. To finish our proof of semantic completeness, we must show that every $\mathbf{M}$-saturated set Γ is simultaneously satisfiable. In order to do this, we'll make a model of Γ out of the materials furnished by Γ itself. Since in predicate logic there is more to a model than an assignment of truth-values to sentence parameters, the construction of this model is more complicated than in the proof of VII.M13. To see how this construction can be carried out, let's consider how we would handle a 1-ary predicate parameter P and three individual constants, a, b, and c, in building a model of an $\mathbf{M}$-saturated set Γ. We'll neglect the other components of $\mathbf{M}$ in this discussion.

First, what will we choose as the domain of our model? Keeping in mind that we want to interpret Γ in terms of itself, the most natural thing to do would be to let the domain consist of all the individual terms of $\mathbf{M}$ and to construe them as names of themselves. We would thus have $V(a) = a$, $V(b) = b$, and $V(c) = c$. This idea would work if we didn't have to reckon with identity, but as long as there can be formulas such as $a=b$ in Γ it will run into difficulties. The trouble is that for all formulas A of $\mathbf{M}$ we want $V(A)$ to be $\mathbf{T}$ if and only if $A \in \Gamma$, but since a and b are different symbols $V(a=b)$ will be $\mathbf{F}$ in spite of the fact that $a=b \in \Gamma$.

To overcome this problem we have to arrange things so that a and b name the same thing if and only if $a=b \in \Gamma$. For example, suppose that $a=b \in \Gamma$ and that $a=c \notin \Gamma$. Then we can let $V(a) = a$ and $V(b) = a$, and $V(c) = c$; this will make $V(a=b) = \mathbf{T}$ and $V(a=c) = \mathbf{F}$. Our strategy here is to choose a single representative of those terms that are equivalent to one another. (Terms s and t are equivalent if $s=t \in \Gamma$.) All these equivalent terms are then assigned this representative, just as a and b are both assigned a in our example.

To ensure that this strategy will always work we must show that situations never arise in which, for instance, $a=b \in \Gamma$ and $b=c \in \Gamma$, but $a=c \notin \Gamma$. If this were to happen we would have to assign the same representative to a and b, the same representative to b and c, and yet assign a and c different representatives. This clearly would be impossible. In the proof of M16 we'll show that such things can never happen.

Finally let's consider the 1-ary predicate parameter P. What value will we give to it? This must be a property of members of the domain; i.e., it will be a property of certain terms of $\mathbf{M}$. Since we must choose this property so that $V(Pt)$ will be $\mathbf{T}$ if and only if $Pt \in \Gamma$, we really have only one alternative: we must let the property $V(P)$ apply to those and only those representatives s in the domain such that $Ps \in \Gamma$. If, for example, we have Pa and $\sim Pc$ in Γ, we will let $V(a) \in V(P)$ and $V(c) \notin V(P)$; i.e., $a \in V(P)$ and $c \notin V(P)$.

In the proof of M16 we just go over this again more generally and rigorously, and check that in fact it works.

M16. If Γ is M-saturated, then there is a valuation V of M such that $\Gamma = \{A \mid A \in F_M$ and $V(A) = T\}$.

PROOF. The domain of our valuation will consist of certain terms of M; in order to tell which terms, we have to look more closely at the identities present in Γ. Let's say that terms s and t of M are *equivalent*, $s \simeq t$, if $s=t \in \Gamma$. For each term t of M, there is an *equivalence class* E_t, consisting of those terms s such that $s \simeq t$: $E_t = \{s \mid s \in T_M$ and $s \simeq t\}$. Now, each term t of M belongs to some equivalence class; indeed, we have $t \in E_t$ in view of M7 and X.M45. Also, no term of M falls into two different equivalence classes. For suppose that $t \in E_r$ and $t \in E_s$; then $t=r \in \Gamma$ and $t=s \in \Gamma$. Let t' be an arbitrary member of E_s. Then $t'=s \in \Gamma$ and by M5, X.M46 and X.M47 $t'=r \in \Gamma$; i.e., $t' \in E_r$. By the same argument any member of E_r is in E_s, and therefore $E_r = E_s$.

Now we pick one member t_E of each equivalence class E; t_E is the *representative* of the equivalence class E. The domain D of our valuation V will be the set of all these representatives. Furthermore, we'll assign to each term the representative of the equivalence class to which it belongs: $V(s) = t_{E_s}$. This has the following two consequences, for all terms s and t of M:

1. $s=V(s) \in \Gamma$.
2. $s=t \in \Gamma$ if and only if $V(s) = V(t)$.

To complete our definition of the valuation V we must specify how V acts on the predicate parameters of M. First, if P is a 0-ary predicate parameter of M (i.e., a sentence parameter), we let $V(P) = T$ if and only if $P \in \Gamma$, just as we did in proving VII.M13. Second, if P is an n-ary predicate parameter of M, where $n > 0$, we let $V(P) = \{\langle t_1, \ldots, t_n \rangle \mid t_1, \ldots, t_n \in D$ and $Pt_1 \cdots t_n \in \Gamma\}$.

We now have to show that for all formulas A of M, $V(A) = T$ if and only if $A \in \Gamma$; we do this by induction on the complexity of A. In case A is atomic, A is either a sentence parameter P, an identity $s=t$, or a formula $Qr_1 \cdots r_n$. If A is P then by definition of V, $V(A) = T$ if and only if $A \in \Gamma$. And if A is $s=t$ then by 2, above, $A \in \Gamma$ if and only if $V(s) = V(t)$; i.e., $A \in \Gamma$ if and only if $V(A) = T$. Finally, if A is $Qr_1 \cdots r_n$, $V(A) = T$ if and only if $\langle V(r_1), \ldots, V(r_n) \rangle \in V(P)$. But $V(P)$ was defined so that $\langle V(r_1), \ldots, V(r_n) \rangle \in V(P)$ if and only if the formula $PV(r_1) \cdots V(r_n)$ is a member of Γ. Since by 1, above, we have $r_i = V(r_i) \in \Gamma$ for all i, $1 \le i \le n$, it follows by M5 and X.M47 that $PV(r_1) \cdots V(r_n) \in \Gamma$ if and only if $Pr_1 \cdots r_n \in \Gamma$. Therefore we again have $V(A) = T$ if and only if $A \in \Gamma$. This completes the basis step of the induction.

In the inductive step we let A be a complex formula of **M** and assume as inductive hypothesis that for all formulas B of **M** less complex than A, $V(B) = T$ if and only if $B \in \Gamma$. As usual there are three cases: A may be an implication, a negation, or a universal quantification. The first two cases are handled in precisely the same way as in the proof of VII.M13 and do not need to be repeated here.

Suppose, then, that A is a universal quantification $(x)C^{\,x}/u$, where x is free for u in C. Then $V(A) = T$ if and only if for all $t \in D$, $V^{\,t}/u(C) = T$. Since if $t \in D$ then $V(t) = t$, we know by XI.M32 that, for all $t \in D$, $V^{\,t}/u(C) = T$ if and only if $V(C^{\,t}/u) = T$. Therefore $V(A) = T$ if and only if for all $t \in D$, $V(C^{\,t}/u) = T$. But C is less complex than A, so the hypothesis of induction ensures that for any $t \in D$, $V(C^{\,t}/u) = T$ if and only if $C^{\,t}/u \in \Gamma$. So $V(A) = T$ if and only if for all $t \in D$, $C^{\,t}/u \in \Gamma$. But $C^{\,t}/u \in \Gamma$ for all $t \in D$ if and only if for all terms s of **M**, $C^{\,s}/u \in \Gamma$. (The reason is that for all terms s of **M** there is a term r in D—namely, $V(s)$— such that $s = r \in \Gamma$. Thus $C^{\,s}/u \in \Gamma$ if $C^{\,r}/u \in \Gamma$.) Therefore $V(A) = T$ if and only if for all $s \in T_M$, $C^{\,s}/u \in \Gamma$; but by M10, $C^{\,s}/u \in \Gamma$ for all $s \in T_M$ if and only if $(x)C^{\,x}/u \in \Gamma$. Therefore $V(A) = T$ if and only if $A \in \Gamma$.

This completes the induction, and the proof of M16.

Having finished the proof of the above metatheorems, most of our work is done. It's only necessary to reap corollaries and explore their significance. First come a variety of results concerning semantic completeness.

*M17. Let Γ be a set of formulas of a morphology **M**. If Γ is consistent then Γ is simultaneously satisfiable.*

PROOF. Use M15 and M16 just as VII.M11 and VII.M13 are used in the proof of VII.M14.

*M18. Let Γ be any set of formulas of **M**. Γ is consistent if and only if Γ is simultaneously satisfiable.*

M19. If $\Gamma \Vdash A$ then $\Gamma \vdash A$.

M20. $\Gamma \Vdash A$ if and only if $\Gamma \vdash A$.

M21. If $\Vdash A$ then $\vdash A$.

M22. $\Vdash A$ if and only if $\vdash A$.

These last metatheorems are direct corollaries of M17 and their proofs are left as exercises. In view of X.M61, we also have a semantic completeness theorem for the system S_k of natural deduction.

M23. $A_1, \ldots, A_n \vdash_{S_k} B$ if and only if $\{A_1, \ldots, A_n\} \Vdash B$.

7. As we pointed out in Chapter VII, the correlation between semantic and syntactic notions established in the above metatheorems helps to justify the system proved complete. They show, for instance, that every theorem obtainable in $H_{p=}$ is desirable and, conversely, that every formula that is desirable as a theorem can be proved in $H_{p=}$. This completeness result for $H_{p=}$ is much more interesting than the corresponding result for H_s because so much more reasoning can be formalized in predicate logic than in sentence logic. Indeed, most logicians would agree that all known mathematical theories—i.e., all theories actually used by mathematicians—can be rendered by taking a suitable morphology for $H_{p=}$ and adding a set Γ of postulates to the logical axioms of $H_{p=}$. The *theorems* of such a theory would thus be represented by those formulas A of **M** such that $\Gamma \vdash A$. And there is no reason why this sort of thing can't be done for any subject-matter in which deductive reasoning is prominent; for instance, physics, economics, or logic itself.

Thus, we can regard sets Γ of formulas of any morphology for $H_{p=}$ as sets of postulates for theories or *axiomatizations* of theories. A model of such a set corresponds to a situation in which the postulates of the theory are realized, a situation the theory is "about". We can regard a *theory*, on the other hand, as a set of theorems generated by some set of postulates. More precisely, a theory in a morphology **M** is a deductively closed set Δ of formulas of **M**; i.e., a set such that for all formulas A of **M**, $A \in \Delta$ if $\Delta \vdash A$. An *axiomatization* or *postulate set* for a theory Δ will be a set Γ of formulas of **M** such that $\Delta = \{A \mid A \in F_M$ and $\Gamma \vdash A\}$. Clearly, there will be many different axiomatizations of any one theory. (In this connection, see E11.)

This way of looking at things sheds new light on M18, M20, and M22. Among theories, there will be some which have no models at all; M16 tells us that these are precisely those theories that are inconsistent. This corresponds to a time-honored way of showing theories consistent by imagining or "distinctly conceiving" situations in which these theories are realized. In the semantics of predicate logic these notions of *distinct conception* and *realization* (or *truth*) are replaced by the mathematical concepts of a *valuation* (or *relational structure*) and of *satisfaction*.

More generally, M20 shows that those formulas of a morphology **M** which are true in all models of a theory Δ in **M** are precisely the theorems of Δ. That is, any theorem of Δ is true in all models of Δ, and any formula of **M** which is true in all models of Δ is a theorem of Δ. This sounds trivial, but it is really a restatement of M20, which took so much trouble to prove. The fact that it seems trivial is an indication of how fundamental semantic completeness is. If M20 were to fail, our logical theory would be in serious trouble.

Every theory Δ in a morphology M corresponds to a set of relational structures of type M: the relational structures that are models of Δ. If Δ is empty or contains only theorems of $H_{p=}$, the set of models of Δ will be the set of *all* relational structures of type **M**. Conversely, if a formula *A* of **M** is satisfied in all relational structures of type **M**, it is a theorem of $H_{p=}$. This is expressed by M22, which says that the theorems of predicate logic are precisely those formulas that hold in every possible situation. As we begin to think of some subject-matter or other, we start to add postulates which are not mere theorems of logic. For instance, if we are thinking of geometry, we will add geometrical postulates. M20 tells us that as we "strengthen" a theory by adding such postulates, we also restrict what it is about by decreasing the models of the theory. (See E9 in this connection.)

Thus, we can use the set of models of a theory as a measure of its abstractness. The more inclusive this set of models, the less particular the content of the theory, since the theory will admit more sorts of realizations, or have to do with more kinds of things. At the extreme of particularity would be theories that determine essentially only one model. This notion is made precise by speaking of *categorical* theories; a theory is said to be categorical if all its models are isomorphic to some model. (See XI.P1 in this connection.) One of the more surprising results of model theory is that there are very few categorical theories; e.g., no theory rich enough to encompass material of mathematical interest can be categorical. In particular, there is no theory Δ of *being less than* whose models are all isomorphic to the positive integers $\{1, 2, \ldots\}$ ordered by $<$. A conclusion suggested by this result is that every sufficiently rich theory is *essentially abstract* in that it must admit non-isomorphic models.

The role of metatheorems such as M20 is crucial to this way of thinking. If it were not for this equivalence of the syntactic and semantic notions of consequence, we could not pass freely between results about the models of a theory and results about the deductive structure of the theory. Theorems of logic would not be doing their proper job of asserting only what holds in *all possible* situations, and would thus interfere with the relationship between a theory and its models. This clearly would be unwelcome, if not intolerable; it would complicate the further development of our logical theory at almost every point.

8. In this section we will illustrate some applications of our completeness results by using them to prove two important metatheorems about predicate logic: the compactness theorem and the Löwenheim–Skolem theorem. Compactness is established in the same way as in Chapter VII; the proofs of the following metatheorems, therefore, are left as exercises.

M24. (Compactness.) If every finite subset of a set Γ has some model, then Γ itself has some model.

M25. Every finite subset of a set Γ has some model if and only if Γ has some model.

M26. If $\Gamma \Vdash A$, then for some finite subset Δ of Γ, $\Delta \Vdash A$.

M27. $\Gamma \Vdash A$ if and only if for some finite subset Δ of Γ, $\Delta \Vdash A$.

The compactness theorem has many applications; for instance, we can use it to deduce strong completeness from weak completeness (see E8, below). Another example of an application of compactness is the following result.

M28. If Γ is not simultaneously satisfiable in any infinite domain, then there is an n ($n \geq 0$) such that for all $i > n$, Γ is not simultaneously satisfiable in any domain of cardinality i.

PROOF. Let Γ be a set of formulas of **M** which is not simultaneously satisfiable in any infinite domain, and suppose for *reductio* that for every number n, there is an $i > n$ such that Γ is simultaneously satisfiable in a domain of size i. Now, where $k \geq 1$, let A_k be the formula

$$(\exists x_1) \cdots (\exists x_k)(\sim x_1 = x_2 \,\wedge\, \sim x_1 = x_3 \,\wedge \cdots \wedge\, \sim x_1 = x_k \,\wedge\, \sim x_2 = x_3$$
$$\wedge\, \sim x_2 = x_4 \,\wedge \cdots \wedge\, \sim x_2 = x_k \,\wedge\, \sim x_3 = x_4 \,\wedge \cdots \wedge\, \sim x_{k-1} = x_k),$$

where $x_1, \ldots, x_k$ are individual variables of **M**. The formula A_k clearly is satisfiable only in domains containing at least k members. Now, let $\Delta = \Gamma \cup \{A_1, A_2, \ldots\}$, and let Θ be any finite subset of Δ. Since Θ is finite, there is an n such that for all $i > n$, $A_i \notin \Theta$. By assumption, there is a model V of Γ whose domain has more than n elements; V will thus satisfy each A_i such that

$i < n$, and so V is also a model of Θ. Therefore, Θ is simultaneously satisfiable.

We have now shown that every finite subset of Δ is simultaneously satisfiable, and hence we know by compactness that Δ is simultaneously satisfiable, so that Δ has some model U. But U satisfies A_k for *all* $k \geq 1$, and hence the domain of U is infinite, contrary to assumption. Thus it cannot be the case that for every n there is an $i > n$ such that Γ is simultaneously satisfiable in a domain of size i, and so there is an n such that for all $i > n$, Γ is not simultaneously satisfiable in any domain of size i.

This metatheorem can be restated in more perspicuous fashion. By the *size* of a model, let's understand the size of its domain; thus, a model is finite if its domain is finite. What M25 establishes, in those terms, is that if a set Γ has arbitrarily large finite models, then it has an infinite model.

The Löwenheim–Skolem theorem states that every theory that has an infinite model has a denumerable model. It is possible to prove this theorem directly, using only semantic notions; roughly speaking, this is done by showing that any infinite model V of a set Γ of formulas has a part which is denumerable and is also a model of Γ. This direct argument requires a fairly advanced mathematical argument, and rather than developing it further we will prove the theorem indirectly, using our proof of M16.

M26 (*Löwenheim–Skolem theorem*). *Let Γ be a set of formulas of a morphology* $\mathbf{M}$ *for* $\mathbf{H_{p=}}$, *where* $\mathbf{F_M}$ *is denumerable. If Γ has an infinite model then Γ has a denumerable model.*

PROOF. Let the formulas $A_1, A_2, \ldots$ be defined as in the proof of M25, above, and let V be an infinite model of Γ. Since V is infinite, it is a model of Δ, where $\Delta = \Gamma \cup \{A_1, A_2, \ldots\}$. Therefore Δ is simultaneously satisfiable, and so by M5, Δ is consistent. Let $\mathbf{M}'$ be an S-extension of the morphology $\mathbf{M}$; M13 and M14 tell us that there is an $\mathbf{M}'$-saturated set Θ of formulas of $\mathbf{M}'$ such that $\Delta \subseteq \Theta$. Now, the proof of M16 constructs under these circumstances a model U of Θ, whose domain is made up of individual terms of $\mathbf{M}'$; since there are only denumerably such terms, the model U can be at most denumerable. Since on the other hand we have $A_k \in \Theta$ for each $k \geq 1$, and any model of A_k must contain at least k elements, U must be *at least* denumerable. Therefore, U is denumerable; and since U is a model of Θ, U is also a model of Γ.

The Löwenheim–Skolem theorem tells us a great deal concerning what cardinalities we may expect the models of a theory to have. In fact, it can be generalized to obtain an even stronger result: for any infinite cardinality, a set Γ of formulas (of a denumerable morphology) has a model of that cardinality if and only if it has a denumerable model (see P3 and P4, below, in this regard). Thus, a theory has a denumerable model if and only if it has some model in *every* infinite cardinality. Putting this together with M28, we can also see that if Γ has no denumerable models, then all of its models (if it has any) will be smaller in size than some positive integer k.

9. At this point we'll end our discussion of applications of the completeness theorems; more uses of these results are given in the exercises and problems below. You may have wondered why we didn't state the existence of a *decision procedure* for $H_{p=}$ as a corollary of M20; but if you consider the matter, you'll see that merely showing the equivalence of validity and provability does not suffice to ensure a method of deciding questions regarding the provability of formulas. This will only be the case if the notion of validity is decidable. Now, since truth-tables are all finite structures, the notion of validity for H_s *is* decidable. But this is not the case in $H_{p=}$; in cases where the domain of a valuation is infinite, a finite procedure will not suffice to calculate the truth-value given to a formula by a valuation. Thus, in spite of our successful demonstration of the semantic completeness of $H_{p=}$, we are just as much in the dark as ever about whether $H_{p=}$ is decidable. (As it turns out, $H_{p=}$ is *not* decidable, but the proof of this is a long story.)

Another point that may have struck you as puzzling is the Löwenheim–Skolem theorem; indeed, this result has also been called the "Löwenheim–Skolem paradox". What causes wonder here is that the theory of sets can itself be formulated using $H_{p=}$; the postulates of set theory will then appear as a set Γ of formulas of a morphology **M**. We can assume that **M** has just one predicate parameter, a 2-ary one that stands for the membership relation. Among the theorems that can be obtained from Γ will be a formula A asserting the existence of nondenumerably infinite cardinalities. Now, according to M17, if Γ is consistent, it has a model. But any decent set Γ of postulates for set theory can easily be shown to have no finite models; by the Löwenheim–Skolem theorem, if Γ is consistent, it must have a denumerable model V. Since $Γ \vdash A$, A must be true in V. But how is this possible, since V is denumerable? Does this mean that Γ has *no* models, and so is inconsistent?

In fact, the difficulty can be resolved without drawing the conclusion that set theory is inconsistent. First, we must be more critical regarding the notion of *denumerability*; we must distinguish it as it occurs in our set-theoretic metalanguage and as it occurs in the formula A. To say that a set X is denumerable is to say that there is a one-one correspondence of X with the positive integers; i.e., that *there is* a set Y which is a one-one correspondence of X with the positive integers. For convenience, now, let's suppose that the domain of V in fact contains only sets, and that P actually is interpreted by V as standing for membership. Thus, if s and t are terms of **M**, $V(Pst) = T$ if and only if $V(s) \in V(t)$.

We know on the one hand that the domain D of V is denumerable from the standpoint of our metalanguage. This implies (though we won't go through the steps here) that every member of the domain D must be a set of at most denumerable cardinality. Hence, for every infinite set X of D, there is a one-one correlation C_X of X with the positive integers.

The formula A, however, says that there are infinite sets Y in D such that there exist no one-one correspondences in D of Y with the positive integers. (We assume there is a collection of sets in D doing duty for the positive integers.) Since A is true in V, there must in fact be infinite sets Y in D for which no one-one correspondences of Y with the positive integers can be found in D. But this is no impossibility; it merely means, in particular, that the set C_Y is not to be found in D.

Thus, the appearance of contradiction presented by the Löwenheim–Skolem theorem stems from taking the universal quantifier to be unequivocal in its metalinguistic and its object-linguistic uses. But it *is* equivocal. When we talk about "all sets" in our metalanguage, we mean all sets in a sense that is meant to be unqualified; but in **M**, as interpreted by V, "all sets" means only all sets in D. Thus, the perplexity and sense of contradiction is removed here. Nevertheless, it remains surprising that a denumerable domain D of sets exists in which the postulates of set theory are satisfied. But although this is surprising, it is guaranteed by the proof of M29, provided only that these postulates are consistent.

We may view the Löwenheim–Skolem theorem as revealing a limitation on the nature of deductive theories; no theory formulated using a morphology for $H_{p=}$ can characterize unequivocally the notion of a nondenumerable set. No matter how we formulate the theory of sets by means of a set Γ of postulates, the theory will have denumerable models if it has infinite models at all. It follows that if Γ characterizes the relational structure it is intended to characterize, it must also have models which are radically different from the intended one.

When construed in this way, the Löwenheim–Skolem theorem is the first of a family of *limitative* metatheorems: metatheorems about what cannot be done with any formal system. These limitative results have been developed in great detail and variety in the last thirty-five years, and constitute one of the most fascinating and characteristic areas of modern logic. Although these results are beyond the scope of this work, we have at least come to the threshold beyond which they lie.

Exercises

1. Show that the following formulas are not provable in $H_{p=}$.
   (a) $(\exists x)Px \supset (\exists x)\sim Px$
   (b) $(x)(Px \equiv (\exists y)Py)$
   (c) $(x)(y)(\exists z)Pxyz \supset (x)(\exists z)(y)Pxyz$
   (d) $(x)(y)(Pxy \supset x=y) \supset (x)Pxx$
   (e) $(x)Pxx \supset (x)(y)(Pxy \supset x=y)$

2. Decide whether or not the following formulas are provable in $H_{p=}$.
   (a) $Q \equiv (x)Q$
   (b) $(x)(Px \supset (\exists y)Py)$
   (c) $(x)Px \equiv (Pa \wedge ((x)Px \vee (x)\sim Px))$
   (d) $((x)(y)(z)((Pxy \wedge Pyz) \supset Pxz) \wedge (x)(\exists y)Pxy) \supset (\exists x)(y)Pxy$
   (e) $Pa \equiv (\exists x)(x=a \wedge Pa)$
   (f) $(x)Px \supset Q \supset (x)(Px \supset Q)$
   (g) $(x)(y)((\exists z)Pxzz \supset (\exists z)Pxyz)$
   (h) $\sim(x)(Px \supset Qx) \supset. \sim(x)Px \supset \sim(x)Qx$

3. Let **M** have just one binary predicate parameter P, and let Γ consist of the following formulas of **M**.
$$(x)(\exists y)(\exists z)(Pxy \wedge Pzx)$$
$$(x)(y)(z)(Pxy \supset. Pyz \supset Pxz)$$
$$(x)(y)(Pxy \supset \sim Pyx)$$
$$(x)(y)(\sim x=y \supset (Pxy \vee Pyx))$$
   (a) Show that Γ is consistent.
   (b) Let $\Delta = \Gamma \cup \{(x)(y)(\sim x=y \supset (\exists z)(Pxz \wedge Pzy))\}$. Show that Δ is consistent.
   (c) Let $\Theta = \Delta \cup \{(\exists x)(y)x=y\}$. Show that Θ is inconsistent.
   (d) Let $\Xi = \Gamma \cup \{\sim A_{117}\}$, where A_{117} is the 117th formula in the sequence $A_1, A_2, \ldots$ defined in the proof of M28. Show by a semantic argument that Ξ is inconsistent.

4. Show that if a set Γ is **M**-saturated then for all formulas A, individual parameters u and individual variables x of **M**, if u is free for x in A and $(\exists x)A\,^x/u \in \Gamma$ then there is a term t of **M** such that $A\,^t/u \in \Gamma$.

5. It is not in general true that if **M** is a morphology for $H_{p=}$ and A is a formula, u an individual parameter and x an individual variable of **M** with u free for x in A, then if $\vdash (\exists x)A\,^x/u$ there is a term t of **M** such that $\vdash A\,^t/u$. Establish this by finding a counterexample and showing that it is in fact a counterexample.

6. Say that a set Γ of formulas of **M** is *omega-complete* with respect to **M** if for all formulas A, individual parameters u and individual variables x of **M** with u free for x in A, $\Gamma \vdash (x)A\,^x/u$ whenever $\Gamma \vdash A\,^t/u$ for all terms t of **M**. Likewise, say that Γ is *omega-consistent* with respect to **M** if it is never the case for any formula A, individual parameter u and individual variable x of **M** with u free for x in A that $\Gamma \vdash \sim(x)A\,^x/u$ and $\Gamma \vdash A\,^t/u$ for all terms t of **M**. Show the following.

(a) If Γ is omega-consistent with respect to **M** and negation-complete with respect to **M**, then it is omega-complete with respect to **M**.

(b) If for all formulas A, individual parameters u and individual variables x of **M** with u free for x in A, there is a term t of **M** such that $\Gamma \vdash A\,^t/u$ whenever $\Gamma \vdash (\exists x)A\,^x/u$, then Γ is omega-complete with respect to **M**.

(c) If Γ is omega-complete with respect to **M** and A is any formula of **M**, then $\Gamma \cup \{A\}$ is omega-complete with respect to **M**.

7. Let $H^1_{p\,=}$ be the logic having in addition to the axioms and rules of $H_{p\,=}$ the axiom $(x)(y)x = y$. Show, using M20, that $H^1_{p\,=}$ is semantically complete in the following sense: $\Gamma \vdash_{H^1_{p\,=}} A$ if and only if Γ implies A in every domain containing exactly one element.

8. (a) Use M28 and M21 to prove M20. (b) Use M18 to prove M15.

9. Where Γ is a set of formulas of **M**, let $\Gamma^{\mathbf{M}}$ be the set of relational structures of type **M** which are models of Γ. And let $cl(\Gamma)$ be the set $\{A \mid A \in F_{\mathbf{M}}$ and $\Gamma \vdash A\}$; i.e., $cl(\Gamma)$ is the deductive closure of Γ. Establish the following, using any metatheorems in this chapter.

(a) $A \in cl(\Gamma)$ if and only if $V(A) = T$ for all $V \in \Gamma^{\mathbf{M}}$.

(b) If $\Gamma_{\mathbf{M}} \subseteq \Delta^{\mathbf{M}}$ then $cl(\Delta) \subseteq cl(\Gamma)$.

(c) If $cl(\Delta) \subseteq cl(\Gamma)$ then $\Gamma^{\mathbf{M}} \subseteq \Delta^{\mathbf{M}}$.

10. Using any metatheorems established previously to them, prove the following metatheorems.

(a) M4	(b) M5	(c) M6	(d) M7
(e) M8	(f) M9	(g) M10	(h) M11
(i) M18	(j) M19	(k) M20	(l) M21
(m) M22	(n) M23	(o) M24	(p) M25
(q) M26	(r) M27		

11. Let Δ be a theory of a morphology **M**; i.e., Δ is a deductively closed set of formulas of **M**. Show that there are infinitely many axiomatizations of Δ; i.e., infinitely many sets Γ such that $\Delta = \{A \mid \Gamma \vdash A\}$.

12. Using any metatheorems and proofs given in the text, establish the following.

(a) Let V be a valuation of a morphology **M** on a domain D, such that for all $d \in D$ there is a $t \in T_{\mathbf{M}}$ such that $V(t) = d$. Let Γ be the set of formulas of **M** satisfied by V: $\Gamma = \{A \mid A \in F_{\mathbf{M}}$ and $V(A) = T\}$. Then Γ is **M**-saturated.

(b) Let Γ be an M-saturated set of formulas of M. Then there is a valuation V of M on some domain D, such that for all $d \in D$ there is a $t \in T_M$ such that $V(t) = d$ and such that $\Gamma = \{A \mid A \in F_M$ and $V(A) = T\}$.

Problems

1. This is an example of a notion of satisfaction which is weakly complete but strongly incomplete for $H_{p=}$. Where Γ is a set of formulas of M, say that Γ is *simultaneously omega-satisfiable* (with respect to M) if there is a model of Γ in which every element of the domain has a name in T_M. Show that for all formulas A of M, A is simultaneously omega-satisfiable with respect to M if and only if A is a consistent formula of $H_{p=}$. Go on to show that it is not the case for all sets Γ of formulas of M that Γ is simultaneously omega-satisfiable with respect to M if and only if Γ is a consistent set of formulas of M.

2. Define a logical system $H_=$ as follows. A morphology for $H_=$ is just like a morphology for $H_{p=}$; the formulas of a morphology M for $H_=$ consist of those formulas of M for $H_{p=}$ which have no quantifiers. Let a set Γ of formulas of a morphology M for $H_=$ be *simultaneously satisfiable* if Γ is simultaneously satisfiable as a set of formulas of $H_{p=}$. Let $H_=$ have those axioms of $H_{p=}$ which are formulas of $H_=$, and the rule *modus ponens*. Show that $H_=$ is semantically complete, in the sense that for all formulas A of $H_=$, $\vdash_{H_=} A$ if and only if A is valid. (*Hint:* Adopt the strategy used in this chapter to show $H_{p=}$ semantically complete.)

3. Generalize the completeness theorems of this chapter to morphologies of arbitrary cardinality.

4. Prove the so-called "upwards Löwenheim–Skolem theorem": if a set Γ has a model of infinite cardinality α, then for any cardinality β exceeding α there is a model of Γ having cardinality β. (*Hint:* Use the result of problem 3 on an extension of Γ obtained by adding lots of negated identities.)

5. Show that if a set Γ of formulas of a *denumerable* morphology M is omega-complete with respect to M (see E6), then there is an M-saturated extension Δ of Γ.

6. Find a semantic proof of the interpolation theorem for $H_{p=}$. (*Note:* This is a difficult problem. There is no straightforward way to generalize the proof of VII.M24 to obtain this result.)

XIII Informal

Set Theory

1. At many places in the preceding chapters we made use of concepts and techniques borrowed from mathematics. The purpose of this chapter is to explain some of the most important of these, which belong to that part of mathematics called the *theory of sets*.

A discussion of this topic is appropriate in a book such as this for many reasons; set theory is intimately connected with logic. Especially when dealing with more powerful systems of logic, such as *higher-order* systems having quantifiers corresponding to predicate parameters, it is difficult to tell where logic ends and set theory begins. And not only are set-theoretic techniques used in the study of logic, but logical techniques are frequently used in set theory. In recent years, its most important results have been obtained by metamathematical means. In work of this kind, set theory must be treated *formally*: that is, it must be presented as a first-order theory of the sort discussed in XII.7.

At present, however, our main purpose is to develop enough set theory to provide background for its applications in the metatheory of logic, and so we can be satisfied with an informal treatment of the subject. Although our discussion will provide a rough idea of what a formal version of a set theory would look like, we will rely for the most part on intuitive conceptions in developing the theory.

2. A *set* is many things, considered as a unity. For example, there are the various planets of our solar system: Mercury, Venus, and so on. In thinking of them as *planets*, we're in a way already thinking of them as one, though in itself this creates nothing new. But we can also think of these planets as together constituting a new object, the *set* of the planets. At present counting there are nine planets, taken severally. But taken together, as one, there is a single object: the set (*collection, multitude, aggregate, class*) of the planets. In other contexts of this sort, we might speak of bunches, crowds, heaps, or the like; some of these words have spatial connotations and other complicating features, but at bottom they all involve the concept of sethood.

In giving an abstract account of this concept, it will be illuminating to investigate the relation of *membership* in a set. To talk about this relation we'll use, as before, the Greek letter '∈'. Thus,

Mars ∈ the set of planets

means that Mars is to be found in the set of the planets, and

12 ∈ the set of numbers greater than 10

means that 12 is a member of the set of numbers greater than 10.

3. Sometimes, people confuse set-theoretic *membership* with set-theoretic *inclusion*; so before going any further, let's disentangle the two. The set of the planets is *included in* (or is a *subset of*) the set of satellites, because every planet is a satellite. But the set of planets is *not* a member of the set of satellites. If we made a catalog of satellites, we wouldn't put the set of planets in the list, although, of course, we *would* inscribe each of the planets. All of the planets can be found orbiting the sun, can be seen in telescopes, and so forth, whereas the *set* of the planets cannot.

You might jump to the conclusion that this difference between membership and inclusion turns on the fact that the planets are "concrete", whereas the set of the planets is "abstract". But by taking a slightly different example which involves only sets we can show that this isn't so. Let's think of animal species as sets of animals, so that the species of lions is the set of all lions, the species of whooping cranes is the set of all whooping cranes, and so forth.

The set of all animal species will then be a set of sets; each of its members will be a set, which will then in turn have members of its own. Now the set of pigs will be a member of the set of animal species: the set of pigs $\in$ the set of animal species. The set of pigs, however, is not *included* in the set of animal species. In fact, take any pig; the pig will be a particular animal, but will not itself be an animal species. Thus there is a member of the set of pigs which is not a member of the set of animal species; not every pig is an animal species.

On the other hand, take the set of animals. This set differs from the set of animal species, being made up of animals rather than sets of animals. Since every pig is an animal, the set of pigs is included in the set of animals. But the set of pigs is an animal *species*, not an animal; thus, the set of pigs is not a member of the set of animals.

Letting the sign '$\subseteq$' represent set-theoretic inclusion, we can sum all this up as follows.

> The set of pigs $\in$ the set of animal species.
> The set of pigs $\nsubseteq$ the set of animal species.
> The set of pigs $\subseteq$ the set of animals.
> The set of pigs $\notin$ the set of animals.

Here, the stroke '/' has the effect of negating, so that 'The set of pigs $\nsubseteq$ the set of animal species' means that the set of pigs is not a subset of the set of animal species.

4. This example of sets X, Y, and Z such that $X \in Y$ but $X \nsubseteq Y$, and $X \subseteq Z$ but $X \notin Z$ should make it clear that membership and inclusion are different relations. One set can be included in another without being a member of it, and can be a member of another without being included in it. However, this doesn't mean that the two notions are unrelated; indeed, we can define inclusion in terms of membership.

D1. $X \subseteq Y$ *if for all* u, *if* $u \in X$ *then* $u \in Y$.

That is, X is a subset of Y in case every member of X is a member of Y. Notice that D1 entails that for all sets X, $X \subseteq X$. We can also define a stronger kind of inclusion (called *strict* or *proper* inclusion) which does not have this reflexive property: $X \subset Y$ if $X \subseteq Y$ and $X \neq Y$. In other words, $X \subset Y$ if for all u, $u \in Y$ if $u \in X$ and for some u, $u \in X$ and $u \notin Y$.

Another important set-theoretic notion is that of the *union* of two sets, which is the set formed by joining together the members of these sets. Thus, the union of the set of mothers and the set of fathers is the set of parents. Using

'∪' to stand for the operation of forming unions, this can be written as follows.

> The set of mothers ∪ the set of fathers = the set of parents.

Given any two sets, we can also form their *intersection*, the set of things common to both of them. The intersection of the set of males with the set of parents is the set of fathers. We use '∩' to represent the operation of forming intersections, and write this as follows.

> The set of males ∩ the set of parents = the set of fathers.

Like inclusion, both of these notions can be characterized in terms of membership.

D2. u ∈ X ∪ Y *if* u ∈ X *or* u ∈ Y.

D3. u ∈ X ∩ Y *if* u ∈ X *and* u ∈ Y.

In D2, 'or' is to be taken in the inclusive sense, so that if u ∈ X *and* u ∈ Y, then u ∈ X ∪ Y. As a consequence, X ∩ Y ⊆ X ∪ Y.

5. A question we've not yet discussed is how sets are individuated. Under what conditions are sets identical, and when are they different? Our original description of sets, "many things, considered as a unity", suggests a simple answer to this question: sets are identical if and only if they have the same members. If a set is nothing more than a unity constituted by its members, it's hard to see how sets could have the same members and yet be different. This idea has a further merit: it enables us to state the criterion of identity in terms of inclusion, as follows.

(*i*)   X = Y if and only if X ⊆ Y and Y ⊆ X.

If we liked, we could view i as a *definition* of the notion of identity of sets. Many set-theoreticians, however, prefer to regard notion of identity as independent, and consider i as a postulate, called the *postulate of extensionality*. But in any case, the net result is the same: to show sets X and Y identical you try to show that X ⊆ Y and Y ⊆ X, and to show X and Y different you try to find some u such that u ∈ X and u ∉ Y, or u ∈ Y and u ∉ X.

Notice, by the way, that postulate i justifies the technique we used in D2 and D3. In D2, for instance, we didn't define X ∪ Y directly, but instead gave conditions for membership in X ∪ Y. But in view of the postulate of extensionality, to give conditions for membership in a set and to say what the set is amount to the same thing.

6. Using D1 to D3 and postulate i, we can show a number of things about sets; for instance, that for any sets X and Y, $X \cup Y = Y \cup X$. In view of i, to establish this we must show two things: first, that $X \cup Y \subseteq Y \cup X$; and second, that $Y \cup X \subseteq X \cup Y$.

First, then, take an arbitrary member u of $X \cup Y$; by D2, we know that $u \in X$ or $u \in Y$. But then clearly $u \in Y \cup X$. This shows that $X \cup Y \subseteq Y \cup X$. Reversing this argument shows likewise that if $u \in Y \cup X$, then $u \in X \cup Y$, so that $Y \cup X \subseteq X \cup Y$. By i, then, $X \cup Y = Y \cup X$.

A similar problem is to show that for all sets X and Y, $X \cap (Y \cup X) = X$. To do this, first let u be an arbitrary member of X. Then $u \in Y \cup X$ by D2, and since $u \in X$, it follows by D3 that $u \in X \cap (Y \cup X)$. Thus, $X \subseteq X \cap (Y \cup X)$. On the other hand, if $u \in X \cap (Y \cup X)$, then by D3, $u \in X$, so that $X \cap (Y \cup X) \subseteq X$. By i, then, $X \cap (Y \cup X) = X$.

In the exercises for this chapter there are a number of similar identities which can be established by means of the postulate of extensionality.

7. In applying set theory to a subject-matter, we naturally want to talk about particular sets; for instance, in logic we want to talk about sets of formulas. To do this, it's useful to have a notation for naming sets. Since we have decided that sets are determined by their members, it is natural to form names of sets out of names of their members. Thus, it's convenient to use curly brackets in discussing sets like the set of integers between 3 and 9 and the set of planets: {4, 5, 6, 7, 8} is the former set, and {Mercury, Venus, Earth, Mars, Jupiter, Saturn, Uranus, Neptune, Pluto} is the latter.

D4. $Y \in \{X_1, X_2, \ldots, X_n\}$ *if* $Y = X_1$ *or* $Y = X_2$ *or* $\cdots$ *or* $Y = X_n$.

Besides giving us a useful vocabulary for naming sets, this notation is perspicuous in yielding insights into general points. For instance, consider the sets {1, 2, 3}, {3, 1, 2}, and {2, 1, 1, 3, 2}. The principle of exensionality guarantees that these are identical, since they all have the same members. Similarly, {1, 2} = {2, 1} and {4, 6, 8, 8} = {6, 4, 4, 8}. These examples show that *order* and *repetition* of members are not taken into account in forming sets; in determining what a set is, we abstract from these factors.

When we have considered various objects—1, 2, and 3, for instance—as together constituting a set, we then have a new object at our disposal: the set {1, 2, 3}. There is no reason why we shouldn't use this new set in forming another one: say, $\{1, 2, \{1, 2, 3\}\}$. The three members of this last set are 1, 2, and the set $\{1, 2, 3\}$. We can do this again, obtaining sets such as $\{1, 2, \{1, 2, \{1, 2, 3\}\}\}$; this collecting together of new totalities may be continued *ad infinitum*.

This enables us to construct many examples of the sort we wanted in Section 4, above. For instance, take the sets $\{1, 2\}$, $\{1, 2, 3\}$, and $\{1, \{1, 2\}\}$. The following relations hold between these sets.

$$\{1, 2\} \in \{1, \{1, 2\}\}$$
$$\{1, 2\} \nsubseteq \{1, \{1, 2\}\}$$
$$\{1, 2\} \subseteq \{1, 2, 3\}$$
$$\{1, 2\} \notin \{1, 2, 3\}$$

8. There is nothing to prevent us from putting curly brackets around just one name; we obtain in this way names of sets such as $\{2\}$, which contain just one object. Sets of this sort are called *unit* sets, and though the idea of such things may seem strange, they're useful sets to have. If there were no unit sets, we'd have to say that the set of moons of the Earth didn't exist, and we wouldn't be able to call $\{1, 2\} \cap \{2, 3\}$ a set.

Notice that $\{X\}$ needn't be the same as X. In fact, rather strange consequences follow from the supposition that $\{X\} = X$, and in most versions of set theory it can be shown that for all X, $X \neq \{X\}$. The difference between X and $\{X\}$ is illustrated by $\{1, 2\}$ and $\{\{1, 2\}\}$. These sets differ because they have different members; for instance, $\{1, 2\} \in \{\{1, 2\}$ but $\{1, 2\} \notin \{1, 2\}$.

Unit sets can be useful when we want to talk about the result of adding an element to a set. Suppose, for example, that we need to consider the result of putting 2 into a set X. This will yield the set $X \cup \{2\}$; in view of D2, the members of this set are just the members of X together with the element 2. It would in general be incorrect to use '$X \cup 2$' as a name of the set made by adding 2 to X. In the first place, unless we conceive of 2 as itself a set, the expression '$X \cup 2$' doesn't make sense, since it would be mistaken to speak of 2 as having members. But even if the number 2 *were* a set (according to most set-theoretic accounts, it is), $X \cup 2$ would in general differ from $X \cup \{2\}$. (For instance, see E5(c), below.)

Having swallowed the concept of a unit set, you probably won't strain at the notion of the *empty set*. Set-theoreticians acknowledge the existence of an empty set for the same reasons that lead them to countenance unit sets. If there were no empty set, there would be no set of moons of Venus, and $\{1, 2\} \cap \{3, 4\}$ wouldn't be a set. Most set theories, then, have a postulate or theorem to the effect that there is a set having no members.

Once we've granted the existence of an empty set, it's easy to show that there is one and only one such set, because the principle of extensionality can be used to prove that any sets that have no members are identical. (If X and Y are sets having no members, then it's vacuously true that X and Y have the same members. For instance, if an arbitrary object Z is a member of X, then $Z \in Y$ because *nothing* is a member of X.) This justifies our speaking of *the* empty set, since there is a unique set of this sort. We will use '$\varnothing$' as a name of the empty set; thus, for all X, it is not the case that $X \in \varnothing$.

D5. $X \in \varnothing$ *for no* X.

9. The notation introduced in the above section has its limitations, especially where large sets are concerned. If we want to refer to such a set, it may be difficult or impossible to write down a complete list of its members. Fortunately, however, there is another natural way to name sets; for instance, to refer to the set of the planets, we can simply call it 'the set of the planets'. Here, we've used a *property* (the property of being one of the planets) to form a name of a set. Rather than using locutions such as 'the set of people over six feet tall' or 'the set of positive integers less than 10 or greater than 20', we will use a more mathematical notation:

$$\{X \ / \ X \text{ is a person and } X \text{ is over six feet tall}\}$$

and

$$\{X \ / \ X \text{ is a positive integer, and } X < 10 \text{ or } X > 20\}.$$

These can be read 'the set of X such that X is a person and X is over six feet tall' and 'the set of X such that X is a positive integer, and $X < 10$ or $X > 20$'. This is a very flexible and general notation; whenever we can form a predicate in our language, the notation permits us to make a name purporting to refer to the set of things satisfying that predicate.

It is tempting to say that corresponding to any predicate of our language there is the set of things satisfying the predicate; but this would be incorrect. In general, when we use the definite article 'the' to form names, there is no guarantee that the name will refer to anything; a stock example of this is 'the present king of France'. And in set theory, we have to be particularly cautious in this regard; if we grant that any predicate whatsoever determines a set, we are liable to be caught in contradictions. (In this connection, see P7, below.) This, of course, leaves completely unsettled the question of which predicates do actually correspond to sets. Modern set theories attempt to resolve this question by means of postulates of set existence: for instance, a postulate that the empty set exists, or that if sets X and Y exist, then $X \cup Y$

exists. A variety of such postulates can be devised, which in part accounts for the many set theories that have been proposed.

Fortunately for us these refinements are largely independent of everyday applications of set theory to areas such as logic. Rather than arising in the practical employment of set theory, questions of set existence have most often troubled only those who have concerned themselves with the foundations of set theory itself, and hence with the general question of what sets there are. Since in this book we will be considering only noncontroversial portions of set theory, we will employ our new notation for naming sets without requiring proof of existence. It will be understood that these can be furnished in any of the standard axiomatic versions of set theory.

10. In Section 7 we pointed out that in forming a set we abstract from any arrangement of the elements that constitute the set. Often, however, we wish to take arrangement into account. A written word of English, for instance, is a whole composed of letters. But we couldn't regard such a word as a set of letters, for then we wouldn't be able to distinguish 'dog' from 'good': {'d', 'o', 'g'} = {'g', 'o', 'o', 'd'}.

Considerations of this sort lead us to the notions of an *ordered pair*, *ordered triple*, and in general to the notion of an *ordered n-tuple*. An ordered *n*-tuple is a linear array of objects containing exactly *n* entries. Angle brackets are used to name *n*-tuples; thus, $\langle 1, 2 \rangle$ is the ordered pair whose first entry is 1 and whose second entry is 2. Repetitions are allowed, so that ordered triples such as $\langle 1, 1, 2 \rangle$ and $\langle 1, 1, 1 \rangle$ are perfectly correct.

A kind of principle of extensionality applies to *n*-tuples:

(ii)   If $X_1 = Y_1$, $X_2 = Y_2, \ldots,$ and $X_n = Y_n$, then $\langle X_1, \ldots, X_n \rangle = \langle Y_1, \ldots, Y_n \rangle$.

Anything that a set-theoretician would want to establish about *n*-tuples is a consequence of this principle and its converse, so that if we wish to define the notion of an *n*-tuple in terms of familiar concepts, we need only find a definition that will enable us to show that $\langle X_1, X_2, \ldots, X_n \rangle = \langle Y_2, Y_2, \ldots, Y_n \rangle$ if and only if $X_1 = Y_1$, $X_2 = Y_2, \ldots,$ and $X_n = Y_n$. A definition permitting this in most versions of set theory is the following. Let $\langle X_1, X_2 \rangle = \{X_1, \{X_1, X_2\}\}$; let $\langle X_1, X_2, X_3 \rangle = \langle\langle X_1, X_2 \rangle, X_3 \rangle$; let $\langle X_1, X_2, X_3, X_4 \rangle = \langle\langle X_1, X_2, X_3 \rangle, X_4 \rangle$; and so on. Although this definition works, we won't bother with it here; we'll simply postulate the principle of extensionality for *n*-tuples, as well as its converse.

Using these principles, we can show, for instance, that $\langle 1, 2 \rangle \neq \langle 2, 1 \rangle$ and that $\langle \{1, 2\}, 1 \rangle = \langle \{2, 1\}, 1 \rangle$. The first follows by the converse of ii from the fact that $1 \neq 2$, and the second by ii from the fact that $\{1, 2\} = \{2, 1\}$.

11. One of the most important applications of n-tuples is their use as *coordinated locations*. To take a simple case, suppose that we have a rectangle divided into five units one way and three units the other way, as follows.

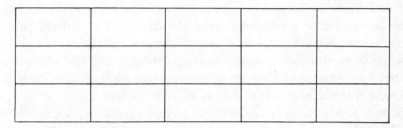

Think of the various small rectangles into which the large rectangle is divided as *locations*; the natural way to refer to these locations is in terms of their position horizontally and vertically. For instance, we can speak of the location 4 spaces to the right and 2 up. Now, as long as we adhere to the convention of giving horizontal position first, we can identify locations with ordered pairs; we can say, e.g., that $\langle 2, 2 \rangle$ *is* the location 2 spaces to the right and 2 up. The fact that we're dealing with *ordered* pairs here is essential; the location $\langle 3, 2 \rangle$ isn't the same as the location $\langle 2, 3 \rangle$.

Thus, the set of all locations in this grid is the set of ordered pairs $\{\langle i, j \rangle \mid i \in \{1, 2, 3\}$ and $j \in \{1, 2, 3, 4, 5\}\}$, i.e., the set of ordered pairs whose left members are drawn from $\{1, 2, 3\}$ and right members from $\{1, 2, 3, 4, 5\}$. This set is called the *Cartesian product* $\{1, 2, 3\} \times \{1, 2, 3, 4, 5\}$ of the sets $\{1, 2, 3\}$ and $\{1, 2, 3, 4, 5\}$: "Cartesian" in honor of DesCartes, who thought of this numerical way of representing geometrical notions, and "product" because the operation $\times$ of "Cartesian multiplication" bears some resemblance to ordinary multiplication. (Notice, for instance, that if X has n members and Y has m members, then $X \times Y$ will have $n \cdot m$ members.)

If we generalize this idea, we arrive at the notion of a *state space*. Suppose, for instance, that we're interested not only in the location of things in the above grid, but in certain other features; e.g., their absolute temperature (to the nearest whole number), and whether or not they are metallic. First, let's use the numbers 1 and 2 to represent whether or not a thing is metallic; 1 represents, say, a "yes" answer to this question and 2 a "no". Then possible temperatures will correspond to the set $\omega = \{0, 1, 2, \ldots\}$, and possible outcomes of observations of "metallicness" to the set $\{1, 2\}$. We think of a *state* of a thing, then, as a possible outcome with regard to all four factors: horizontal location, vertical location, temperature, and "metallicness". And this in turn can be viewed as an ordered *quadruple* $\langle i, j, m, n \rangle$, where $i \in \{1, 2, 3\}$, $j \in \{1, 2, 3, 4, 5\}$, $m \in \omega$, and $n \in \{1, 2\}$. Thus, the set of possible states (or *state space*) under consideration here is the Cartesian product $\{1, 2, 3\} \times \{1, 2, 3, 4, 5\} \times \omega \times \{1, 2\}$.

It frequently happens with such spaces that the factors of this product are identical; Euclidean spaces are cases of this sort. For instance, the Euclidean plane is regarded by mathematicians as the set $X \times X$ of ordered pairs of real numbers. (Here, X is the set of real numbers. A real number is a positive or negative number corresponding to the points of a line; real numbers can be thought of as given by decimal expressions which may continue infinitely to the right of the decimal point.) Just as we regard $n \cdot n$ as a *power* n^2 of n, we look at $X \times X$ as a *Cartesian power* of X, and say that $X \times X = X^2$. The set X^3, then, consists of all ordered triples of real numbers; X^3 is three-dimensional Euclidean space. And, in general, X^n is the n-dimensional Euclidean space of all n-tuples of real numbers.

12. We can use the notion of a set of ordered pairs to develop an account of *functions*. The function concept is one of the most important and fundamental ideas of mathematics. Intuitively, we can characterize a function as a rule which, given certain objects, will determine an object corresponding to them. For example, *squaring* and *doubling* are functions taking positive integers into positive integers; the result of squaring a positive integer n is n^2, and the result of doubling it is $2n$. Both of these functions are operations of a computational sort that can be performed on numbers, but not every function need be thought of as operational. For instance, the relationship between a person and his or her (biological) mother is functional, since every person has a unique mother, and likewise the relationship between a person and the number that is his or her age is functional. But we aren't likely to think of either of these items as recovered from the person by a kind of operation. Thus, all that is essential to a function is that the relationship it expresses between *argument* and *value* be unique; every argument of a function must be given one and only one value by the function.

Squaring and doubling are functions of one argument; only a single number is needed as argument to determine the value of the function. Multiplication, however, requires two numbers. To compute $n \cdot m$, we must be given both n and m. Such functions are called functions of two arguments, and generalizing this we can speak of functions having any number of arguments.

Fortunately, by using the notion of an n-tuple, we can regard any function having many arguments as a function of just one argument. For instance, we can think of multiplication as a function taking *ordered pairs* of numbers as arguments, rather than two separate numbers. And in general, given any function of *n* arguments, we can regard it as a function operating on *n*-tuples.

13. Until quite recently in the history of mathematics, people were content to leave the general concept of a function undefined, and to think of arithmetical functions pictorially. For example, functions that take real numbers into real numbers can be graphed using Cartesian coordinates. Thus, the function f such that $f(x) = x^2 - 2$ is represented graphically as follows.

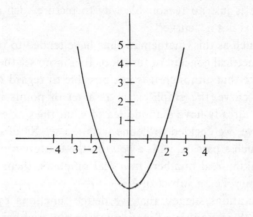

Examples of this sort make it tempting to identify functions of real numbers with curves in the Euclidean plane (in a general sense of "curve" in which straight lines, as well as parabolas, are curves). But gradually, it was realized that this concept of functionality was too narrow; for instance, it does not include discontinuous functions.

A function f with just one discontinuity is the function f defined as follows: $f(x) = -1$ if $x \leq 0$, and $f(x) = 1$ if $x > 0$. This function is *constant* for the nonpositive numbers, assigning them all the value -1, and also constant for the positive numbers. The discontinuity, or "jump", occurs at the value 0. By introducing special conventions, it is possible to picture this function.

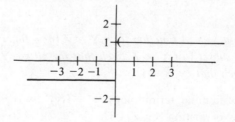

Here, the left parenthesis indicates that f does not assume the value 1 at the argument 0.

Already, this method of picturing functions is beginning to break down, and it fails completely in cases where there are discontinuities at *every* point. A case of this kind is the function g such that $g(x) = 1$ for rational x, and $g(x) = -1$ for irrational x. (A real number x is *rational* if there exist integers *m* and *n* such that $x = m/n$; otherwise, x is *irrational*. Rational numbers, then, are fractions or *ratios*.) Now, between every two rational numbers there is an irrational number, and between any two irrational numbers there is a rational number (see P2, below). This means that g "jumps" from -1 to 1 at *every* point, and there is just no reasonable way to picture such a function; certainly, its graph is not a "curve".

For reasons such as this, mathematicians have tended to move away from a pictorial, geometrical concept of functions to a more set-theoretical characterization. Notice that although it is not possible to regard the graph of the function g as a curve, the graph exists as a set of points in the Cartesian plane. Now, we already have a good idea of what the Cartesian plane is. In Section 12, above, we decided to define it as the set X^2 of ordered pairs of real numbers; such a pair $\langle x, y \rangle$ is a *point* in the Cartesian plane. The graph of a function taking real numbers into real numbers, then, will be a set of points in the plane: i.e., a subset of X^2.

These considerations suggest that we define functions by simply identifying them with their graphs; a function taking real numbers into real numbers, then, will in fact *be* a subset of X^2. But not every subset of X^2 is such a function. For instance, the set $\{\langle 1, 2 \rangle, \langle 2, 4 \rangle\}$ isn't a function taking real numbers into real numbers, because it isn't defined for every real number; its *domain* is not the set of all real numbers. Also, the set $\{\langle x, y \rangle \mid y^2 = x\}$ is not a function taking real numbers into real numbers, since all of its values are not real numbers; $\sqrt{-1}$, for instance, is not a real number. Finally, $\{\langle x, y \rangle \mid x < y\}$ isn't a function taking real numbers into real numbers, since the uniqueness condition fails; for instance both $\langle 1, 2 \rangle$ and $\langle 1, 3 \rangle$ are in this set so there is no unique number associated with 1.

Generalizing these ideas and making them explicit, we arrive at the following definition.

D6. Let Y and Z be sets. A function from Y to Z (or a function with domain Y and range Z) is a subset f of Y $\times$ Z, such that for all y $\in$ Y, there is a unique member z of Z such that $\langle y, z \rangle \in$ f.

We can retain the familiar terminology '$z = f(y)$' by regarding this as just an alternative way of writing '$\langle y, z \rangle \in$ f'.

14. You may have noticed it is inessential that the range Z of a function f from Y to Z be exhausted by f; there may be members z of Z such that for all $y \in Y$, $f(y) = z$. In case the range *is* exhausted, mathematicians often speak of f as being a function from Y *onto* Z, and in case it isn't, as being a function from Y *into* Z; the preposition 'to' is noncommittal in this respect. A more systematic terminology, popular in Europe, refers to functions to their range as *injections* and onto their range as *surjections*.

Also, it need not be true that every value of a function is the image of only one argument. For instance, take the function of squaring on the (positive and nonpositive) integers. Every integer has a unique square, but no square is the result of squaring only one integer. The number 4, for instance, is the result of squaring both 2 and -2. Many interesting functions, however, do have this property of "reversibility"; such functions are said to be *one-one* (or to be *bijections*.)

D7. Let f *be a function from a set* Y *to a set* Z; f *is said to be one-one if for every* u, v $\in$ Y, *if* f(u) = f(v) *then* u = v.

The doubling function on the domain ω of nonnegative integers is one-one, since if $2n = 2m$, then $n = m$. Notice that this function is not *onto* the set ω; 3, for instance, is not the result of doubling any integer. On the other hand, the halving function on the domain ω is a one-one function onto ω; $\frac{1}{2}n = \frac{1}{2}m$ if $n = m$, and for any nonnegative integer n there is a nonnegative integer m (namely, $2n$) such that $\frac{1}{2}m = n$.

One-one functions have an interesting property; if their graphs are rotated diagonally, the resulting graph is also the graph of a function. For instance, the doubling function on domain ω, when graphed, appears as the following array of dots.

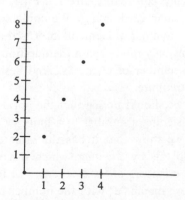

Rotating this graph so that the horizontal and vertical axes are interchanged, we obtain a graph of the halving function on the domain $\{2n \mid n \in \omega\}$.

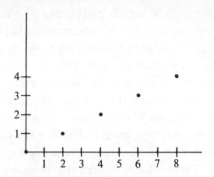

Another way of describing this feature of one-one functions is to say that any result of reversing one of them is also a function. If f is a one-one function from X onto Y and $g = \{\langle U, V \rangle \mid \langle V, U \rangle \in f\}$, then g is a function from Y onto X. Moreover, g is one-one.

15. One-one functions can be used to develop a general theory of the magnitude or *cardinality* of sets. It's clear that sets such as $\{1, 2, 4\}$, $\{\{2, 3, 4\}, \varnothing, \{3\}\}$, and $\varnothing$ each have a definite number of elements: three, three, and zero. Thus, we can say that the first two sets have the same number of elements, or are *alike in cardinality*, and both have *greater cardinality* than the third. In the case of sets such as these, we have a way of settling these questions, because we can *count* them. However, we have to reckon with infinite sets too, if our account of cardinality is to be properly general.

In carrying out this generalization, it's useful to concentrate on the relational notions of *having the same cardinality* and *having less cardinality*, rather than trying to define cardinality directly. First, when can we say that sets Y and Z have the same cardinality? We could say that X and Y are alike in cardinality if the number of elements of Y is the same as the number of elements of Z, but this only raises again the question of what it means for a set to have a certain number of elements. And besides, it seems to presuppose that Y and Z are finite.

To break this circle, we should notice that the notion of having the same cardinality is used in assigning a number to a finite set. To determine that a set Y has n members, we show that it has the same cardinality as the set $\{1, 2, \ldots, n\}$; and we do this by *counting*, which is a way of matching the members of Y with the members of $\{1, 2, \ldots, n\}$. For instance, to count the letters of the alphabet, we match 'a' with the number 1, 'b' with 2, 'c' with

3, and so forth. When we come to the last letter, 'z', we find that it is matched with the number 26; we then say that there are 26 letters. Thus, we take this procedure of *matching* to show that $\{1, 2, \ldots, 26\}$ has the same cardinality as $\{\text{'a'}, \text{'b'}, \ldots, \text{'z'}\}$.

If we think about this notion of "matching", it's clear that the order in which we run through a set is irrelevant in counting; if we count properly, we'll obtain the same answer no matter in what order we take the letters of the alphabet. There are, however, two sorts of mistakes we can make in counting a set; we can count the same element twice, or we can fail to count every member of the set. In other words, we can match the same member of the given set with two different numbers, or some member of the set can fail to be matched with any number.

If we think of this process of "matching" as a function whose domain is a set of numbers $\{1, 2, \ldots, n\}$ and whose range is the set Y to be counted, then a correct matching—one which does not fail in either of these two ways—is a function which is *one-one* and *onto* Y. This is precisely what is meant by saying that nothing in Y is counted twice, and everything in Y is counted. The process of counting a finite nonempty set Y, then, can be characterized as the determination of a one-one function onto Y, whose domain is $\{1, 2, \ldots, n\}$ for some n. The existence of such a function shows that Y has the same cardinality as $\{1, 2, \ldots, n\}$, and hence that Y has n members.

Now, let's generalize this to obtain a criterion for having the same cardinality. A one-one function from Y onto Z will match the members of Y in one-one fashion with the members of Z, so that if there is such a function, Y and Z must have the same cardinality. The existence of a one-one function from Y onto Z, then, is the condition we want.

D8. A set Y is said to have the same cardinality as a set Z, Y $\simeq$ Z, if there exists a one-one function from Y onto Z.

According to this definition, for instance, $\{1, 2, 3\}$ has the same cardinality as $\{2, 4, 6\}$, since $\{\langle 1, 2 \rangle, \langle 2, 4 \rangle, \langle 3, 6 \rangle\}$ is a one-one function from $\{1, 2, 3\}$ onto $\{2, 4, 6\}$. On the other hand, $\{1, 2, 3\}$ does not have the same cardinality as $\{1, 2\}$, because every function from $\{1, 2, 3\}$ onto $\{1, 2\}$ must assign at least two members of $\{1, 2, 3\}$ the same value.

To obtain a better understanding of the ins and outs of D8, we'll develop a few consequences of this definition. In order to present these consequences systematically, we will number them as theorems.

T1. For any set Y, Y $\simeq$ Y.

    PROOF. $f = \{\langle U, U \rangle / U \in Y\}$ is a subset of Y^2 such that for any member U of Y, there is a unique Z (namely, U) such that $\langle U, Z \rangle \in f$. Thus, f is a function; and clearly, f is onto Y. (f is called the *identity function* on the domain Y.) Therefore, $Y \simeq Y$.

T2. For any sets Y and Z, if $Y \simeq Z$ then $Z \simeq Y$.

PROOF. Suppose that $Y \simeq Z$; then there exists a one-one function f from Y onto Z. Let $g = \{\langle z, y \rangle \mid y \in Y$ and $f(y) = z\}$. Now, if z is any member of Z, there is a member y of Y such that $f(y) = z$, since f is onto Z. And since f is one-one, there is at most one $y \in Y$ such that $f(y) = z$. Also, since f is a function, for every $y \in Y$ there is a $z \in Z$ such that $g(z) = y$; i.e., g is onto Y.

We have now shown that if $Y \simeq Z$, then there is a one-one function from Z onto Y; in other words, if $Y \simeq Z$, then $Z \simeq Y$.

T3. For all sets U, V, and W, if $U \simeq V$ and $V \simeq W$, then $U \simeq W$.

Proving T3 is assigned below as an exercise; the method of proof resembles that of T2. This theorem is often used implicitly in counting; for instance, instead of directly counting the number of people in an audience, the theatre manager might count the number of tickets sold, on the assumption that everyone in the audience bought a ticket, and everyone who bought a ticket is in the audience. If these assumptions are correct, T3 guarantees that if the set of tickets sold has the same cardinality as $\{1, 2, \ldots, n\}$, then the audience has the same cardinality as $\{1, 2, \ldots, n\}$.

16. Our treatment of sameness of cardinality suggests how to account for *order relations* of magnitude between sets. If we can map a set X one-one *to* a set Y, X will then be in one-one correspondence with a subset of Y. It seems reasonable to say under these circumstances that X is less-than-or-equal to Y in cardinality. This idea enables us to define a relation $\preceq$ among sets which is analogous to the relation $\leq$ among numbers.

D9. Let Y and Z be sets; $Y \preceq Z$ if there is a one-one function from Y to Z.

For example, $\{1, 2\} \preceq \{2, 4, 6\}$, since $\{\langle 1, 2 \rangle, \langle 2, 4 \rangle\}$ is a one-one function from $\{1, 2\}$ to $\{2, 4, 6\}$. And by the same token, $\{1, 2\} \preceq \{1, 2\}$. To take an example involving infinite sets, $\{0, 2, 4, \ldots\} \preceq \{0, 1, 2, \ldots\}$, since the identity function on $\{0, 2, 4, \ldots\}$ (i.e., the function $\{\langle n, n \rangle \mid n \in \{0, 2, 4, \ldots\}\}$) is a one-one function from $\{0, 2, 4, \ldots\}$ to $\{0, 1, 2, \ldots\}$.

Our first theorem about this relation establishes that it is *transitive*.

T4. For all sets U, V, *and* W, *if* $U \preceq V$ *and* $V \preceq W$, *then* $U \preceq W$.

PROOF. Suppose that $U \preceq V$ and $V \preceq W$; then there exists a one-one function f from U to V and a one-one function g from V to W. Let h = $\{\langle u, w \rangle \mid u \in U$ and $w = f(g(u))\}$. (The function h is said to be the *composition* of g with f.) Since f is one-one and g is one-one, h is one-one (this is assigned as an exercise below). And the existence of h shows that $U \preceq W$.

Although the relation $\preceq$ is transitive, it is *not* symmetric; it is not always the case that if $Y \preceq Z$, then $Z \preceq Y$. For instance, we've shown that $\{1, 2\} \preceq \{2, 4, 6\}$. But there can be no one-one function from $\{2, 4, 6\}$ to $\{1, 2\}$, since every function from $\{2, 4, 6\}$ to $\{1, 2\}$ must give the same value to at least two members of $\{2, 4, 6\}$. Thus, $\{2, 4, 6\} \npreceq \{1, 2\}$; it is not the case that $\{2, 4, 6\} \preceq \{1, 2\}$.

In number theory it is most natural to define weak ordering, $\leq$, in terms of strict ordering, $<$, by saying that $n \leq m$ if $n < m$ or $n = m$. But in the theory of cardinality, it is easiest to do the opposite and define strict ordering in terms of weak ordering and sameness of cardinality.

D10. Let Y *and* Z *be sets;* $Y \prec Z$ *if* $Y \preceq Z$ *and* $Y \not\simeq Z$.

In other words, $Y \prec Z$ if there is a one-one function from Y to Z, but there is no one-one function from Y *onto* Z. In the counterexample we just gave to the symmetry of $\preceq$, we also showed that $\{1, 2\} \prec \{1, 2, 3\}$, since what we established was that there is no one-one function from $\{1, 2\}$ onto $\{2, 4, 6\}$. More generally, whenever $Y \npreceq Z$, then $Y \nprec Z$.

T5. For any sets Y *and* Z, *if* $Y \prec Z$ *then* $Y \preceq Z$.

This follows directly from D8.

Questions that arise naturally about these ordering relations lead at once to some rather difficult problems. For instance, we may ask whether if $Y \preceq Z$ and $Z \preceq Y$, then $Y \simeq Z$; this is certainly something that *should* be true. To settle this question positively, we would have to show, given a one-one function f from Y to Z and a one-one function g from Z to Y, that there always is a one-one function from Y onto Z. In fact, this can be done, and once it has been accomplished the proof is not awfully long, although it is rather complicated and difficult to find. We won't present the proof here, but if you are interested, see XIV.P3, below.

Another question that comes to mind is whether any two sets are *comparable*; i.e., is it the case for any sets Y and Z that $Y \prec Z$ or $Z \prec Y$ or $Y \simeq Z$?

A proof of this is not only difficult to find, but is extremely long and complicated even after it has been worked out. Not only that, but even after a "proof" of comparability has been given, the status of this proof is somewhat problematic, since it rests on one of the more questionable principles of set theory. (Comparability can be shown to be equivalent to the *axiom of choice*.) For more information on these matters, consult any of the general works on set theory listed in the bibliography.

17. So far, we've said little about how the above definitions can be applied to infinite sets, although in discussing D9 we did point out that $\{0, 2, 4, \ldots\} \preceq \{0, 1, 2, \ldots\}$. Let's look at this example more closely.

Since $\{0, 2, 4, \ldots\} \preceq \{0, 1, 2, \ldots\}$, it can't be the case that $\{0, 1, 2, \ldots\} \prec \{0, 2, 4, \ldots\}$; this, however, does not decide whether $\{0, 2, 4, \ldots\} \prec \{0, 1, 2, \ldots\}$ or $\{0, 2, 4, \ldots\} \simeq \{0, 1, 2, \ldots\}$. Now, you might try to settle this question by arguing that the identity function f on $\{0, 2, 4, \ldots\}$ is a one-one function from $\{0, 2, 4, \ldots\}$ to $\{0, 1, 2, \ldots\}$; but, since f is not *onto* $\{0, 1, 2, \ldots\}$, the two sets must not have the same cardinality. This argument, however, is fallacious. In order to prove that $\{0, 2, 4, \ldots\} \not\simeq \{0, 1, 2, \ldots\}$, it is insufficient to show that a single function f is not onto $\{0, 1, 2, \ldots\}$. We must show that *any* one-one function from $\{0, 2, 4, \ldots\}$ to $\{0, 1, 2, \ldots\}$ can't be onto $\{0, 1, 2, \ldots\}$. And of course, no proof of this is possible, because in fact there *are* one-one functions from $\{0, 2, 4, \ldots\}$ onto $\{0, 1, 2, \ldots\}$. We can define such a function by simply lining the two sets alongside one another in numerical order; let $g = \{\langle 2n, n \rangle \mid n \in \{0, 1, 2, \ldots\}\}$. This is one-one, since if $n = m$ then $2n = 2m$; it is a function, since if $2n = 2m$, then $n = m$. And it is from $\{0, 2, 4, \ldots\}$ onto $\{1, 2, 3, \ldots\}$. Thus, by D6, $\{0, 2, 4, \ldots\} \simeq \{1, 2, 3, \ldots\}$; there are as many even numbers as there are numbers.

When put in this way, this consequence of D7 may seem paradoxical; you may feel that there are "more" numbers than even numbers, since $\{0, 2, 4, \ldots\} \subset \{0, 1, 2, \ldots\}$. But if we are to achieve a treatment of the magnitude of infinite sets which is at all successful, we must learn to accept this "paradox" as a truth about infinite sets. Our definition of sameness of cardinality is not at fault; the concept of one-to-one correspondence is so deeply involved in our notion of counting, that we *must* admit that if two sets can be put into one-to-one correspondence, then they have the same cardinality. If we stick to this criterion, things aren't as bad as they seem at first. We can show (see XIV.2, below) that D8 does entail that if $Y \subset Z$ then $Y \prec Z$, *provided* Y *is finite*. For finite parts, then, it does hold true that a part is smaller than the whole. (Here, of course, "part" means "proper subset".) To get our bearings in thinking about the cardinality of infinite sets, we must realize that this principle applies only to finite sets, and doesn't hold in general. Failure to achieve this insight was one of the major obstacles to the development of a successful theory of the infinite. But once this difficulty is overcome, it becomes possible to build up a large body of positive results concerning the magnitude (or "cardinality") of infinite sets.

18. In discussing these results, the set ω is a good place to begin. This set represents a minimal infinite cardinality, in the following sense: there are no infinite sets which ω exceeds in cardinality. That is, if $U \prec \omega$ then U is finite. (For hints concerning the proof of this result, see E17. It is more difficult to show that ω has a *smallest* infinite cardinality; i.e., that for all infinite sets X, $\omega \leq X$. See P1 in this connection.) The sets that have the same cardinality as ω will share this "minimal grade of infinity"; we will say that any such set is *denumerable*, or *denumerably infinite*.

D11. A set U is denumerable if $U \simeq \omega$.

A one-one function from U onto ω will arrange U in an order just like that of the natural numbers. Thus, U is denumerable if and only if U can be arranged in the form $\{u_0, u_1, u_2, \ldots\}$, where $u_i \neq u_j$ if $i \neq j$.

At this point it's natural to ask whether *every* infinite set is denumerable. If this were so, all infinite sets would be alike in cardinality and there would only be one infinite magnitude. Since, as we said above, there are no infinite sets U such that $U \prec \omega$, it's reasonable to look for sets exceeding ω in cardinality among the supersets of ω.

If we add only a few elements to ω, say -1, -2, and -3, there is no difficulty in showing the resulting set denumerable; simply arrange it in the following order.

$$-3, -2, -1, 0, 1, 2, 3, \ldots.$$

What if we add infinitely many elements to ω? Consider, say, the set $\{\ldots, -2, -1, 0, 1, 2, \ldots\}$ of all integers, positive and negative. Here we must do some rearranging to get a one-one correspondence with ω: where $i \in \omega$ let $f(i) = i/2$ if i is even and $f(i) = -(i + 1)/2$ if i is odd. The function f defined in this way is one-one, from ω onto the set of all integers, and thus shows the latter set to be denumerable. In effect, what we have done here is to interlace the integers as follows.

$$0, -1, 1, -2, 2, -3, 3, \ldots.$$

Still another way to add elements to ω is to fill in the spaces between the members of ω with *fractions*. We may represent nonnegative fractions by ordered pairs $\langle i, j \rangle$, where i and j are members of ω such that $j > 0$ and $\langle i, j \rangle$ is in lowest terms; in other words, where i and j share no integral divisors other than 1. The set Y of nonnegative fractions is *dense*, in that between any two members of Y there is another member; nevertheless, Y turns out to be denumerable. The easiest way of showing this is first to show that the set ω^2 of ordered pairs of members of ω is denumerable. To put ω^2 into one-one correspondence with ω, we first arrange ω^2 in a grid, as follows.

$$
\begin{array}{cccc}
(0,0) & (0,1) & (0,2) & \ldots \\
(1,0) & (1,1) & (1,2) & \ldots \\
(2,0) & (2,1) & (2,2) & \ldots \\
(3,0) & (3,1) & (3,2) & \ldots \\
\vdots & \vdots & \vdots &
\end{array}
$$

Now, start a path through this grid at the upper left with the pair $(0, 0)$ and continue it by zigzagging downwards and to the right, as follows.

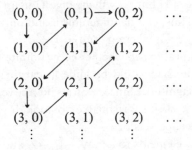

This clearly provides a one-one function f from ω onto ω^2; $f(0) = (0, 0)$, $f(1) = (1, 0)$, and in general $f(n)$ is the $(n - 1)$th pair to appear along the path. So the set of ω^2 of ordered pairs of nonnegative integers is denumerable.

Thus, since we defined the set Y of nonnegative fractions so that Y is a subset of ω^2, Y also is denumerable, in view of E16. Since the set of all fractions, negative and nonnegative, has the same cardinality as Y (see P4), this set also is denumerable.

19. At this point, it may seem as if *all* infinite sets will turn out to be denumerable. But this isn't so. One of the most astonishing discoveries of set theory is Cantor's ingenious argument showing that there exist certain sets that are nondenumerably infinite. An example of such a set is the set X of real numbers.

Intuitively, the real numbers are numbers that represent positions on a geometrical line, but in order to reproduce Cantor's argument we must characterize the reals more precisely than this. To do so, we'll use the notion of a *nonending decimal*, which consists of a nonnegative integer i and a sequence $n_1, n_2, n_3, \ldots$ of nonnegative integers less than 10. We may write decimals using the usual notation; e.g., $17.54333\ldots$ is a decimal. Also, we can speak of negative decimals, so that, for instance,

$$4.000\ldots - 5.444\ldots = -1.444\ldots.$$

Any fraction may be represented as a nonending decimal. For instance, $9/5 = 1.8000\ldots$, $2/3 = 0.666\ldots$, and $8/7 = 1.14285714285714\ldots$. However, not every nonending decimal represents a fraction; $\sqrt{2}$ and π, for instance, are not fractions but can both be represented as nonending decimals.

Two decimals $i.m_1m_2m_3\ldots$ and $j.n_1n_2n_2\ldots$ are said to *represent the same real number* if $i.m_1 \cdots m_k$ and $j.m_1 \cdots m_k$ become arbitrarily close as k increases. More precisely, $i.m_1m_2m_3\ldots$ and $j.n_1n_2n_3\ldots$ represent the same real if for all integers p such that $p > 0$, there is an integer q such that $|i.m_1 \cdots m_q - j.n_1 \cdots n_q| < 1/p$. (Here the bars represent *absolute value*: $|r| = r$ if $r > 0$, and $|r| = -r$ if $r < 0$.) Now, it's almost true that if $i.m_1m_2m_3\ldots$ and $j.n_1n_2n_3\ldots$ represent the same real, then $i = j$ and for all k, $n_k = m_k$. That is, it's almost true that only identical decimals can represent the same real. The only exceptions to this rule are cases such as $0.999\ldots$ and $1.000\ldots$, or $4.53999\ldots$ and $4.54000\ldots$, in which one decimal terminates in a nonending block of 9's and another terminates in a nonending block of 0's. The decimals $4.53999\ldots$ and $4.54000\ldots$ represent the same real, because the difference between closer approximations of these decimals becomes arbitrarily small.

To avoid situations of this sort, let's call a nonending decimal *standard* if it does not end in an infinite block of 9's. It can be shown that if standard nonending decimals $i.n_1n_2n_3\ldots$ and $j.m_1m_2m_3\ldots$ represent the same real, then $i = j$ and $n_k = m_k$ for all k. If we like, then, we may actually identify real numbers with standard nonending decimals; the problem of whether the set of reals is denumerable then reduces to the problem of whether the set of standard nonending decimals is nondenumerable.

Now we can go ahead with Cantor's argument. For simplicity, consider the reals between 0 and 1; this amounts to considering standard decimals of the sort $0.n_1n_2n_3\ldots$, where $n_k > 0$ for at least one k. Let the set of such decimals be U. Suppose that U is denumerable; this means that there exists a one-one function, say f, from ω onto U. Thus, we can list all the members of U in the order determined by f, as follows.

$$
\begin{array}{ll}
f(0): & 0.n_{00} \quad n_{01} \quad n_{02} \quad n_{03} \quad \cdots \\
f(1): & 0.n_{10} \quad n_{11} \quad n_{12} \quad n_{13} \quad \cdots \\
f(2): & 0.n_{20} \quad n_{21} \quad n_{22} \quad n_{23} \quad \cdots \\
f(3): & 0.n_{30} \quad n_{31} \quad n_{32} \quad n_{33} \quad \cdots \\
\ \ \vdots & \qquad \vdots
\end{array}
$$

In this diagram, n_{ij} is the jth digit of the ith decimal in the enumeration determined by f.

The trick to which we will now resort is to use properties of this array itself to construct a member of U which cannot occur in the purported enumeration. We do this by taking the diagonal and changing it systematically. The sequence n_{00}, n_{11}, n_{22}, ... represents the diagonal path through the above array; the kth member, n_{kk}, of this sequence, is the kth digit of the kth decimal in the enumeration. Here, n_{kk} is a nonnegative integer less than 10; let b_k be 1 if $n_{kk} \neq 1$ and 2 if $n_{kk} = 1$. (It doesn't matter how b_k is defined, as long as b_k always differs from n_{kk} and $0.b_0 b_1 b_2 \ldots$ is a standard decimal.)

Now, consider the decimal $0.b_0 b_1 b_2 \ldots$; no digits occurring in it at all are 9's, so this is a standard decimal between 0 and 1 and so is in U. But this decimal is defined so that for all k, $b_k \neq n_{kk}$. Thus, the kth digit of $0.b_0 b_1 b_2 \ldots$ differs from the kth digit of the kth decimal of the enumeration, and hence for all $k \in \omega$, $0.b_0 b_1 b_2 \ldots$ differs from $f(k)$. Since $0.b_0 b_1 b_2 \ldots$ is a member of U, f is not a function onto the set U. But this contradicts our hypothesis about f.

Since we've made no assumptions at all about f, except that it was to be a one-one function from ω onto U, our argument shows that *any* such function is impossible. Thus, *there is no* one-one function from ω onto U; and this means that $\omega \not\approx U$. To show that $\omega \prec U$, we must also establish that there is a one-one function g from ω *into* U. But there is no difficulty in defining such a function; for instance, let g(n) be the standard decimal expansion of

$$
\frac{1}{n+1}.
$$

We may conclude, then, that $\omega \prec U$; U is greater in cardinality than the set of nonnegative integers.

The set U is a subset of the set of all standard decimals, which we have identified with the set X of real numbers; therefore, $\omega \prec X$. (See E14, below.)

20. The argument of the above section shows that not all infinite sets are alike in cardinality; but it doesn't decide whether there are just two infinite magnitudes or whether there is a largest infinite magnitude. Both of these questions are settled negatively by a generalization of the proof that the reals are nondenumerable, which shows, given any set V, how to make a set exceeding V in cardinality. The definition of such a set is not complicated; the power-set of V, i.e., the set of all subsets of V, has this property.

T6. Let V *be any set, and* $\mathscr{P}(V)$ *be the power-set of* V. (*Remember that* $\mathscr{P}(V) = \{W \mid W \subseteq V\}$.) *Then* $V \prec \mathscr{P}(V)$.

PROOF. As in the proof of Section 16, we assume that $V \simeq \mathscr{P}(V)$; then there is a one-one function, say f, from V onto $\mathscr{P}(V)$. Where $w \in V$, $f(w)$ will be a subset of V; and either $w \in f(w)$ or $w \notin f(w)$. Let $Z = \{w \mid w \in V$ and $w \notin f(w)\}$. Now, for all $w \in Z$, $w \in V$, so that $Z \subseteq V$; i.e., $Z \in \mathscr{P}(V)$. Since f is a function onto $\mathscr{P}(V)$, there is a member z of V such that $f(z) = Z$; either $z \in f(z)$ or $z \notin f(z)$. If $z \in f(z)$, then by definition of Z, $z \notin Z$; but since $Z = f(z)$ it follows that $z \notin f(z)$. But then, again by definition of Z, $z \in Z$, which is impossible since $f(z) = Z$.

This contradiction follows from the assumption that $V \simeq \mathscr{P}(V)$; therefore, $V \not\simeq \mathscr{P}(V)$. Now, where $g(u) = \{u\}$ for $u \in V$, g will be a one-one function from V into $\mathscr{P}(V)$. Therefore, $V \prec \mathscr{P}(V)$.

It may not be obvious that this argument is a generalization of our proof in Section 16 that the reals are nondenumerable. To make this clear, let's reprove T6 by another method. In this second proof, we will suppose that $V = \{v_0, v_1, v_2, \ldots, v_\xi, \ldots\}$. Although this may seem tantamount to assuming that $V \simeq \omega$, it is not meant to be so restrictive a supposition, since the index 'ξ' may range over a larger set of "numbers" than ω. The subscripts are used only to indicate that V has been ordered in a definite way and do not impose any restriction on the cardinality of V. (For more information on this technique, consult any of the set-theoretical texts given in the bibliography. Look under the topics "ordinal numbers", "well-ordering", and "transfinite induction".)

Once the set V is ordered in this fashion, we can picture its subsets using rows of 0's and 1's; 0 in the ξth place indicates that v_ξ is not a member of the subset, 1 that v_ξ is a member of the subset. For instance, the subset $\{v_1, v_3\}$ of V would be represented as follows.

$$\begin{array}{ccccccccccc} 0 & 1 & 2 & 3 & 4 & 5 & 6 & \ldots & \xi & \ldots \\ 0 & 1 & 0 & 1 & 0 & 0 & 0 & \ldots & 0 & \ldots \end{array}$$

This representation will enable us to construct a grid resembling the array we used in proving that the reals are nondenumerable.

Assume, now that $V \simeq \mathscr{P}(V)$; then there is a one-one function, say f, from V onto $\mathscr{P}(V)$. Representing $f(v_0)$, $f(v_1)$, and so on by sequences of 0's and 1's, we obtain the following pattern.

	0	1	2	3	...	ξ	...
$f(v_0)$:	n_{00}	n_{01}	n_{02}	n_{03}	...	$n_{0\xi}$	...
$f(v_1)$:	n_{10}	n_{11}	n_{12}	n_{13}	...	$n_{1\xi}$	...
$f(v_2)$:	n_{20}	n_{21}	n_{22}	n_{23}	...	$n_{2\xi}$	...
$f(v_3)$:	n_{30}	n_{31}	n_{32}	n_{33}	...	$n_{3\xi}$	...
$\vdots$	$\vdots$	$\vdots$	$\vdots$	$\vdots$		$\vdots$	
$f(v_\xi)$:	$n_{\xi 0}$	$n_{\xi 1}$	$n_{\xi 2}$	$n_{\xi 3}$	...	$n_{\xi\xi}$	...
$\vdots$	$\vdots$	$\vdots$	$\vdots$	$\vdots$		$\vdots$	

Here, $n_{\xi\xi}$ is either 0 or 1; if $n_{\xi\xi} = 0$, then $v_\zeta \in f(v_\xi)$, and if $n_{\xi\xi} = 1$, then $v_\zeta \notin f(v_\xi)$. Again, consider the diagonal $n_{00}n_{11}n_{22} \ldots n_{\xi\xi} \ldots$ of this array. Switching every member of the diagonal, let $b_\xi = 1$ if $n_{\xi\xi} = 0$, and $b_\xi = 0$ if $n_{\xi\xi} = 1$; $b_0 b_1 b_2 \ldots b_\xi$ is an array of 0's and 1's, and represents a subset Z of V. By definition of Z, for every ξ, $v_\xi \in Z$ if and only if $v_\xi \notin f(v_\xi)$ for every ξ and so cannot be in the range of f. But this contradicts our assumption that f is onto $\mathscr{P}(Z)$; so again, we conclude that there can be no one-one function from V onto $\mathscr{P}(V)$.

T6 readily yields us as many infinite magnitudes as we could wish; consider, for instance, the sequence of sets ω, $\mathscr{P}(\omega)$, $\mathscr{P}(\mathscr{P}(\omega))$, and so forth. T6 guarantees that any member of this sequence exceeds any previous member in cardinality; thus we have here infinitely many infinite sets, any two of which will differ in cardinality. And this is only the beginning; we can generate sets of still greater cardinality, by taking the union of the above sequence (i.e., the set consisting of those elements that belong to some member of the sequence). This set must be greater in cardinality than any member of the sequence. Then we can go on, taking the power set of *this* set, and so on. This process continues indefinitely.

21. The above sections provide two ways of generating nondenumerably infinite sets—one by filling in the gaps between the integers to form the continuum of real numbers—the other by taking power-sets, starting with the set ω of nonnegative integers. These two methods can be seen to be closely related; in fact, $\mathscr{P}(\omega)$ has the same cardinality as the set of standard decimals. (See P3, below.) The hierarchy of sets discussed above—ω, $\mathscr{P}(\omega)$, $\mathscr{P}(\mathscr{P}(\omega))$, and so on—thus contains as its second member a set identical in cardinality to the set of real numbers.

A question that arises immediately is whether there are any sets *between* ω and $\mathscr{P}(\omega)$ in cardinality; is there a set U such that $\omega \prec U \prec \mathscr{P}(\omega)$? This question, originally raised by Cantor, is known as the *continuum problem*; the more general question whether there is an infinite set V such that $V \prec U \prec \mathscr{P}(V)$ for some set U is called the *generalized continuum problem*. The thesis that there is no set U such that $\omega \prec U \prec \mathscr{P}(\omega)$ is Cantor's *continuum hypothesis*.

The continuum hypothesis and its generalization have been among the most stimulating and profound problems that the mathematicians of this century have tried to settle. So far, all attempts to prove or disprove even the continuum hypothesis on the basis of plausible set-theoretic principles have failed. In spite of the lack of success in solving the problem straightforwardly, some very deep *metamathematical* results have been obtained concerning the continuum problem. It has been shown of a large number of axiomatic theories of sets that they do not decide the continuum problem.

This result falls into two parts. Let **M** be a morphology for the theory of sets (often **M** will have just one two-place predicate for set-theoretic membership), let Γ be the set of formulas of **M** postulated in the theory, and let A be a formula representing the continuum hypothesis. Then

1. If Γ is consistent then it is not the case that $\Gamma \vdash \sim A$, and
2. If Γ is consistent then it is not the case that $\Gamma \vdash A$.

In other words, (1) if the theory is consistent, then the continuum hypothesis is consistent with the theory, and (2) if the theory is consistent, then the continuum hypothesis is not provable in the theory. Result 1 is called the *relative consistency* of the continuum hypothesis ("relative" because it depends on the assumption that Γ itself is consistent), and was proved by K. Gödel in 1938; result 2 is called the *relative independence* of the continuum hypothesis, and was proved by P. Cohen in 1964. These results obviously won't hold for *any* set Γ of "postulates" for the theory of sets (for instance, they fail if $A \in \Gamma$ or $\sim A \in \Gamma$); but they have been established for a wide variety of postulates which in fact have been proposed for the theory of sets.

These results show one way in which the metamathematical method may be applied to mathematics itself. When a mathematician fails to solve a problem concerning some subject matter, he is able in some cases to reflect on this failure and succeed in showing on the metamathematical level that this problem could not be solved. As we pointed out in concluding Chapter XII, it is in this area that modern logicians have made many of their most remarkable and interesting achievements.

Exercises

1. Establish the following identities.
   (a) $X \cap Y = Y \cap X$
   (b) $X \cup (X \cap Y) = X$
   (c) $X \cap (Y \cup Z) = (X \cap Y) \cup (X \cap Z)$
   (d) $X \cup (Y \cap Z) = (X \cup Y) \cap (X \cup Z)$

2. Show that $X \subseteq Y$ if and only if $X \cap Y = X$.

3. Where X and Y are sets, let $u \in X - Y$ if and only if $u \in X$ and $u \notin Y$.
   (a) Find an example showing that for some X and Y, $X - Y \neq Y - X$.
   (b) Show that if $X - Y = Y - X$ then $X = Y$.
   (c) Show that $X - Y = \varnothing$ if and only if $X \subseteq Y$.
   (d) Show that $(X - Y) - Z = X - (Y \cup Z)$.
   (e) Show that if $X \subset Y$ and $U \subseteq X$ then $X - U \subset Y - U$.

4. Show that for all sets X, if $\varnothing \neq X$ then $\varnothing \subset X$.

5. Establish the following.
   (a) For all sets X, $X \cup \{X\} \neq \varnothing$. (*Hint:* Show that if $X \cup \{X\} = \varnothing$ then $X = \{\varnothing\}$.)
   (b) Show that for all sets X, $X \cup \{X\} \neq \{\{\varnothing\}\}$.
   (c) Show that if $X \cup \{Y\} = X \cup Y$ then $Y \in Y$ or $Y \cup \{Y\} \subseteq X$.

6. Let f be a function from X to Y, and g be a function from Y to Z; let $\langle u, v \rangle \in h$ if and only if $u \in X$ and $g(f(u)) = v$. In other words, let h be the composition of f with g.
   (a) Show that h is a function from X to Z.
   (b) Show that if f is onto Y and g is onto Z then h is onto Z.
   (c) Show that if f and g are one-one then h is one-one.
   (d) Show that if h is one-one and f is onto Y then both f and g are one-one.

7. Show that if f is a one-one function from U onto V and $u \in U$ then $f - \{\langle u, f(u) \rangle\}$ is a one-one function from $U - \{u\}$ onto $V - \{f(u)\}$.

8. Let f be a function on a domain V and let $U \subseteq V$. The *restriction* of f to U is the set $f \mid U = \{\langle u, f(u) \rangle / u \in U\}$. Show that $f \mid U$ is a function, and that if f is one-one then $f \mid U$ is one-one.

9. Prove T3; i.e., show that if $U \simeq V$ and $V \simeq W$ then $U \simeq W$.

10. Show that if $X \cap Y = \varnothing$ and $U \cap V = \varnothing$, then $X \cup Y \simeq U \cup V$ if $X \simeq U$ and $Y \simeq V$.

11. Show that if $X \simeq U$ and $Y \simeq V$ then $X \times Y \simeq U \times V$.

12. Show that if $\mathbf{M'}$ is an S-extension of $\mathbf{M}$ then $F_{\mathbf{M'}}$ is denumerable if and only if $F_{\mathbf{M}}$ is denumerable.

13. Establish the following.
    (a) $\{0, 1, 2, \ldots\} \simeq \{\cdots -4, -2, 0, 2, 4, \ldots\}$
    (b) $\{0, 1, 2, 3, 4, 5\} \simeq \{2, 4\} \times \{1, 2, 3\}$
    (c) $\{1, 2, 3\} \prec \{4, 5, 6, 7\}$
    (d) For all sets X, $X \precsim X^2$.
    (e) For all sets X, $\varnothing \prec X$ if $X \neq \varnothing$. (*Note:* It follows from D6 that $\varnothing$ is a function from $\varnothing$ to X.)
    (f) For all sets X, if $\varnothing \simeq X$ then $X = \varnothing$.

14. Show that if $U \prec V$ and $V \simeq W$ then $U \prec W$.

15. Where X is any set, let 2^X be the set of functions from X to $\{0, 1\}$. Show that for all sets X, $\mathscr{P}(X) \simeq 2^X$.

16. Show that if $Y \subseteq \omega$ and Y has no largest member (i.e., for all $n \in Y$ there is an $m \in Y$ such that $n < m$), then $Y \simeq \omega$. (*Hint:* Use the natural ordering of Y to define a one-one function from ω onto Y.)

17. Show that no infinite set has cardinality less than ω. (*Hint:* Use the result of E16. Recall that to say that Y is infinite is to say that for all n, $Y \not\precsim \{m \mid m < n\}$.)

Problems

1. Let X be a set of nonempty sets. A *choice*-function for X is a function f from X to $\{u \mid$ for some $Y \in X, u \in Y\}$, such that for all $Y \in X, f(Y) \in Y$. Thus a choice-function for X picks a member of each set in X. The *axiom of choice* states that there is a choice-function for each set of nonempty sets. Derive the following consequences of the axiom of choice.
   (a) If there is a function from Y onto Z then $Z \precsim Y$.
   (b) If Y is infinite then $\omega \prec Y$. (*Hint:* Let f be a choice-function for $\mathscr{P}(Y) - \{\varnothing\}$ and consider the sequence X, $X - \{f(X)\}$, $X - \{f(X), f(X - \{f(X)\})\}, \ldots$.)
   (c) If Y is infinite then for some Z, $Z \subset Y$ and $Z \simeq Y$. (*Hint:* Use (b).)

2. Show that between every two rational real numbers there is an irrational real number, and that between every two irrational real numbers there is a rational real number. (*Hint:* If $r < s$, what is the cardinality of the interval of real numbers between r and s?)

3. Show that $\mathscr{P}(\omega)$ is identical in cardinality with the set X of standard decimals. (If you are unable to do this, show that $\mathscr{P}(\omega) \precsim X$ and $X \precsim \mathscr{P}(\omega)$. It will then follow from XIV. P3 that $\mathscr{P}(\omega) \simeq X$.)

4. Show that the nonnegative rational numbers are identical in cardinality with the rational numbers. (*Hint:* Let Y be the nonnegative rationals and Z the

positive rationals. First show that $Y \simeq Z$ by mapping the whole numbers in Y onto the whole numbers in Z. Then show that Z is identical in cardinality with the set of all rationals.)

5. An *algebraic number* is a real number x which satisfies an equation of the form $k_m x^m + k_{m-1} x^{m-1} + \cdots + k_1 x + k_0 = 0$, where $k_0, k_1, \ldots, k_m$ are (negative or nonnegative) integers. Show that the set of algebraic numbers is denumerable.

6. The *postulate of restriction* says that for all sets X there is a set Y such that $Y \in X$ and $Y \cap X = \varnothing$. Derive the following consequences from the postulate of restriction.
   (a) For all sets X, $X \notin X$.
   (b) For all sets $X_1, X_2, \ldots, X_n$ it is never the case that $X_1 \in X_2, X_2 \in X_3, \ldots, X_{n-1} \in X_n$ and $X_n \in X_1$.
   (c) There does not exist a sequence $X_1, X_2, \ldots$ of sets such that for all i, $X_{i+1} \in X_i$.

7. Let $R = \{X \mid X \notin X\}$. Show that if R is a set then it follows that both $R \in R$ and $R \notin R$. On pain of inconsistency, then, we must deny that, where P is a condition expressed in the language of set theory, there will exist a set $\{X \mid X$ has $P\}$. Try to find ways of restricting this principle so as to avoid contradiction.

XIV Mathematical Induction

1. Our approach to logic has relied heavily on inductive techniques; in our metatheoretic work we have continually used inductive definitions and proofs. Here we will give a separate account of these techniques, which may be helpful in understanding their employment in logic. Also, we may be able to explain how a theory of the nonnegative integers can be developed within set theory.

Let ω be the set $\{0, 1, 2, 3, \ldots\}$ of nonnegative integers. Every member of ω is produced from the initial element 0 by the process of successively adding 1. We can use this generative process to prove things about the set ω. If we want to show that every member of ω possesses a certain property, our goal is to establish something about infinitely many objects. In some cases this task will be trivial; for instance, we may be asked to show that for all n, n is either greater than 5 or not greater than 5. Since this is a logical truth, it can be established using techniques such as those of Chapter IV. There also are problems in which only a finite number of things need to be verified in order to obtain the desired conclusion. If, for instance, we wanted to show that for all n, n^2 is less than 10 if n is less than 4, we need only check that 0, 1, 4, and 9 are less than 10.

But besides cases such as these, more complicated questions arise which call for more powerful methods of proof. A good example is the problem of finding a rule for determining the sum of the first n nonnegative integers. Let's call this sum $f(n)$, and agree that $f(0) = 0$. Testing n less than 5 we find that $f(0) = 0$, $f(1) = 1$, $f(2) = 3$, $f(3) = 6$, and $f(4) = 10$. Considering these and other instances, we may guess eventually that in general $f(n) = \frac{1}{2}n(n + 1)$.

To verify this conjecture we need to prove that it holds true for all members n of ω; we will do this inductively. The idea of the proof is first to show that $f(0) = \frac{1}{2}n(n + 1)$ and then to show that for any n, if $f(n) = \frac{1}{2}n(n + 1)$ then $f(n + 1) = \frac{1}{2}(n + 1)(n + 1 + 1)$.

We can do this as follows. First, we agreed to let $f(0)$ be 0. But $\frac{1}{2}0(0 + 1) = 0$, so that $f(0) = \frac{1}{2}0(0 + 1)$. Second, suppose for an arbitrary n that $f(n) = \frac{1}{2}n(n + 1)$. Now we calculate to show that $f(n + 1) = \frac{1}{2}(n + 1)(n + 1 + 1)$. Since $f(n + 1)$ is the sum

$$0 + 1 + \cdots + n + (n + 1)$$

it follows that $f(n + 1) = f(n) + (n + 1)$. And since $f(n) = \frac{1}{2}n(n + 1)$, we know that $f(n + 1) = \frac{1}{2}n(n + 1) + (n + 1)$. But $\frac{1}{2}n(n + 1) + (n + 1)$ is $\frac{1}{2}(n(n + 1) + 2(n + 1))$, which in turn is $\frac{1}{2}(n + 1)(n + 2)$. Therefore, $f(n + 1) = \frac{1}{2}(n + 1)(n + 1 + 1)$, as desired.

This shows that for all n, if $f(n) = \frac{1}{2}n(n + 1)$ then

$$f(n + 1) = \frac{1}{2}(n + 1)(n + 1 + 1)$$

and completes the inductive argument showing that for all n, $f(n) = \frac{1}{2}n(n + 1)$.

Let's look more closely at this argument. What we wanted to prove was that all n possess a certain property: the property that $f(n) = \frac{1}{2}n(n + 1)$. To do this we first established that 0 has the property; this is called the *basis step* of the argument. Second, we showed that if any n has the property, then so does $n + 1$; this is called the *inductive step* of the argument. In the inductive step we let n be an arbitrary member of ω and assumed that n has the property; this is called the *hypothesis of induction* or *inductive hypothesis*. Then, given the inductive hypothesis, we showed that $n + 1$ must also have the property. Having done this, we concluded that any member of ω whatsoever has the property.

What makes the argument work is the fact that any nonnegative integer m can be reached as the last member of a finite sequence 0, 1, 2, ..., m. The basis step shows that 0 possesses the given property, and the inductive step shows that the property will be carried upwards along the sequence, so that eventually m has the property. It's like a row of dominoes falling.

Although they may seem so, inductive arguments aren't circular. In such an argument we don't assume what is to be proved when we make the inductive hypothesis. What was to be proved in the above example was that for all n, $f(n) = \frac{1}{2}n(n + 1)$. What we supposed in the hypothesis of induction was that for an unspecified number n, $f(n) = \frac{1}{2}n(n + 1)$. Nothing was assumed about numbers other than n.

2. In XIII.17 we mentioned a result about finite sets which is another good example of a theorem proved by induction: if Y is a finite set and Y $\subset$ Z then Y $\prec$ Z. Before proving this we first need to rephrase it so that it is explicitly a statement about the members of ω: for all n, for all sets Y having exactly n members there is no set Z such that Y $\subset$ Z and Y $\simeq$ Z.

In the basis step we must show that if a set Y has exactly 0 members then there is no Z such that Y $\subset$ Z and Y $\simeq$ Z. But if Y has exactly 0 numbers then Y is the empty set $\varnothing$; and if $\varnothing \simeq$ Z then Z $= \varnothing$. Thus there is no set Z such that Y $\subset$ Z and Y $\simeq$ Z.

In the inductive step we assume as hypothesis of induction that for all sets Y having exactly n members there is no set Z such that Y $\subset$ Z and Y $\simeq$ Z. Suppose for the sake of argument that there is a set U having exactly $n + 1$ members, and a set V such that U $\subset$ V and U $\simeq$ V. Let v $\in$ V and v $\notin$ U; there is such a v, since U $\subset$ V. Since U $\simeq$ V, there is a one-one function from U onto V, say f; let $f(x) = v$. Now, consider the set W $=$ U $-$ {x} and let g be the restriction of f to W, so that g $=$ f $- \{\langle x, v\rangle\}$. Finally, let S $=$ V $-$ {v}. We can say the following things about W and S: (1) W has exactly n members, (2) W $\simeq$ S, and (3) W $\subset$ S. Since U has exactly $n + 1$ members, (1) follows from the fact that W is formed by removing one element from U. As for (2), this holds because g is a one-one function from W onto S (see XIII.E7 in this connection). Finally, suppose w $\in$ W; then w $\in$ U and since U $\subset$ V, w $\in$ V. Also w $\neq$ v because v $\notin$ U. Thus for all w, if w $\in$ W then w $\in$ V $-$ {v}, so that W $\subseteq$ V $-$ {v}; i.e., W $\subseteq$ S. Now, if x $\neq$ v, x $\in$ S but x $\notin$ W, so that W $\subset$ S. On the other hand, if x $=$ v, clearly U $-$ {x} $\subset$ V $-$ {x}, so that in any case S $\subset$ W. This establishes (3).

The above paragraph constitutes the inductive step of our argument. To simplify things, let's call a set Y *peculiar* if there is a set Z such that Y $\subset$ Z and Y $\simeq$ Z. What we have just shown is that if a set U of size $n + 1$ is peculiar, then there is a set S of size n that also is peculiar. This, however, contradicts our hypothesis of induction, which states that no set of size n is peculiar. Thus we know that if no sets of size n are peculiar, then no sets of size $n + 1$ are peculiar, and the induction is finished.

3. The inductive arguments we have considered up to now have relied on the principle that if zero has a property and the successor of any number having the property also has the property, then any number whatsoever has the property. This is often called the principle of *weak induction*.

This method of argument is not well adapted to some problems. For instance, suppose we try to show that every set containing a nonnegative integer contains a least nonnegative integer. To prove this, let W be a set; we will show inductively that for all n, if $n \in W$ then there is a least nonnegative integer in W. The basis of this induction is easy, since if $0 \in W$ then 0 itself is the least nonnegative integer in W.

If we proceed by weak induction, we must assume as our hypothesis of induction that if $n \in W$ then there is a least nonnegative integer in W. We then suppose that $n + 1 \in W$, and try to show that W contains a least nonnegative integer. If $n + 1$ is itself the least nonnegative integer in W, we have our conclusion; if it is not, then there is some m less than $n + 1$ in W. In this case, we should be able to use our hypothesis of induction to show that W contains a least nonnegative integer, but unfortunately we aren't able to do this. The hypothesis that we have framed applies only when $m = n$; if $m < n$ we can't use it.

Evidently, what is needed here is an inductive hypothesis to the effect that for all $m < n + 1$, if $m \in W$ then there is a least nonnegative integer in W. With this hypothesis, the argument goes through smoothly; if there is some m less than $m + 1$ in W, then the hypothesis of induction guarantees that there is a least nonnegative integer in W.

The general principle involved in this argument seems to be as follows.

If 0 has a property and if for all n, $n + 1$ has the property whenever all m such that $m < n + 1$ have the property, then all n have the property.

$$(i)$$

In the above example, the property in question is a complex one: m has the property if and only if there is a least nonnegative integer in W if $m \in W$.

The principle i is just as valid as weak induction. If its premises are true, then 0 has the property. Then, since 0 is the only nonnegative integer less than 1, 1 has the property as well. And since 0 and 1 are the only nonnegative integers less than 2, 2 also has the property. Since this procedure can be continued indefinitely, all nonnegative integers must have the property.

Although i is a correct formulation of the principle of strong induction, there is a simpler way of expressing it. This is the form in which the principle usually appears.

If for all n, n has a given property whenever all m such that $m < n$ have the property, then all n whatsoever have the property.

(ii)

That is, if for all n, n has a given property whenever all previous m have the property, then all n whatsoever have the property.

It's hard to believe that ii is valid, since it assumes no basis step. Surprisingly enough, however, the basis step doesn't need to be included since it already is implied by the inductive step of ii. That is, if for all n, n has a given property whenever all m such that $m < n$ have the property, then 0 has the property.

The proof of this is as follows: suppose that for all n, n possesses the property whenever all previous m have the property. In particular, then, if all m such that $m < 0$ have the property, then 0 does. But *there are* no m such that $m < 0$; it therefore is *vacuously true* that every m such that $m < 0$ has the property. And thus 0 has the property.

This argument will appear less contrived if it is formalized. (The following few paragraphs, then, will presuppose Chapters VIII and IX.) Let the domain consist of all nonnegative integers, let a stand for '0', and let P represent the property under consideration. Let Qxy stand for 'n is less than m'. Then ii is rendered as follows.

(iii) $(x)((y)(Qyx \supset Py \supset Px) \supset (x)Px$

Above, we argued that Pa follows from $(x)((y)(Qyx \supset Py) \supset Px)$; in this argument we also used the fact that no nonnegative integer is less than zero, which may be translated formally by $(x) \sim Qxa$. In formal notation, then, our claim is that Pa follows from $(x)((y)(Qyx \supset Px) \supset Px)$ and $(x) \sim Qxa$. We can derive this in the system S_p as follows.

1	$(x)((y)(Qyx \supset Py) \supset Px)$	hyp
2	$(x) \sim Qxa$	hyp
3	$(y)(Qya \supset Py) \supset Pa$	1, uq elim
4	u $\quad$ Qua	hyp
5	$\sim Pu$	hyp
6	Qua	4, reit
7	$(x) \sim Qxa$	2, reit
8	$\sim Qua$	7, uq elim
9	$\sim \sim Pu$	5–8, neg int
10	Pu	9, neg elim
11	$Qua \supset Pu$	4–10, imp int
12	$(y)(Qya \supset Py)$	11, uq int
13	Pa	3, 12, m p

(iv)

The validity of strong induction for ω is closely associated with a principle called the *well-ordering principle* for ω:

(*v*)   Every nonempty subset of ω has a least element.

At the beginning of this section, when we gave an example of a proof using strong induction we used this technique to establish v. Conversely, v can be employed to justify the principle of strong induction. Given a property of nonnegative integers, let U be the set of members of ω which *do not* possess the property. Suppose that the premiss for strong induction holds: for all n, n has the property whenever all previous m have the property. This means that for all n, $n \notin U$ if for all m such that $m < n$, $m \notin U$. Now, assume that U has a least member, say k. It must then be the case that for all m such that $m < k$, $m \notin U$; but then $k \notin U$, contrary to our assumption that k is a least member of U. Therefore, U has no least member; and in view of v, U is empty. Since no n is in U, every n must possess the given property.

   4. Inductive principles do not apply to all mathematical structures. The fact that the principle of strong induction is equivalent to v shows that this principle holds because the nonnegative integers are arranged in such a way that from every subset of ω which contains any members at all, we can choose a least member of the subset. Many mathematical structures aren't arranged in this way: the (positive and nonpositive) integers, for instance. The set $\{\ldots, -3, -2, -1, 0\}$ is nonempty, but has no least element. And the principle of strong induction does not apply to this set. It's vacuously true for all integers x that if for all integers y less than x, y is positive, then x is positive. (This holds because there are always negative integers less than any integer x, so that it's never true that all integers y less than x are positive.) But it's false that all integers are positive.

   There are, however, many structures besides the nonnegative integers which *are* well ordered and to which inductive principles may be applied. As a very simple example, let's consider the nonnegative integers beginning with some number n different from zero. The principle of weak induction for $\{i \mid i \in \omega$ and $i \geq n\}$ is as follows.

   If n has a property and for all $i \geq n$, $i + 1$ has the property if i does, then every i such that $i \geq n$ has the property.

                                (*vi*)

As an illustration of this principle for $n = 2$, we'll show by weak induction that for all $n \geq 2$, $n^2 > n + 1$. First, $4 > 3$, so that $2^2 > 2 + 1$; this furnishes the basis step. For the inductive step, suppose that $n^2 > n + 1$; then

$n^2 \geq n + 2$. Now, $n + 1 > n$, so that $(n + 1)^2 > n^2$; therefore $(n + 1)^2 > (n + 2)$; i.e., $(n + 1)^2 > (n + 1) + 1$. This shows that for all $n \geq 2$, if $n^2 > n + 1$ then $(n + 1)^2 > (n + 1) + 1$. It follows by weak induction that for all $n \geq 2$, $n^2 > n + 1$.

The principle of strong induction for $i \geq n$ is as follows.

> If for every $i \geq n$, i has a property provided that all j such that $n \leq j < i$ do, then every i such that $i \geq n$ has the property.

$$(vii)$$

An important application of vii for $n = 2$ is found in the proof of the so-called *fundamental theorem of arithmetic*. This theorem says that every $n \geq 2$ can be represented uniquely as a product of powers of prime numbers. A *prime number* is an integer greater than 1 that is divisible only by itself and 1. For instance 2, 3, 7, 19, and 41 are prime numbers.)

We will leave it as an exercise to prove the fundamental theorem in full force; here we will show just that every $n \geq 2$ can be represented as a product of powers of primes. Suppose as inductive hypothesis that, where $m \geq 2$ for all k such that $2 \leq k < m$, there is a way to represent k as a product of powers of primes. We want to show there is a way to represent m in this manner. If m is prime, then since $m = m^1$ we can represent m as a product of powers of primes. And if m is not prime, there exist integers k and j such that $j \cdot k = m$ and $2 \leq j < m$ and $2 \leq k < m$. The inductive hypothesis ensures that there are primes $p_1, \ldots, p_h$ and $q_1, \ldots, q_i$ such that $j = p_1^{j_1} \cdot \cdots \cdot p_h^{j_h}$ and $k = q_1^{k_1} \cdot \cdots \cdot q_i^{k_i}$, where $j_1, \ldots, j_h, k_1, \ldots, k_i$ are positive integers. But then $m = p_1^{j_1} \cdot \cdots \cdot p_h^{j_h} \cdot q_1^{k_1} \cdot \cdots \cdot q_n^{k_n}$ and thus is representable as a product of powers of primes.

5. Mathematical induction is useful in carrying out definitions as well as proofs. Although by now, we've said something about inductive proofs, we've said nothing about inductive definitions.

Let's begin by considering how we might go about defining the set ω of nonnegative integers. Perhaps the simplest way to do this is just to repeat what we have already said, that the members of ω are just 0, 1, 2, and so forth.

$$(ix) \qquad \omega = \{0, 1, 2, \ldots\}$$

In many ways this technique is perfectly satisfactory; it will get the idea across to anyone who understands the notation involved. But the use of 'and so forth' and of the triple dots suggests that ix could perhaps be made more explicit.

It plainly is impossible to accomplish this by writing down a complete list of the members of ω; we must therefore attempt to revise ix by some other clarification of the triple dots. These dots succeed in communicating because we can expect the reader to figure out from the first three members of ω how to continue the sequence. A person who understands ix will know what the members of ω are because he will see how they are generated. Since ω is infinite, this process of generation will never be complete after finitely many steps. But nevertheless, any member of ω will be produced by a finite number of steps of the process.

Lying behind ix, then, is a *rule of generation* for the members of ω, a rule that a person can grasp after he is given a few instances of it. It's possible to state this rule explicitly; it is just the operation of adding one. This means that the following information, at least, is contained in ix.

1. $0 \in \omega$.
2. If $z \in \omega$ then $z + 1 \in \omega$.

Together, 1 and 2 ensure that everything we want to be in ω is in ω. However, in order to characterize ω adequately, we must also see to it that nothing that should not be in ω is in this set. These two conditions must therefore be completed by a clause stating that anything *not* generated from 0 by a finite number of applications of the rule is not a member of ω.

There is a difficulty here. We can't accomplish this directly, by saying that $z \in \omega$ only if z is generated from 0 by adding 1 finitely many times. The reason for this is that above, in Chapter XIII, we defined the notion of finitude by appealing to the set of natural numbers. So now we can't use the notion of finitude to define ω without leading ourselves in a circle.

This difficulty can be overcome by noticing that the set we wish to define is the *least inclusive* set satisfying 1 and 2. We want to say, then, that ω is included in any set that satisfies 1 and 2; this third clause will guarantee that the only way anything can get into ω will be by virtue of successive applications of 1 and 2.

3. For all sets Y, $\omega \subseteq Y$ if $0 \in Y$ and for all z, if $z \in Y$ then $z + 1 \in Y$.

Since clause 3 makes no use of the concept of finitude, our definition of ω is not circular.

Together, clauses 1, 2, and 3 constitute an *inductive definition* of the set ω of nonnegative integers; they define ω by specifying how it is generated. Clause 1 of this definition is called the *basis clause*, clause 2 the *inductive clause*, and clause 3 the *extremal clause*.

The extremal clause of an inductive definition is always completely determined by the basis and inductive clauses. For this reason it often is omitted when inductive definitions are presented. We ourselves haven't made the extremal clause a part of the inductive definitions of previous chapters. Rather, we have followed these definitions by a statement that captures the intent of the extremal clause. In the definition of ω, for instance, we would present clauses 1 and 2 and then say that an object is an element of ω only if it qualifies as such by successive applications of 1 and 2.

6. Our account of inductive definition has left several matters unsettled. The most important of these is the question of existence and uniqueness; an "inductive definition" would be pointless unless it succeeded in defining a unique thing. We therefore must show that for any inductive definition there exists a unique set satisfying this definition.

This leads us to the problem of specifying the general form of an inductive definition. We can do this using set-theoretic notions. Let X be any set and $f_1, \ldots, f_n$ be any n functions, where f_i is k_i-ary. Given these, it is possible to define a set Y inductively, as follows.

　1. If $u \in X$ then $u \in Y$;
2.1. If $\{u_1, \ldots, u_{k_1}\} \subseteq Y$ then $f_1(u_1, \ldots, u_{k_1}) \in Y$;
　　$\vdots$
2.n. If $\{u_1, \ldots, u_{k_n}\} \subseteq Y$ then $f_n(u_1, \ldots, u_{k_n}) \in Y$;
　3. For all sets W, if W satisfies 2.1–2.n then $Y \subseteq W$.

$$(x)$$

This is the general form of the definition we gave above of ω; there, X was $\{0\}$, n was 1, and f_1 was the function such that $f(v) = v + 1$.

Our problem is now to prove that there exists one and only one set Y corresponding to x. This breaks down into two parts: showing that there exists at most one such Y, and showing that there exists at least one such Y. The former of these tasks is easy, and is left as an exercise. The latter is more difficult, since it requires the use of some set-theoretic principles we didn't discuss in Chapter XIII. It is left as a problem, with some hints.

Another problem with our definition of ω is that it doesn't suffice to tell us what the members of ω are, since it doesn't tell us what 0 is, and in what the operation of adding 1 consists. These two questions can be settled by appealing, as usual, to set theory, choosing a particular set to be 0 and a particular set-theoretic function to be the operation of adding 1. To a large extent these decisions are arbitrary: any set X can be chosen to be 0 and any function f to be the operation of adding 1, as long as each new set picked by f differs from every previous set.

One choice which is now widely accepted because of its simplicity was suggested by J. von Neumann. Von Neumann's idea was to let 0 be the empty set $\varnothing$, and, where X is any set, to let $X + 1$ be $\{X\} \cup X$. Thus, $1 = \{\varnothing\}$, $2 = \{\varnothing, \{\varnothing\}\}$, $3 = \{\varnothing, \{\varnothing\}, \{\varnothing, \{\varnothing\}\}\}$, and so forth. One nice consequence of this choice is that strict set-theoretic inclusion, $\subset$, can be identified with the usual ordering relation for nonnegative integers; $n < m$ if and only if $n \subset m$. Another is that the set n will have exactly n members.

Given the von Neumann definition, we can provide an example of how the extremal clause is used to show that certain sets are *not* in ω. For example, take the set $\{\{\varnothing\}\}$; clearly this set will not occur in the sequence $\varnothing$, $\{\varnothing\}$, $\{\varnothing, \{\varnothing\}\}, \ldots$; and so we ought to be able to use the extremal clause to show that $\{\{\varnothing\}\} \notin \omega$.

Perhaps the best way to do this is first to show that the principle of weak inductive proof holds for ω, as we have defined this set. To formulate this principle, let 'P' represent an arbitrary property of sets: according to weak induction, if P holds of 0 and holds of $X + 1$ whenever it holds of any set X, then P holds of all members of ω. It is easy to prove this, using the extremal clause. Let $Y = \{Z \mid Z \in \omega$ and P holds of $Z\}$. (The standard postulates of set theory guarantee that Y exists, provided ω does.) Y plainly satisfies clauses 1 and 2 of the definition of ω, and the extremal clause then ensures that $\omega \subseteq Y$, and therefore P must hold of every member of ω.

Armed with the principle of weak induction we can show that $\{\{\varnothing\}\} \notin \omega$ by showing that $0 \neq \{\{\varnothing\}\}$ and that if $X \neq \{\{\varnothing\}\}$ then $X \cup \{X\} \neq \varnothing$, for any set X. The first part of this is easy, since if $0 = \{\{\varnothing\}\}$ then we would have $\{\varnothing\} \in \varnothing$, which is impossible because $\varnothing$ has no members. And since it isn't difficult to show that for no set X does $X \cup \{X\} = \{\{\varnothing\}\}$ (see XIII.E5), the second part also follows readily. Weak induction then ensures that no member of ω equals $\{\{\varnothing\}\}$; i.e., $\{\{\varnothing\}\} \notin \omega$.

7. Inductive techniques can be used to define many sets besides ω. For instance, the following clauses define the set E of even numbers.

1. $0 \in E$;
2. If $X \in E$ then $(X + 1) + 1 \in E$;
3. For all sets Y, $E \subseteq Y$ if $0 \in Y$ and for all Z, if $Z \in Y$ then $(Z + 1) + 1 \in Y$.
   (xi)

Another example is the following definition of the set H of *hereditarily finite sets* (a hereditarily finite set is a finite set of finite sets of finite sets of $\cdots$ of finite sets).

1. $\varnothing \in H$;
2. If $\{X_1, \ldots, X_n\} \subseteq H$ then $\{X_1, \ldots, X_n\} \in H$;
3. For all sets Y, $H \subseteq Y$ if $\varnothing \in Y$ and for all $X_1, \ldots, X_n$, $\{X_1, \ldots, X_n\} \in Y$ if $\{X_1, \ldots, X_n\} \subseteq Y$.

$$(xii)$$

It also is common to give inductive definitions of functions; the following definition of addition for members of ω is an example.

1. $0 + n = n$;
2. $((m + 1) + n) = (m + n) + 1$.

$$(xiii)$$

We have given this definition in abbreviated form, and it calls for some clarification. First, it uses the operation of adding 1; this is not circular, since we have defined this operation separately. Second, the extremal clause is omitted. Third, we must recall that a function is a set of n-tuples; in particular, $+$ is a set of triples and we have $\langle m, n, k \rangle \in +$ if and only if $m + n = k$. Example xiii is thus, like our other inductive definitions, a definition of a set. To establish this we can rewrite it in the following way.

1. For all $X \in \omega$, $\langle 0, X, X \rangle \in +$;
2. If $V, X \in \omega$ then $\langle V \cup \{V\}, X, W \cup \{W\} \rangle \in +$ if $\langle V, X, W \rangle \in +$;
3. For all sets Y, $+ \subseteq Y$ if $\langle 0, X, X \rangle \in Y$ for all $X \in \omega$ and $\langle V \cup \{V\}, X, W \cup \{W\} \rangle \in Y$ if $\langle V, X, W \rangle \in Y$, for all $V, X, W \in \omega$.

$$(xiv)$$

On the basis of xiv, $+$ can be shown to be a function on the domain ω^2; furthermore, it can be shown to have the properties usually associated with addition.

8. The examples we have provided in this chapter should indicate how pervasive and flexible a technique mathematical induction is. It can be used to define a wide variety of mathematical structures, and to demonstrate the properties of these structures. Indeed, where a set such as ω or the set F_M of formulas of some morphology M for H_s is defined inductively, you usually find that the most basic theorems about these sets depend on mathematical induction for their proof. This is true, for instance of the fundamental theorem of arithmetic and the replacement theorem, V.M29.

The research of logicians in syntax (especially in *proof theory*, the theory of proofs and deductions) is therefore very dependent on mathematical induction. For a long time, the most profound results in this area have pivoted on increasingly difficult and complicated inductive arguments. Most of the proofs of the interpolation theorem for $\mathbf{H}_{p=}$, for instance, are like this.

Our set-theoretic characterization of the notions involved in the inductive definition of ω may have suggested to you a similar procedure in syntax. Can we replace syntactic operations such as negation by set-theoretic concepts? This is easily done and, indeed, for denumerable morphologies can be performed using only notions from the arithmetic of nonnegative integers. This procedure, called the *arithmetication of syntax*, is one of the most important techniques used in proving the limitative metatheorems we mentioned above in XII.9.

Exercises

1. Show by weak induction that if a set X has exactly n members, then the power-set $\mathscr{P}(X)$ of X has exactly 2^n members.

2. (a) Determine a formula for the number $t(n)$ of truth-tables for n parameters, and show by induction that the formula is correct.
   (b) Determine a formula for the number $c(m, n)$ of members of the Cartesian product $X \times Y$, where X has exactly m members and Y exactly n members. Show by induction that the formula is correct.
   (c) Determine a formula for the number $p(m, n)$ of members of the Cartesian power X^n, where X has exactly m members and $n \geq 2$. Show by induction that the formula is correct.
   (d) Determine a formula for the number $r(m, n)$ of n-ary relations on a domain having exactly m members, and show that the formula is correct. (*Hint:* Use E1 and E2(c), together with the fact that an n-ary relation on D is a subset of the Cartesian power D^n.)

3. Where X and Y are sets, let X^Y be the set of functions from Y to X. Show by induction that if X has exactly m members and Y exactly n members then X^Y has exactly m^n members.

4. Discover what is wrong with the following "proof" that all finite sets are alike in cardinality.
   We will show by weak induction that for all n, $X \simeq Y$ for all sets X and Y having no more than n members. In the basis case, suppose that X and Y have no more than 0 members. Then $X = \varnothing$ and $Y = \varnothing$, and so $X \simeq Y$. In the inductive step, assume that for all sets X and Y having no more than n members, $X \simeq Y$, and let U and V have no more than $n + 1$ members. Let $u \in U$ and $v \in V$; since $U - \{u\}$ and $V - \{v\}$ have fewer than n members, the hypothesis of induction ensures that $U - \{u\} \simeq V - \{v\}$. Therefore $U \simeq V$, and the induction is finished.

5. Show by weak induction that for all n the Cartesian power ω^n of ω is denumerable. (See XIII.18 for the basis step.)

6. Following the hint given in XIII.10, let $\langle X, Y \rangle = \{X, \{X, Y\}\}$ and $\langle X_1, \ldots, X_n, X_{n+1} \rangle = \langle\langle X_1, \ldots, X_n \rangle, X_{n+1} \rangle$. Assume that it cannot be the case that $U \in V$ and $V \in U$ for any sets U and V. Use this in showing inductively that $X_1 = Y_1$, $X_2 = Y_2, \ldots$, and $X_n = Y_n$ if and only if $\langle X_1, X_2, \ldots, X_n \rangle = \langle Y_1, Y_2, \ldots, Y_n \rangle$.

7. Use strong induction to prove the fundamental theorem of arithmetic, in the following form. Let p_i, where $i \geq 1$, be the ith prime number; $p_1 = 2$, $p_2 = 3$, $p_3 = 5$, and so on. Where $n > 2$, let a *decomposition* of n be an ordered m-tuple $\langle k_1, \ldots, k_m \rangle$ such that $k_m > 0$ and $p_1^{k_1} \cdot \cdots \cdot p_m^{k_m} = n$. Then for all $n \geq 2$, there exists one and only one decomposition of n.

8. Give inductive definitions of the following sequences.
   (a) $0, 3, 6, 9, 12, \ldots$
   (b) $1, 2, 4, 8, 16, \ldots$
   (c) $1, 1, 1, 1, 1, \ldots$
   (d) $1, 0, 1, 0, 1, \ldots$
   (e) $1, 2, 6, 24, 120, \ldots$
   (f) $2, 2, 3, 6, 17, 66, 327, \ldots$

9. Show that if sets Y and Z satisfy the inductive definition x, then $Y = Z$.

10. Show by induction that, where ω is given by the von Neumann definition, $X = \{Y \mid Y \in \omega \text{ and } Y < X\}$ for all $X \in \omega$.

11. Show that the following sets are not members of ω.
    (a) $\{\{\varnothing\}\}$
    (b) $\{\{\varnothing\}, \{\varnothing, \{\varnothing\}\}\}$
    (c) ω (*Hint:* Show by induction that for all $X \in \omega$, $X \notin X$.)

12. Let $+$ be the set defined by xiii (or, more precisely, by xiv).
    (a) Show that $+$ is a function from ω^2 to ω.
    (b) Show that for all $m, n, m + n = n + m$.
    (c) Give an inductive definition of multiplication, $\cdot$, in terms of addition.
    (d) Show that for all $k, m, n, k \cdot (m + n) = (k \cdot m) + (k \cdot n)$.
    (e) Show that for all $m, n, m \cdot n = n \cdot m$.

13. Let H be defined as in xii.
    (a) Show that if $\{X, Y\} \subseteq H$ then $X \cup Y \in H$ and $X \cap Y \in H$.
    (b) Show that if $X \in Y$ and $Y \in H$ then $X \in H$.
    (c) Show that if $X \subseteq Y$ and $Y \in H$ then $X \in H$.

Problems

1. Among the postulates of set existence commonly used in set theory are the following.
   1. There is a set X such that $\varnothing \in X$ and for all sets Y, if $Y \in X$ then $Y \cup \{Y\} \in X$. (*Postulate of infinity.*)
   2. For all sets X and properties P, the set $\{Z / Z \in X$ and Z has $P\}$ exists. (*Postulate of subsets.*)
   3. For all sets X, the set $\{Z /$ for all Y, $Z \in Y$ if $Y \in X\}$ exists. (*Postulate of intersections.*)
   Use these to show that there exists a set ω satisfying the conditions given in x.

2. Use the principle of weak induction for ω to prove the principle of strong induction for ω. That is, assume that for all properties P, if 0 has P and for all n, $n + 1$ has P if n does, then every n has P. Show that if for all n, n has P if every k less than n does, then every n has P. (*Hint:* Consider the property possessed by n if and only if for all $k \leq n$, k has P.)

3. Prove the Schröder–Bernstein theorem; i.e., show that if $X \preceq Y$ and $Y \preceq X$ then $X \simeq Y$. (*Hint:* If $X \preceq Y$, there is a one-one function f from X to Y and if $Y \preceq X$ there is a one-one function g from Y to X. Let $Z = \{g(y) / y \in Y\}$, and define a subset U of X inductively, as follows.
   1. $X - Z \subseteq U$
   2. If $u \in U$ then $g(f(u)) \in U$
   3. For all sets V, if $X - Z \subseteq V$ and $g(f(u)) \in V$ if $u \in V$, then $U \subseteq V$.
      Define a function h by letting $h(x) = f(x)$ if $x \in U$, and $h(x) = g^{-1}(x)$ if $x \notin U$, where $x \in X$. Show that h is a one-one function from X onto Y.)

Bibliography

The books cited below are chosen from works most likely to be of help to those wanting further information relating to matters discussed in the text. I have made no attempt to furnish a complete list of such works, but many of the books mentioned below contain comprehensive bibliographies. For convenience I have divided the list into four parts: general and miscellaneous works, history of logic, philosophical logic, and set theory. Many of the works listed under the first heading are treatises of considerable scope and contain material relevant to other headings.

General and miscellaneous works

BETH, E., *The Foundations of Mathematics*. Amsterdam: North-Holland Publishing Company, 1959.
CHURCH, A., *Introduction to Mathematical Logic*, vol. 1. Princeton, N.J.: Princeton University Press, 1956.

CHURCH, A., "Logic," *Encyclopaedia Britannica*, William Benton, Chicago, 1966, vol. 14, pp. 209–219.

CURRY, H., *Foundations of Mathematical Logic*. New York: McGraw-Hill Book Company, 1963.

FITCH, F., *Symbolic Logic*. New York: The Ronald Press Company, 1952.

KERSCHNER, R., and L. WILCOX, *The Anatomy of Mathematics*. New York: The Ronald Press Company, 1950.

KLEENE, S., *Introduction to Metamathematics*. Princeton, N.J.: D. Van Nostrand Company, Inc., 1952.

KREISEL, G., and J. KRIVINE, *Elements of Mathematical Logic*. Amsterdam: North-Holland Publishing Company, 1967.

MENDELSON, E., *Introduction to Mathematical Logic*. Princeton, N.J.: D. Van Nostrand Company, Inc., 1964.

MOSTOWSKI, A., *Thirty Years of Foundational Studies*. New York: Barnes & Noble, Inc., 1966.

QUINE, W., *Mathematical Logic*. Cambridge, Massachusetts: Harvard University Press, 1958.

ROGERS, H., *Theory of Recursive Functions and Effective Computability*. New York: McGraw-Hill Book Company, 1968.

SHOENFIELD, J., *Mathematical Logic*. Reading, Massachusetts: Addison-Wesley Publishing Company, Inc., 1967.

TARSKI, A., *Logic, Semantics, Metamathematics*. Oxford: Oxford University Press, 1956.

History of logic

BOCHEŃSKI, I., *A History of Formal Logic*. Notre Dame: Notre Dame University Press, 1961.

CHURCH, A., "Logic, History of," *Encyclopaedia Britannica*, William Benton, Chicago, 1966, vol. 14, pp. 219–237.

KNEALE, W., and M. KNEALE, *The Development of Logic*. Oxford: Oxford University Press, 1962.

Philosophical logic

CARNAP, R., *Meaning and Necessity*. Chicago: University of Chicago Press, 1947.

FREGE, G., *Translations from the Philosophical Writings of Gottlob Frege*, translated by P. Geach and M. Black. Oxford: Basil Blackwell, 1960.

HINTIKKA, J., *Knowledge and Belief*. Ithaca, New York: Cornell University Press, 1962.

PRIOR, A., *Formal Logic*, 2nd ed. Oxford: Oxford University Press, 1962.

QUINE, W., *From a Logical Point of View*. Cambridge, Massachusetts: Harvard University Press, 1953.

STRAWSON, P., *Introduction to Logical Theory*. London: Methuen and Company, 1952.

Set theory

ABIAN, A., *The Theory of Sets and Transfinite Arithmetic*. Philadelphia: W. B. Saunders Company, 1965.

FRAENKEL, A., *Abstract Set Theory*, 3rd ed. Amsterdam: North-Holland Publishing Company, 1966.

FRAENKEL, A., and Y. BAR-HILLEL, *Foundations of Set Theory*. Amsterdam: North-Holland Publishing Company, 1958.

GÖDEL, K., *The Consistency of the Continuum Hypothesis*. Princeton: Princeton University Press, 1940.

QUINE, W., *Set Theory and Its Logic*. Cambridge: Harvard University Press, 1963.

STOLL, R., *Set Theory and Logic*. San Francisco: W. H. Freeman and Company, 1961.

Index of Symbols

F_M 210–11

V^{d}/u 241

$\subset$ 283

$\times$ 289

ω 289, 315–16

$\simeq$ 295

$\leq$ 296

$\prec$ 297

$\mathscr{P}$ 303

Solutions to Selected Exercises

Chapter I

1. The following are formulas of S_0: (a), (f), (g), (h).

5. (a)

1	$(p \supset (q \supset p))$	A1
2	$(r \supset (q \supset r))$	1, subst
3	$(r \supset (r \supset r))$	2, subst
4	$((r \supset (r \supset r)) \supset (q \supset (r \supset (r \supset r))))$	1, subst
5	$(q \supset (r \supset (r \supset r)))$	3, 4, m p
6	$(p \supset (r \supset (r \supset r)))$	5, subst

(b)

1	$((\sim p \supset \sim q) \supset (q \supset p))$	A3
2	$((\sim\sim p \supset \sim q) \supset (q \supset \sim p))$	1, subst
3	$((p \supset (q \supset r)) \supset ((p \supset q) \supset (p \supset r)))$	A2
4	$(((\sim\sim p \supset \sim q) \supset (q \supset r)) \supset (((\sim\sim p \supset \sim q) \supset q)$ $\supset ((\sim\sim p \supset \sim q) \supset r)))$	3, subst
5	$(((\sim\sim p \supset \sim q) \supset (q \supset \sim p))$ $\supset (((\sim\sim p \supset \sim q) \supset q) \supset ((\sim\sim p \supset \sim q) \supset \sim p)))$	4, subst
6	$(((\sim\sim p \supset \sim q) \supset q) \supset ((\sim\sim p \supset \sim q) \supset \sim p))$	2, 5, m p

(c) 1 $((p \supset (q \supset r)) \supset ((p \supset q) \supset (p \supset r)))$ A2
     2 $((p \supset ((p \supset p) \supset r)) \supset ((p \supset (p \supset p)) \supset (p \supset r)))$ 1, subst
     3 $((p \supset ((p \supset p) \supset p)) \supset ((p \supset (p \supset p)) \supset (p \supset p)))$ 2, subst
     4 $(p \supset (q \supset p))$ A1
     5 $(p \supset ((p \supset p) \supset p))$ 4, subst
     6 $((p \supset (p \supset p)) \supset (p \supset p))$ 3, 5, m p
     7 $(p \supset (p \supset p))$ 4, subst
     8 $(p \supset p)$ 6, 7, m p

(d) 1 $((\sim p \supset \sim q) \supset (q \supset p))$ A3
     2 $(p \supset (q \supset p))$ A1
     3 $(p \supset (\sim q \supset p))$ 2, subst
     4 $(((\sim p \supset \sim q) \supset (q \supset p))$
        $\supset (\sim q \supset ((\sim p \supset \sim q) \supset (q \supset p))))$ 3, subst
     5 $(\sim q \supset ((\sim p \supset \sim q) \supset (q \supset p)))$ 1, 4, m p
     6 $((p \supset (q \supset r)) \supset ((p \supset q) \supset (p \supset r)))$ A2
     7 $((s \supset (q \supset r)) \supset ((s \supset q) \supset (s \supset r)))$ 6, subst
     8 $((s \supset ((\sim p \supset \sim q) \supset r))$
        $\supset ((s \supset (\sim p \supset \sim q)) \supset (s \supset r)))$ 7, subst
     9 $((\sim q \supset ((\sim p \supset \sim q) \supset r))$
        $\supset ((\sim q \supset (\sim p \supset \sim q)) \supset (\sim q \supset r)))$ 8, subst
    10 $((\sim q \supset ((\sim p \supset \sim q) \supset (q \supset p)))$
        $\supset ((\sim q \supset (\sim p \supset \sim q)) \supset (\sim q \supset (q \supset p))))$ 9, subst
    11 $((\sim q \supset (\sim p \supset \sim q)) \supset (\sim q \supset (q \supset p)))$ 5, 10, m p
    12 $(p \supset (r \supset p))$ 2, subst
    13 $(\sim q \supset (r \supset \sim q))$ 12, subst
    14 $(\sim q \supset (\sim p \supset \sim q))$ 13, subst
    15 $(\sim q \supset (q \supset p))$ 11, 14, m p

(e) 1 $((p \supset (q \supset r)) \supset ((p \supset q) \supset (p \supset r)))$ A2
     2 $((p \supset (s \supset r)) \supset ((p \supset s) \supset (p \supset r)))$ 1, subst
     3 $((q \supset (s \supset r)) \supset ((q \supset s) \supset (q \supset r)))$ 2, subst
     4 $(p \supset (q \supset p))$ A1
     5 $(p \supset ((s \supset r) \supset p))$ 4, subst
     6 $(((q \supset (s \supset r)) \supset ((q \supset s) \supset (q \supset r))) \supset ((s \supset r)$
        $\supset ((q \supset (s \supset r)) \supset ((q \supset s) \supset (q \supset r)))))$ 5, subst
     7 $((s \supset r) \supset ((q \supset (s \supset r)) \supset ((q \supset s) \supset (q \supset r))))$ 3, 6, m p
     8 $((s \supset (q \supset r)) \supset ((s \supset q) \supset (s \supset r)))$ 1, subst
     9 $((s \supset (q \supset p)) \supset ((s \supset q) \supset (s \supset p)))$ 8, subst
    10 $(((s \supset r) \supset (q \supset p)) \supset (((s \supset r) \supset q)$
        $\supset ((s \supset r) \supset p)))$ 9, subst
    11 $(((s \supset r) \supset ((q \supset (s \supset r)) \supset p)) \supset (((s \supset r)$
        $\supset (q \supset (s \supset r))) \supset ((s \supset r) \supset p)))$ 10, subst
    12 $(((s \supset r) \supset ((q \supset (s \supset r)) \supset ((q \supset s) \supset (q \supset r))))$
        $\supset (((s \supset r) \supset (q \supset (s \supset r))) \supset ((s \supset r)$
        $\supset ((q \supset s) \supset (q \supset r)))))$ 11, subst

13   $(((s \supset r) \supset (q \supset (s \supset r)))$
      $\supset ((s \supset r) \supset ((q \supset s) \supset (q \supset r))))$ 7, 12 m p
14   $((s \supset r) \supset (q \supset (s \supset r)))$ 4, subst
15   $((s \supset r) \supset ((q \supset s) \supset (q \supset r)))$ 13, 14, m p
16   $((p \supset r) \supset ((q \supset p) \supset (q \supset r)))$ 15, subst
17   $((p \supset s) \supset ((q \supset p) \supset (q \supset s)))$ 16, subst
18   $((p \supset s) \supset ((r \supset p) \supset (r \supset s)))$ 17, subst
19   $((p \supset q) \supset ((r \supset p) \supset (r \supset q)))$ 18, subst

Chapter II

1. (a) '$(\sim q \supset p)$', where 'p' stands for 'We'll go to the beach today' and 'q' for 'It rains'.
   (b) '$(p \supset \sim q)$', where 'p' stands for 'You do what you're told' and 'q' for 'You'll get along badly here'.
   (c) '$\sim q$', where 'q' stands for 'The dog was treated unkindly'.
   (d) '$(p \supset (q \supset (\sim r \supset s)))$', where 'p' stands for 'I move my pawn', 'q' for 'He castles', 'r' for 'I lose my queen', and 's' for 'I should be able to beat him'.
   (e) 'p', where 'p' stands for 'All mice are mortal'.
   (f) '$(p \supset (q \supset r))$', where 'p' stands for 'The next train is on time', 'q' for 'I miss my train', and 's' for 'I can arrive only five minutes late'.
   (g) 'p', where 'p' stands for 'Sam isn't over five feet tall, unless he has grown'.

Chapter III

1.
1	q	hyp
2	p	hyp
3	p	hyp
4	$(p \supset p)$	3, imp int
5	$(p \supset (p \supset p))$	2-4, imp int

(c)

1	$((p \supset (q \supset p)) \supset r)$	hyp
2	p	hyp
3	q	hyp
4	p	2, reit
5	$(q \supset p)$	3-4, imp int
6	$(p \supset (q \supset p))$	2-5, imp int
7	r	1, 6, m p

(e)

1	p	hyp
2	(((q ⊃ q) ⊃ p) ⊃ r)	hyp
3	(q ⊃ q)	hyp
4	p	1, reit
5	((q ⊃ q) ⊃ p)	3–4, imp int
6	r	2, 5, m p

(h)

1	((p ⊃ q) ⊃ p)	hyp
2	((p ⊃ r) ⊃ q)	hyp
3	r	hyp
4	p	hyp
5	p	hyp
6	r	3, reit
7	(p ⊃ r)	5–6, imp int
8	((p ⊃ r) ⊃ q)	2, reit
9	q	7, 8, m p
10	(p ⊃ q)	4–9, imp int
11	p	1, 10, m p

(j)

2.

1	r	hyp
2	(p ⊃ q)	hyp
3	s	hyp
4	(p ⊃ q)	2, reit
5	(s ⊃ (p ⊃ q))	3–4, imp int
6	((p ⊃ q) ⊃ (s ⊃ (p ⊃ q)))	2–5, imp int
7	(r ⊃ ((p ⊃ q) ⊃ (s ⊃ (p ⊃ q))))	1–6, imp int

(b)

1	((p ⊃ p) ⊃ p)	hyp
2	p	hyp
3	(p ⊃ p)	2, imp int
4	p	1, 3, m p
5	(((p ⊃ p) ⊃ p) ⊃ p)	1–4, imp int

(c)

1	(p ⊃ (p ⊃ q))	hyp
2	p	hyp
3	(p ⊃ (p ⊃ q))	1, reit
4	(p ⊃ q)	2, 3, m p
5	q	2, 4, m p
6	(p ⊃ q)	2–5, imp int
7	((p ⊃ (p ⊃ q)) ⊃ (p ⊃ q))	1–6, imp int

(d)

1	$((p \supset (q \supset r)) \supset s)$	hyp
2	r	hyp
3	p	hyp
4	q	hyp
5	r	2, reit
6	$(q \supset r)$	4–5, imp int
7	$(p \supset (q \supset r))$	3–6, imp int
8	$((p \supset (q \supset r)) \supset s)$	1, reit
9	s	7, 8, m p
10	$(r \supset s)$	2–9, imp int
11	$(((p \supset (q \supset r)) \supset s) \supset (r \supset s))$	1–10, imp int

(e)

1	$((p \supset p) \supset q)$	hyp
2	p	hyp
3	$(p \supset p)$	2, imp int
4	q	1, 3, m p
5	$(((p \supset p) \supset q) \supset q)$	1–4, imp int

(f)

1	$(p \supset q)$	hyp
2	$((r \supset q) \supset s)$	hyp
3	$(r \supset p)$	hyp
4	r	hyp
5	$(r \supset p)$	3, reit
6	p	4, 5, m p
7	$(p \supset q)$	1, reit
8	q	6, 7, m p
9	$(r \supset q)$	4–8, imp int
10	$((r \supset q) \supset s)$	2, reit
11	s	9, 10, m p
12	$((r \supset p) \supset s)$	3–11, imp int
13	$(((r \supset q) \supset s) \supset ((r \supset p) \supset s))$	2–12, imp int
14	$((p \supset q) \supset (((r \supset q) \supset s) \supset ((r \supset p) \supset s)))$	1–13, imp int

(g)

Chapter IV

1. (a) '$(\sim p \supset q)$', where 'p' stands for 'His car breaks down on the way' and 'q' for 'He'll come tomorrow'.
   (b) '$(p \land q)$', where 'p' stands for 'Baltimore is in Maryland' and 'q' for 'Hagerstown is in Maryland'.
   (c) '$(p \land (q \supset r))$', where 'p' stands for 'I never learned to speak German well', 'q' for 'You speak slowly', and 'r' for 'I can understand you'.

(d) Untranslatable, since it is a question.

(e) '$((p \equiv \sim q) \land (\sim r \land \sim s))$', where 'p' stands for 'The accused is guilty', 'q' for 'He was at home on the night of July 15', 'r' for 'His wife will testify against him', and 's' for 'There are other witnesses'.

(f) '$(p \land (q \land r))$', where 'p' stands for 'I've only been in town a week', 'q' for 'I've already been to five parties', and 'r' for 'I've already been to a concert'.

(g) 'p', where 'p' stands for 'Everyone in this room is unable to read music'.

(h) '$((p \supset q) \land r)$', where 'p' stands for 'You are allowed to walk your dog', 'q' for 'You have him on a leash', and 'r' for 'The dog must have a license'. '$((p \supset q) \land (p \supset r))$' is also an acceptable translation, but results from a less likely interpretation of the sentence.

(i) '$(p \equiv (\sim q \land \sim r))$', where 'p' stands for '$2^{10} + 1$ is a prime number', 'q' for '$2^{10} + 1$ is divisible by 17' and 'r' for '$2^{10} + 1$ is divisible by 21'.

(j) '$((\sim(p \lor q) \supset (r \lor (s \land t))) \land (t \supset u))$', where 'p' stands for 'The boss is at home', 'q' for 'The boss is at work', 'r' for 'He is at the golf course', 's' for 'Something extraordinary has happened', 't' for 'He has been detained', and 'u' for 'We'll know about it soon'.

(k) 'p', where 'p' stands for 'New York is nearer to Cleveland than to Kingston'.

(l) '$(q \supset (p \supset r))$', where 'p' stands for 'We get some luck', 'q' for 'We're only two days behind schedule', and 'r' for 'We may be able to catch up'.

(m) Untranslatable, since the sentence is an imperative.

(n) 'p', where 'p' stands for 'The best way to go there is to go five miles down the road and turn left at the fire station'.

(o) '$\sim p$', where 'p' stands for 'He knew that Mozart and his father were musicians'.

(p) '$((\sim p \supset (q \land r)) \land s)$' where 'p' stands for 'The train is late', 'q' for 'I'll stop at a bar', 'r' for 'I'll get a drink', and 's' for 'That's for sure'.

2. (c) From '$(p \lor q)$' and '$(q \supset (r \land s))$' to derive '$(p \lor s)$', where 'p' stands for 'Albert is a fool', 'q' for 'Albert is a liar', 'r' for 'What he told me about my sister is false', and 's' for 'I'll look like a fool'.

1	$(p \lor q)$	hyp
2	$(q \supset (r \land s))$	hyp
3	p	hyp
4	$(p \lor s)$	3, dis int
5	q	hyp
6	$(q \supset (r \land s))$	2, reit
7	$(r \land s)$	5, 6, m p
8	s	7, conj elim
9	$(p \lor s)$	8, dis int
10	$(p \lor s)$	1, 3–4, 5–9, dis elim

(e) From '$(p \supset ((q \land r) \lor (s \land t)))$' and '$(r \supset t)$' to derive '$(p \supset t)$', where 'p' stands for 'John is arrested', 'q' for 'He will plead guilty', 'r' for 'He will have to pay a large fine', 's' for 'He will plead not guilty', and 't' for 'He will go to a lot of trouble'.

1	(p ⊃ ((q ∧ r) ∨ (s ∧ t)))	hyp
2	(r ⊃ t)	hyp
3	p	hyp
4	(p ⊃ ((q ∧ r) ∨ (s ∧ t)))	1, reit
5	((q ∧ r) ∨ (s ∧ t))	3, 4, m p
6	(q ∧ r)	hyp
7	r	6, conj elim
8	(r ⊃ t)	2, reit
9	t	7, 8, m p
10	(s ∧ t)	hyp
11	t	10, conj elim
12	t	5, 6–9, 10–11, dis elim
13	(p ⊃ t)	1–12, imp int

(f) From '~(p ⊃ q)' to infer '(p ∧ ~q)', where 'p' stands for 'God exists' and 'q' for 'There is unnecessary evil in the world'.

1	~(p ⊃ q)	hyp
2	~p	hyp
3	p	hyp
4	~q	hyp
5	p	3, reit
6	~p	2, reit
7	~~q	4–6, neg int
8	q	7, neg elim
9	(p ⊃ q)	3–8, imp int
10	~(p ⊃ q)	1, reit
11	~~p	2–10, neg int
12	p	11, neg elim
13	q	hyp
14	p	hyp
15	q	13, reit
16	(p ⊃ q)	14–15, imp int
17	~(p ⊃ q)	1, reit
18	~q	13–17, neg int
19	(p ∧ ~q)	12, 18, conj int

3.
1	(p ∨ q)	hyp
2	p	hyp
3	(q ∨ p)	2, dis int
4	q	hyp
5	(q ∨ p)	4, dis int
6	(q ∨ p)	1, 2–3, 4–5, dis elim

(a)

1	p	hyp
2	(p ∨ q)	1, dis int
3	(p ∨ ~q)	1, dis int
4	((p ∨ q) ∧ (p ∨ ~q))	2, 3, conj int

(h)

1	((p ⊃ q) ⊃ q)	hyp
2	(q ⊃ ~q)	hyp
3	~p	hyp
4	p	hyp
5	~q	hyp
6	p	4, reit
7	~p	3, reit
8	~~q	5–7, neg int
9	q	8, neg elim
10	(p ⊃ q)	4–9, imp int
11	((p ⊃ q) ⊃ q)	1, reit
12	q	10, 11, m p
13	(q ⊃ ~q)	2, reit
14	~q	12, 13, m p
15	~~p	3–14, neg int
16	p	15, neg elim

(n)

1	((p ⊃ q) ⊃ (r ⊃ q))	hyp
2	(q ⊃ p)	hyp
3	r	hyp
4	~p	hyp
5	p	hyp
6	~q	hyp
7	p	5, reit
8	~p	4, reit
9	~~q	6–8, neg int
10	q	9, neg elim
11	(p ⊃ q)	5–10, imp int
12	((p ⊃ q) ⊃ (r ⊃ q))	1, reit
13	(r ⊃ q)	11, 12, m p
14	r	3, reit
15	q	13, 14, m p
16	(q ⊃ p)	2, reit
17	p	15, 16, m p
18	~~p	4–17, neg int
19	p	18, neg elim
20	(r ⊃ p)	3–19, imp int

(p)

1	$\sim(p \equiv q)$	hyp
2	$\sim(p \lor q)$	hyp
3	p	hyp
4	$\sim q$	hyp
5	p	3, reit
6	$(p \lor q)$	5, dis int
7	$\sim(p \lor q)$	2, reit
8	$\sim\sim q$	4–7, neg int
9	q	8, neg elim
10	q	hyp
11	$\sim p$	hyp
12	q	10, reit
13	$(p \lor q)$	12, dis int
14	$\sim(p \lor q)$	2, reit
15	$\sim\sim p$	11–14, neg int
16	p	15, neg elim
17	$(p \equiv q)$	3–9, 10–16, eqv int
18	$\sim(p \equiv q)$	1, reit
19	$\sim\sim(p \lor q)$	2–18, neg int
20	$(p \lor q)$	19, neg elim

(u)

4.

1	$\sim(p \lor (p \supset q))$	hyp
2	p	hyp
3	$\sim q$	hyp
4	p	2, reit
5	$(p \lor (p \supset q))$	4, dis int
6	$\sim(p \lor (p \supset q))$	1, reit
7	$\sim\sim q$	3–6, neg int
8	q	7, neg elim
9	$(p \supset q)$	2–8, imp int
10	$(p \lor (p \supset q))$	9, dis int
11	$\sim\sim(p \lor (p \supset q))$	1–10, neg int
12	$(p \lor (p \supset q))$	11, neg elim

(a)

1	(p ⊃ q)	hyp
2	~(~p ∨ q)	hyp
3	p	hyp
4	(p ⊃ q)	1, reit
5	q	3, 4, m p
6	(~p ∨ q)	5, dis int
7	~(~p ∨ q)	2, reit
8	~p	3–7, neg int
9	(~p ∨ q)	8, dis int
10	~~(~p ∨ q)	2–9, neg int
11	(~p ∨ q)	10, neg elim
12	(~p ∨ q)	hyp
13	~p	hyp
14	p	hyp
15	~q	hyp
16	p	14, reit
17	~p	13, reit
18	~~q	15–17, neg int
19	q	18, neg elim
20	(p ⊃ q)	14–19, imp int
21	q	hyp
22	p	hyp
23	q	21, reit
24	(p ⊃ q)	22–23, imp int
25	(p ⊃ q)	12, 13–20, 21–24, dis elim
26	((p ⊃ q) ≡ (~p ∨ q))	1–11, 12–25, eqv int

(b)

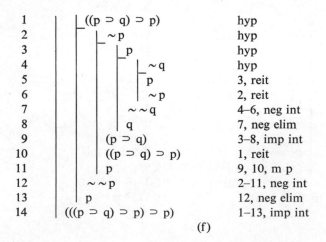

1	((p ⊃ q) ⊃ p)	hyp
2	~p	hyp
3	p	hyp
4	~q	hyp
5	p	3, reit
6	~p	2, reit
7	~~q	4–6, neg int
8	q	7, neg elim
9	(p ⊃ q)	3–8, imp int
10	((p ⊃ q) ⊃ p)	1, reit
11	p	9, 10, m p
12	~~p	2–11, neg int
13	p	12, neg elim
14	(((p ⊃ q) ⊃ p) ⊃ p)	1–13, imp int

(f)

Chapter V

1. P is the same as P; if A is the same as B then $\sim A$ is the same as $\sim B$; if A is the same as B and C is the same as D then $A \supset C$ is the same as $B \supset D$.

3. We use '$\{P, P \supset Q\} \vdash Q$' to say that there is a deduction of Q from hypotheses P and $P \supset Q$. This deduction will be an array $A_1, \ldots, A_n$ of formulas; in fact, $P, P \supset Q, Q$ is such an array. 'P' can only take as values the sentence parameters of $\mathbf{H_s}$; however, the result of putting 'A' and 'B', which represent arbitrary formulas, for 'P' and 'Q' in '$P, P \supset Q, Q$' will represent a deduction. Hence, we know that $\{A, A \supset B\} \vdash B$ for all formulas A and B of $\mathbf{H_s}$.

4. $P_1 \lor P_2$ is a formula of $\mathbf{H_s}$. '$P_1 \lor P_2$' is a name of a formula of $\mathbf{H_s}$, and need not be a formula of $\mathbf{H_s}$.

5. (a) $((P \supset P) \supset Q)$
   (c) $((P \supset P) \supset (P \supset P))$
   (e) $(((\sim(A \supset B) \supset A) \supset \sim A)$
       $\supset (A \supset B))$
   (b) $((P \supset (Q \supset P))$
       $\supset (P \supset (\sim P \supset Q)))$
   (d) $(A \supset (B \supset A))$
   (f) $(\sim P \supset Q)$

6. (a) $A \supset B \supset B \supset . \sim A \supset B$
   (b) $A \supset . A \supset B \supset B$
   (c) $A \supset B \supset B \supset . B \supset A \supset A$
   (d) $\sim(A \supset \sim B) \supset A$
   (e) $A \supset . B \supset \sim(A \supset \sim B)$
   (f) $\sim A \supset \sim B \supset \sim B$
       $\supset \sim\sim(A \supset \sim B)$
   (g) $\sim(A \supset \sim A \supset \sim(\sim A \supset A))$
   (h) $\sim(A \supset B \supset \sim(B \supset A)) \supset \sim(\sim A \supset \sim B \supset \sim(\sim B \supset \sim A))$

8. (a)

1	$P_1 \supset . P_1 \supset P_1$	AS1
2	$(P_1 \supset . P_1 \supset P_1) \supset . P_1 \supset P_1 \supset . P_1 \supset P_1$	AS2
3	$P_1 \supset P_1 \supset . P_1 \supset P_1$	1, 2, m p
4	$(P_1 \supset P_1 \supset . P_1 \supset P_1) \supset . P_1 \supset . P_1 \supset P_1 \supset . P_1 \supset P_1$	AS1
5	$P_1 \supset . P_1 \supset P_1 \supset . P_1 \supset P_1$	3, 4, m p

(b)

1	$\sim P_2 \supset \sim P_1 \supset . P_1 \supset P_2$	AS3
2	$(\sim P_2 \supset \sim P_1 \supset . P_1 \supset P_2) \supset . \sim P_1 \supset . \sim P_2 \supset \sim P_1$ $\supset . P_1 \supset P_2$	AS1
3	$\sim P_1 \supset . \sim P_2 \supset \sim P_1 \supset . P_1 \supset P_2$	1, 2, m p
4	$(\sim P_1 \supset . \sim P_2 \supset \sim P_1 \supset . P_1 \supset P_2)$ $\supset . (\sim P_1 \supset . \sim P_2 \supset \sim P_1) \supset . \sim P_1 \supset . P_1 \supset P_2$	AS2
5	$(\sim P_1 \supset . \sim P_2 \supset \sim P_1) \supset . \sim P_1 \supset . P_1 \supset P_2$	3, 4, m p
6	$\sim P_1 \supset . \sim P_2 \supset \sim P_1$	AS1
7	$\sim P_1 \supset . P_1 \supset P_2$	5, 6, m p

(e)

1	$P_1 \supset . P_1 \supset P_2$	hyp
2	P_1	hyp
3	$P_1 \supset P_2$	1, 2, m p
4	P_2	2, 3, m p

(f)

1	$P_1 \supset . P_1 \supset P_2$	hyp
2	$(P_1 \supset . P_1 \supset P_2) \supset . P_1 \supset P_1 \supset . P_1 \supset P_2$	AS2
3	$P_1 \supset P_1 \supset . P_1 \supset P_2$	1, 2, m p
4	$(P_1 \supset . P_1 \supset P_1 \supset P_1) \supset . (P_1 \supset . P_1 \supset P_1) \supset . P_1 \supset P_1$	AS2

5 $P_1 \supset . P_1 \supset P_1 \supset P_1$ AS1

6 $(P_1 \supset . P_1 \supset P_1) \supset . P_1 \supset P_1$ 4, 5, m p

7 $P_1 \supset . P_1 \supset P_1$ AS1

8 $P_1 \supset P_1$ 6, 7, m p

9 $P_1 \supset P_2$ 3, 8, m p

(h) 1 P_1 hyp

2 $\sim\sim P_1 \supset \sim\sim\sim P_1 \supset . \sim\sim P_1 \supset \sim P_1$ AS3

3 $(\sim\sim P_1 \supset \sim\sim\sim P_1 \supset . \sim\sim P_1 \supset \sim P_1) \supset . \sim\sim\sim P_1$
   $\supset . \sim\sim P_1 \supset \sim\sim\sim P_1 \supset . \sim\sim P_1 \supset \sim P_1$ AS1

4 $\sim\sim\sim P_1 \supset . \sim\sim P_1 \supset \sim\sim\sim P_1 \supset . \sim\sim P_1 \supset \sim P_1$ 2, 3, m p

5 $(\sim\sim\sim P_1 \supset . \sim\sim P_1 \supset \sim\sim\sim P_1 \supset . \sim\sim P_1 \supset \sim P_1)$
   $\supset . (\sim\sim\sim P_1 \supset . \sim\sim P_1 \supset \sim\sim\sim P_1) \supset . \sim\sim\sim P_1$
   $\supset . \sim\sim P_1 \supset \sim P_1$ AS2

6 $(\sim\sim\sim P_1 \supset . \sim\sim P_1 \supset \sim\sim\sim P_1) \supset . \sim\sim\sim P_1$
   $\supset . \sim\sim P_1 \supset \sim P_1$ 4, 5, m p

7 $\sim\sim\sim P_1 \supset . \sim\sim P_1 \supset \sim\sim\sim P_1$ AS1

8 $\sim\sim\sim P_1 \supset . \sim\sim P_1 \supset \sim P_1$ 6, 7, m p

9 $\sim\sim P_1 \supset \sim P_1 \supset . P_1 \supset \sim P_1$ AS3

10 $(\sim\sim P_1 \supset \sim P_1 \supset . P_1 \supset \sim P_1) \supset . \sim\sim\sim P_1 \supset . \sim\sim P_1$
   $\supset \sim P_1 \supset . P_1 \supset \sim P_1$ AS1

11 $\sim\sim\sim P_1 \supset . \sim\sim P_1 \supset \sim P_1 \supset . P_1 \supset \sim P_1$ 9, 10, m p

12 $(\sim\sim\sim P_1 \supset . \sim\sim P_1 \supset \sim P_1 \supset . P_1 \supset \sim P_1)$
   $\supset . (\sim\sim\sim P_1 \supset . \sim\sim P_1 \supset \sim P_1) \supset . \sim\sim\sim P_1 \supset . P_1$
   $\supset \sim P_1$ AS2

13 $(\sim\sim\sim P_1 \supset . \sim\sim P_1 \supset \sim P_1) \supset . \sim\sim\sim P_1 \supset . P_1 \supset \sim P_1$ 11, 12, m p

14 $\sim\sim\sim P_1 \supset . P_1 \supset \sim P_1$ 8, 13, m p

15 $(\sim\sim\sim P_1 \supset . P_1 \supset \sim P_1) \supset . \sim\sim\sim P_1 \supset P_1$
   $\supset . \sim\sim\sim P_1 \supset \sim P_1$ AS2

16 $\sim\sim\sim P_1 \supset P_1 \supset . \sim\sim\sim P_1 \supset \sim P_1$ 14, 15, m p

17 $P_1 \supset . \sim\sim\sim P_1 \supset P_1$ AS1

18 $\sim\sim\sim P_1 \supset P_1$ 1, 17, m p

19 $\sim\sim\sim P_1 \supset \sim P_1$ 16, 18, m p

20 $(\sim\sim\sim P_1 \supset \sim P_1) \supset . P_1 \supset \sim\sim P_1$ AS3

21 $P_1 \supset \sim\sim P_1$ 19, 20, m p

22 $\sim\sim P_1$ 1, 21, m p

10. No. If $A \supset . B \supset A$ were the same as $(C \supset . D \supset E) \supset . C \supset D \supset . C \supset E$ then $C \supset . D \supset E$ would be the same as $C \supset E$, and hence $D \supset E$ would be the same as D. But this is impossible.

12. (c) 1 $A, C, B \vdash C$ M4

     2 $A, C \vdash B \supset C$ 1, M8

     3 $A \vdash C \supset . B \supset C$ 2, M8

     4 $\vdash A \supset . C \supset . B \supset C$ 3, M8

(d) 1 $A, B \vdash B$ M4

     2 $A \vdash B \supset B$ 1, M8

     3 $\vdash A \supset . B \supset B$ 2, M8

13. (b)

1	$A, \sim A \vdash A$	M4
2	$A, \sim A \vdash \sim A$	M4
3	$A \vdash \sim\sim A$	1, 2, M20

(d)

1	$A \supset B, A \vdash B$	*modus ponens*
2	$A \supset B, \sim A \supset B, \sim B, A \vdash B$	1, M5
3	$A \supset B, \sim A \supset B, \sim B, A \vdash \sim B$	M4
4	$A \supset B, \sim A \supset B, \sim B \vdash \sim A$	2, 3, M20
5	$A \supset B, \sim A \supset B, \sim B \vdash \sim A \supset B$	M4
6	$A \supset B, \sim A \supset B, \sim B \vdash B$	4, 5, M11
7	$A \supset B, \sim A \supset B, \sim B \vdash \sim B$	M4
8	$A \supset B, \sim A \supset B \vdash \sim\sim B$	6, 7, M20
9	$A \supset B, \sim A \supset B \vdash B$	8, M19

(e)

1	$\sim A, A \vdash B$	M13
2	$\sim A \vdash A \supset B$	1, M8
3	$A \supset B \supset B, B \supset A, \sim A \vdash A \supset B$	2, M5
4	$A \supset B \supset B, B \supset A, \sim A \vdash A \supset B \supset B$	M4
5	$A \supset B \supset B, B \supset A, \sim A \vdash B$	3, 4, M11
6	$A \supset B \supset B, B \supset A, \sim A \vdash B \supset A$	M4
7	$A \supset B \supset B, B \supset A, \sim A \vdash A$	5, 6, M11
8	$A \supset B \supset B, B \supset A, \sim A \vdash \sim A$	M4
9	$A \supset B \supset B, B \supset A \vdash \sim\sim A$	7, 8, M20
10	$A \supset B \supset B, B \supset A \vdash A$	9, M19
11	$A \supset B \supset B \vdash B \supset A \supset A$	10, M8
12	$A \vee B \vdash B \vee A$	11, D5

(h)

1	$\sim(A \supset \sim\sim A), A, \sim A \vdash A$	M4
2	$\sim(A \supset \sim\sim A), A, \sim A \vdash \sim A$	M4
3	$\sim(A \supset \sim\sim A), A \vdash \sim\sim A$	1, 2, M20
4	$\sim(A \supset \sim\sim A) \vdash A \supset \sim\sim A$	3, M8
5	$\sim(A \supset \sim\sim A) \vdash \sim(A \supset \sim\sim A)$	M4
6	$\vdash \sim\sim(A \supset \sim\sim A)$	4, 5, M20
7	$\vdash \sim(A \wedge \sim A)$	6, D6

Chapter VI

1. (c)

P	$\sim\sim P \supset \sim P$
T	F
F	T

The formula is invalid and satisfiable.

(d)

P	Q	$P \supset Q \supset P \supset P$
T	T	T
T	F	T
F	T	T
F	F	T

The formula is valid and satisfiable.

(f)

P	Q	$\sim(P \supset Q \supset . \sim Q \supset \sim P)$
T	T	F
T	F	F
F	T	F
F	F	F

The formula is invalid and not satisfiable.

(k)

P	Q	R	$P \supset Q \supset R \supset . \sim P \supset R$
T	T	T	T
T	T	F	T
T	F	T	T
T	F	F	T
F	T	T	T
F	T	F	T
F	F	T	T
F	F	F	T

The formula is valid and satisfiable.

2. (a) Let $A \supset . B \supset A$ be a formula of **M**, and V be an arbitrary valuation of **M**. If $V(A) = T$ then $V(B \supset A) = T$, and hence in any case $V(A \supset . B \supset A) = T$. Therefore for any valuation V of **M**, $V(A \supset . B \supset A) = T$; i.e., $A \supset . B \supset A$ is valid.

(d) Let $A \supset B \supset . A \supset \sim B \supset \sim A$ be a formula of **M**, and V be an arbitrary valuation of **M**. If $V(A \supset \sim B \supset \sim A) = F$, then $V(\sim A) = F$ so that $V(A) = T$, and $V(A \supset \sim B) = T$. But if $V(A) = T$ and $V(A \supset \sim B) = T$, then $V(\sim B) = T$ so that $V(B) = F$, and hence $V(A \supset B) = F$. Therefore in any case $V(A \supset B \supset . A \supset \sim B \supset \sim A) = T$. It follows that for any valuation V of **M**, $V(A \supset B \supset . A \supset \sim B \supset \sim A) = T$; i.e., $A \supset B \supset . A \supset \sim B \supset \sim A$ is valid.

3. (a) $\sim(P \supset P)$ is a formula of the sort A, and is not satisfiable. (d) $(P \supset P) \supset \sim(P \supset P) \supset \sim(P \supset P) \supset \sim(P \supset P)$ is a formula of the sort $A \supset B \supset B \supset B$, and is not satisfiable. (e) Let $A \supset A \supset A \supset A$ be a formula of **M**, and V be an arbitrary valuation of **M**. If $V(A) = F$ then, since $V(A \supset A) = T$, $V(A \supset A \supset A) = F$ and therefore $V(A \supset A \supset A \supset A) = T$. $A \supset A \supset A \supset A$ is therefore satisfiable, and in fact is valid.

4. In view of M1, $V(A) = T$ or $V(A) = F$. But if $V(A) = F$ then $V(\sim A) = T$; therefore $V(A) = T$ or $V(\sim A) = T$. Also in view of M1, not both $V(\sim A) = T$ and $V(\sim A) = F$. But if $V(A) = T$ then $V(\sim A) = F$; therefore not both $V(A) = T$ and $V(\sim A) = T$.

8. Let A be a formula of both **M** and **M'**; then **M** and **M'** have at least one sentence parameter in common, say P. Let $A_1, \ldots, A_n$ be a proof of A consisting only of formulas of **M**, and let A_i' be the result of substituting P for each sentence parameter occurring in A_i which is not a sentence parameter of **M'**. Then $A_1', \ldots, A_n'$ is a proof of A_n' consisting only of formulas of **M'**. Since A_n (i.e., A) is a formula of **M'**, A_n is A and this is thus a proof of A. The same procedure shows that if there is a proof of A consisting only of formulas of **M'** then there is a proof of A consisting only of formulas of **M**.

10. (a) No. $\{P\}$ and $\{\sim P\}$ are both simultaneously satisfiable, but $\{P, \sim P\}$ is not.
   (b) Yes. Suppose that Γ is simultaneously satisfiable; then there is a valuation V that simultaneously satisfies Γ. Since $\Gamma \cap \Delta \subseteq \Gamma$, V also simultaneously satisfies $\Gamma \cap \Delta$, which therefore is simultaneously satisfiable.
   (c) Yes. Suppose that Γ is simultaneously satisfiable; then there is a valuation V which simultaneously satisfies Γ. V therefore satisfies $A \vee B$ for each $A \in \Gamma$, and so simultaneously satisfies $\{A \vee B \mid A \in \Gamma$ and $B \in \Delta\}$. This set is therefore simultaneously satisfiable.
   (d) No. $\{P \supset P\}$ is simultaneously satisfiable, but $\{\sim(P \supset P)\}$ is not.

11. $\{P, P \supset Q, \sim Q\}$ is such a set.

Chapter VII

1. (a) Provable.   (b) Not provable.   (c) Provable.
   (d) Not provable.   (e) Provable.   (f) Provable.

2. (a) Correct.   (b) Incorrect.   (c) Correct.
   (d) Correct.   (e) Incorrect.   (f) Incorrect.

3. (a) Consistent.   (b) Inconsistent.   (c) Inconsistent.
   (d) Inconsistent.   (e) Consistent.   (f) Inconsistent.

4. No, because $P \vee Q$ does not imply P, as is shown by letting $V(P) = F$ and $V(Q) = T$.

5. By M16, Γ is simultaneously satisfiable if and only if Γ is consistent, and by M12, Γ is consistent if and only if Γ has at least one M-saturated extension. Therefore Γ is simultaneously satisfiable if and only if Γ has at least one M-saturated extension.

6. Neither P nor $\sim P$ is valid. Therefore neither $\vdash P$ nor $\vdash \sim P$.

7. If both A and $\sim A$ were valid, then we would have both $V(A) = T$ and $V(\sim A) = T$, contradicting VI.M1; therefore if $\Vdash A$ then not $\Vdash \sim A$. By M19, if $\vdash A$ then not $\vdash \sim A$.

9. (a) No. $\Vdash P \vee \sim P$, but neither $\Vdash P$ nor $\Vdash \sim P$. Therefore $\vdash P \vee \sim P$, but neither $\vdash P$ nor $\vdash \sim P$.
   (b) No. $\vdash P \equiv P$, but where $V_1(P) = T$ and $V_2(P) = F$, $V_1(P) \neq V_2(P)$.
   (c) No. P is satisfiable, but $P \wedge \sim P$, a substitution instance of P, is not.
   (d) A is satisfiable if and only if $\{A\}$ is simultaneously satisfiable, and by M16, $\{A\}$ is simultaneously satisfiable if and only if $\{A\}$ is consistent. But by V.M34, $\{A\}$ is consistent if and only if not $\vdash \sim A$. Thus, A is satisfiable if and only if not $\vdash \sim A$.
   (e) Suppose first that Θ is simultaneously satisfiable; then, since $\Gamma \subseteq \Theta$ for each $\Gamma \in X$, each such Γ is simultaneously satisfiable. Conversely, suppose that for each $\Gamma \in X$, Γ is simultaneously satisfiable. Then by M16, Γ is

consistent for each $\Gamma \in X$. Suppose that Θ were inconsistent; then by
V.M33, for some $\{A_1, \ldots, A_n\} \subseteq \Theta$, $\{A_1, \ldots, A_n\}$ would be inconsistent.
Now, for all i, $1 \le i \le n$, $A_i \in \Gamma_i$ for some $\Gamma_i \in X$, and for all such Γ_i and
Γ_j either $\Gamma_i \subseteq \Gamma_j$ or $\Gamma_j \subseteq \Gamma_i$. It follows that there would be a member Γ_k
of X such that $\{A_1, \ldots, A_n\} \subseteq \Gamma_k$, and hence Γ_k would be inconsistent
contrary to our conclusion that every member of X is consistent. There-
fore Θ must be consistent.

16. Suppose that not $\Vdash \sim A$; then there is a valuation V of **M** such that $V(A) = T$,
where **M** is the set of sentence parameters occurring in A. Let **M'** be the set of
sentence parameters occurring in B, and suppose that for some valuation U
of **M'**, $U(B) = F$. Let $\mathbf{M''} = \mathbf{M} \cup \mathbf{M'}$, and define a valuation W on $\mathbf{M''}$ by
letting $W(P) = V(P)$ if $P \in \mathbf{M}$ and $W(P) = U(P)$ if $P \in \mathbf{M'}$. There is no possibility of contradiction here, since **M** and **M'** have no members in common.
But then $W(A \supset B) = F$, which is impossible since $\vdash A \supset B$ and therefore
$\Vdash A \supset B$. It follows that $U(B) = T$ for all valuations U of **M'**, and thus
$\Vdash B$ if not $\Vdash \sim A$. By M19, either $\vdash \sim A$ or $\vdash B$.

Chapter VIII

1. (a), (b), (f), (g), (h), and (j) are formulas. (c), (d), (e), (i), (k), and (l) are not.

2. (a) $(x)(Px \supset Qx)$, where Pu stands for '... is an oak' and Qu for '... is
deciduous'. Domain: all plants.
   (b) Pa, where Pu stands for '... is unhappy' and a for 'Margaret'. Domain:
all people.
   (c) Pab, where Puv stands for '... is married to ___', a for 'John' and b for
'Susan'. Domain: all people.
   (d) $(x)((Px \wedge Qx) \supset \sim Rx)$ where Pu stands for '... is a glass', Qu for
'... is in this shipment' and Ru for '... is broken'. Domain: all physical
objects.
   (e) $(x)(Px \supset Qx)$, where Pu stands for '... is free' and Qu for '... is wise'.
Domain: all people.
   (f) $(x)((Px \wedge Qx) \supset Rax)$, where Pu stands for '... is in Saint Louis', Qu
for '... is worth knowing', Ruv for '... knows ___', and a for 'Bill'.
Domain: all people.
   (g) $(x)((Px \wedge \sim Rax) \supset \sim Qx)$, where Pu stands for '... is in Saint Louis',
Qu for '... is worth knowing', Ruv for '... knows ___', and a for 'Bill'.
Domain: all people.
   (h) $(x)(Px \supset (y)(Qy \supset \sim Rxy))$, where Pu stands for '... is a joke', Qu for
'... is a bone', and Ruv for '... breaks ___'. Domain: all things.
   (i) $(x)((Px \wedge Qax) \supset (\exists y)Ryax)$, where Pu stands for '... is a day', Quv for
'... is at home on ___', $Ruvw$ for '... calls ___ on ___', and a for 'she'.
Domain: all days and persons.
   (j) $(x)(Px \supset (\exists y)(Qy \wedge Ryx))$, where Pu stands for '... is a cloud', Qu for
'... is silver', and Ruv for '... lines ___'. Domain: all things.

(k) $(x)(Px \supset ((\exists y)(Qy \land (\exists z)(Rz \land Sxyz \land \sim Txyz)) \supset (Ux \lor Vx)))$, where Pu stands for '... is a person', Qu for '... is a pair of pants', Ru for '... is a time', $Suvw$ for '... buys ___ at ____', $Tuvw$ for '... tries on ___ at ____', Uu for '... is an optimist', and Vu for '... is a blockhead'. Domain: all people, articles of clothing, and times.

(l) $(x)(Px \supset Qx)$, where Pu stands for '... despises education' and Qu for '... is ignorant'. Domain: all people.

(m) $(x)((Px \land Qx) \supset \sim(\exists y)(Ry \land Sxy))$, where Pu stands for '... is a stone', Qu for '... is rolling', Ru for '... is moss', and Suv for '... gathers ___'. Domain: all physical objects.

(n) $(x)\sim Pxa$, where Puv stands for '... tries harder than ___' and a for 'he'. Domain: all people.

(o) $(x)(\sim Pxx \supset (y)\sim Pxy)$, where Puv stands for '... loves ___'. Domain: all people.

(p) $(x)(\sim Pxx \supset \sim(y)Pxy)$, where Puv stands for '... loves ___'. Domain: all persons.

(q) $(x)((Px \land \sim Qx) \supset Rx)$, where Pu stands for '... writes', Qu for '... writes for money', and Ru for '... is a blockhead'. Domain: all people.

(r) $(x)(Px \supset . (\exists y)(Qy \land Rxy) \supset (y)(Qy \supset Rxy))$, where Pu stands for '... is food', Qu for '... is a person', and Ruv for '... is good enough for ___'. Domain: all people and all foods.

(s) $Pab \equiv (x)(Qx \supset . (y)(Ry \supset . Sya \supset . Txy) \supset Txb)$, where Puv stands for '... implies ___', Qu for '... is a valuation', Ru for '... is a formula', Suv for '... is a member of ___', Tuv for '... makes ___ true', a for 'Γ', and b for 'A'. Domain: all formulas, sets of formulas, and valuations of some morphology **M**.

(t) $(x)(Px \supset x = a)$, where Pu stands for '... is a virtue' and a for 'wisdom'. Domain: all human qualities.

(u) $\sim(x)(Px \supset (y)(Qy \supset Rxy))$, where Pu stands for '... is a shoe', Qu for '... is a foot', and Ruv for '... fits ___'. Domain: all physical objects.

(v) $(x)(Px \supset (y)(\sim y = a \supset Qaxy))$, where Pu stands for '... is a trouble', $Quvw$ for '... is a better remedy for ___ than ____', and a for 'patience'. Domain: all things.

(w) $(\exists x)(Px \land (y)((Qy \land Ry) \supset Syx))$, where Pu stands for '... is a car', Qu for '... is a person', Ru for '... is here', and Suv for '... is going in ___'. Domain: all people and all cars.

(x) $(\exists x)(\exists y)(Pxy \land Qy \land Rxy)$, where Puv stands for '... is a remedy of ___', Qu for '... is a disease', and Ruv for '... is worse than ___'. Domain: all things.

(y) $(x)((Px \land Qx) \supset (y)((Rxy \land Sy) \supset (z)(Pz \supset . Tzy \supset \sim Uxzy)))$, where Pu stands for '... is a person', Qu for '... obeys the law', Ruv for '... owns ___', Su for '... is a restaurant', Tuv for '... is in ___', and $Uuvw$ for '... refuses to serve ___ in ____ on account of ___'s race'. Domain: all people, places of business.

(z) $(x)(Px \supset . Qx \supset (y)((Py \land Ry) \supset \sim(\exists z)(Sz \land Tyzx)))$, where Pu stands for '... is a person', Qu for '... will win the nomination', Ru for '... is on the committee', Su for '... is an objection', and $Tuvw$ for '... has ___ with reference to ___'. Domain: all people, objections. Notice that this translation ignores difficulties that may arise in rendering 'unless' by means of connectives such as $\supset$. Also it involves quantification over objections. This last feature can be removed by using a less informative translation such as $(x)(Qx \supset (y)(Ry \supset \sim Uyx))$, where Uuv stands for '... objects to ___' and the domain consists of all people.

3. (a) $(x)((Px \wedge Qxa) \supset (Rx \vee Sx))$, where Pu stands for '... is a person', Quv for '... is in ___', Ru for '... is sitting', Su for '... is standing', and a for 'the next room'. Domain: all people and places.

(b) $(x)((Px \wedge Qxa) \supset (\exists y)(Ry \wedge Sya \wedge Qxy))$, where Pu stands for '... is a statement', Quv for '... is said at ___', Ru for '... is a time', Suv for '... is earlier than ___', and a for 'now'. Domain: all statements and times.

(c) Untranslatable, since it involves an imperative.

(d) $(x)(\sim Pxa \supset . \sim (\exists y)(Qyx \wedge Pya \wedge Pyb) \supset \sim (\exists z)(Rz \wedge Sxz))$, where Puv stands for '... is endowed with ___', Quv for '... directs ___', Ru for '... is an end', Suv for '... moves toward ___', a for 'knowledge', and b for 'intelligence'. Domain: all things.

(e) $(x)((y)(\sim y = x \supset Pxy) \supset (y)(\sim y = x \supset Qxy))$, where Puv stands for '... laughs later than ___' and Quv for '... laughs better than ___'. Domain: all people in some situation.

(f) P, where P stands for 'There is something going on downtown tonight'.

(g) $(x)(Px \supset (\exists y)(Qy \wedge Rayax))$, where Pu stands for '... is a time', Qu for '... is a glass of water', $Ru_1u_2u_3u_4$ for '... keeps ___ by ___ at time $\sim\sim\sim$', and a for 'I'. Domain: all times and physical objects.

(h) Untranslatable, since it involves an interrogative.

(i) $a = b \wedge \sim (\exists x)Qx$, where Qu stands for '... will care to deny that Harris is the clerk who waited on me', a for 'Harris', and b for 'the clerk who waited on me'. Domain: all people.

(j) $\sim (\exists x)(Px \wedge \sim ((Qx \wedge Rx) \vee (Sx \wedge Rx))$
$$\wedge (\exists y)(((Qy \wedge Ry) \vee (Sy \wedge Ry)) \wedge Txy)),$$
where Pu stands for '... has been contrived by man', Qu for '... is a tavern', Ru for '... is good', Su for '... is an inn', and Tuv for '... produces so much happiness as ___'. Domain: all things.

(k) Untranslatable, since it involves an imperative.

(l) $a = b$, where a stands for 'he' and b for 'the man on the far right'. Domain: all people.

(m) $(x)(Pxa \supset . (y)(Qya \supset Ryx) \supset Sx)$, where Puv stands for '... is a formula of ___', Quv for '... is a valuation of ___', Ruv for '... satisfies ___', Su for '... is valid', and a for '**M**'. Domain: all morphologies, formulas, and valuations.

(n) $(x)(\sim Pax \supset Qax)$, where Puv stands for '... has had enough sleep at ___', Quv for '... feels groggy at ___', and a for 'Harold's wife'. Domain: all people and times.

(o) $(\exists x)(\exists y)(\exists z)(\sim x=y \;\land\; \sim x=z \;\land\; \sim y=z \;\land\; Px \;\land\; Qxa \;\land\; Py \;\land\; Qya \;\land\; Pz \;\land\; Qza)$, where Pu stands for '... is a congressman', Quv for '... is over ___ years old', and a for 'eighty'. Domain: all people and numbers.

(p) $(\exists x)(\exists y)(\exists z)(\sim x=y \;\land\; Pxa \;\land\; Pya \;\land\; Qx \;\land\; Qy \;\land\; Rxz \;\land\; Ryz)$, where Puv stands for '... is in ___', Qu for '... is female', Ruv for '... is married to ___', and a for 'Turkey'. Domain: all people, places.

(q) $\sim(\exists x)Px$, where Pu stands for '... knows whether Marlowe is the author of *Hamlet*'. Domain: all people.

(r) $P \supset (x)(Qxa \supset Rx)$, where P stands for 'It rains today', Quv for '... is going to ___', Ru for '... will be sorry', and a for 'the picnic'. Domain: all people and events.

(s) Pa, where Pu stands for '... believes that every anarchist wears a beard' and a for 'he'. Domain: all people.

(t) $(x)(Pxa \supset Qx)$, where Puv stands for '... made ___', Qu for '... walked with a limp', and a for 'these tracks'. Domain: all things. (According to this translation, the sentence in question does not imply that only one person made the tracks. A different translation that makes this implication hold would be $(\exists x)((y)(x=y \equiv Pxa) \;\land\; Qx)$. In my opinion, the latter translation is less faithful.)

(u) P, where P stands for 'Most donkeys are stubborn'.

(v) $(\exists x)(Px \;\land\; (\exists y)(Qy \;\land\; Ryx \;\land\; (\exists z_1)(Sz_1 \;\land\; Txyaz_1 \;\land\; (\exists z_2)(Sz_2 \;\land\; Uz_2z_1 \;\land\; Vxyaz_2))))$, where Pu stands for '... is a man', Qu for '... is a coat', Ruv for '... belongs to ___', Su for '... is a time', $Tuvw_1w_2$ for '... left at   at time $\sim\sim\sim$', Uuv for '... is later than ___', $Vuvw_1w_2$ for '... returned for ___ to ___ at time $\sim\sim\sim$', and a for 'the theatre'. Domain: all people, places, times, and articles of clothing.

(w) $(\exists x)(Pxa \;\land\; \sim Qx \;\land\; (y)((\sim y=x \;\land\; Pya) \supset Qy))$, where Puv stands for '... is a child of ___', Qu for '... is a boy', and a for 'me'. Domain: all people.

Chapter IX

1. (a) Yes.   (b) Yes.   (c) No.
   (d) No.   (e) No.   (f) Yes.
   (g) Yes.   (h) No.   (i) Yes.
   (j) No.   (k) Yes.   (l) Yes.
   (m) Yes.   (n) No.   (o) No.
   (p) Yes.   (q) Yes.   (r) No.

2.

1	$(\exists x)(y)Pxy$			hyp
2	v	$(\exists x)(y)Pxy$		1, reit
3		u	$(y)Puy$	hyp
4			Puv	3, uq elim
5			$(\exists x)Pxv$	4, eq int
6			$(\exists x)Pxv$	2, 3–5, eq elim
7	$(y)(\exists x)Pxy$			6, uq int

(d)

1	$(\exists x)(y)(Px \supset Qy)$	hyp
2	$(x)Px$	hyp
3	u $(\exists x)(y)(Px \supset Qy)$	1, reit
4	v $(y)(Pv \supset Qy)$	hyp
5	$Pv \supset Qu$	4, uq elim
6	$(x)Px$	2, reit
7	Pv	6, uq elim
8	Qu	5, 7, m p
9	Qu	3, 4–8, eq elim
10	$(y)Qy$	9, uq int
11	$(x)Px \supset (y)Qy$	2–10, imp int

(f)

1	$(x)Px \supset (y)Qy$	hyp
2	$\sim(\exists x)(y)(Px \supset Qy)$	hyp
3	u $\sim Pu$	hyp
4	v Pu	hyp
5	$\sim Qv$	hyp
6	Pu	4, reit
7	$\sim Pu$	3, reit
8	$\sim\sim Qv$	5–7, neg int
9	Qv	8, neg elim
10	$Pu \supset Qv$	4–9, imp int
11	$(y)(Pu \supset Qy)$	10, uq int
12	$(\exists x)(y)(Px \supset Qy)$	11, eq int
13	$\sim(\exists x)(y)(Px \supset Qy)$	2, reit
14	$\sim\sim Pu$	3–13, neg int
15	Pu	14, neg elim
16	$(x)Px$	15, uq int
17	$(x)Px \supset (y)Qy$	1, reit
18	$(y)Qy$	16, 17, m p
19	v Pu	hyp
20	$(y)Qy$	18, reit
21	Qv	20, uq elim
22	$Pu \supset Qv$	19–21, imp int
23	$(y)(Pu \supset Qy)$	22, uq int
24	$(\exists x)(y)(Px \supset Qy)$	23, eq int
25	$\sim\sim(\exists x)(y)(Px \supset Qy)$	2–24, neg int
26	$(\exists x)(y)(Px \supset Qy)$	25, neg elim

(g)

1	$(x)(\exists y)(Px \supset Qy)$	hyp
2	$(\exists x)Px$	hyp
3	u	Pu	hyp
4	$(x)(\exists y)(Px \supset Qy)$	1, reit
5	$(\exists y)(Pu \supset Qy)$	4, uq elim
6	v	$Pu \supset Qv$	hyp
7	Pu	3, reit
8	Qv	6, 7, m p
9	$(\exists y)Qy$	8, eq int
10	$(\exists y)Qy$	5, 6–9, eq elim
11	$(\exists y)Qy$	2, 3–10, eq elim
12	$(\exists x)Px \supset (\exists y)Qy$	2–11, imp int

(h)

1	$a=b$	hyp
2	$a=a$	id int
3	$b=a$	1, 2, id elim

(m)

3.
1	$\sim(\exists x)Px$	hyp
2	u	Pu	hyp
3	$\sim Qu$	hyp
4	Pu	2, reit
5	$(\exists x)Px$	4, eq int
6	$\sim(\exists x)Px$	1, reit
7	$\sim\sim Qu$	3–6, neg int
8	Qu	7, neg elim
9	$Pu \supset Qu$	2–8, imp int
10	$(x)(Px \supset Qx)$	9, uq int
11	$\sim(\exists x)Px \supset (x)(Px \supset Qx)$	1–10, imp int

(a)

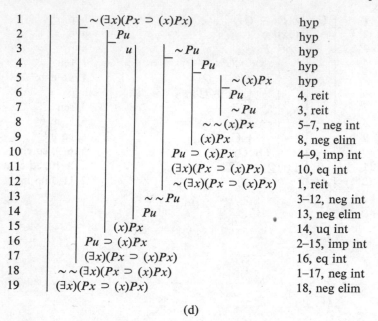

1	$\sim (\exists x)(Px \supset (x)Px)$	hyp
2	Pu	hyp
3	u $\sim Pu$	hyp
4	Pu	hyp
5	$\sim (x)Px$	hyp
6	Pu	4, reit
7	$\sim Pu$	3, reit
8	$\sim\sim (x)Px$	5–7, neg int
9	$(x)Px$	8, neg elim
10	$Pu \supset (x)Px$	4–9, imp int
11	$(\exists x)(Px \supset (x)Px)$	10, eq int
12	$\sim (\exists x)(Px \supset (x)Px)$	1, reit
13	$\sim\sim Pu$	3–12, neg int
14	Pu	13, neg elim
15	$(x)Px$	14, uq int
16	$Pu \supset (x)Px$	2–15, imp int
17	$(\exists x)(Px \supset (x)Px)$	16, eq int
18	$\sim\sim (\exists x)(Px \supset (x)Px)$	1–17, neg int
19	$(\exists x)(Px \supset (x)Px)$	18, neg elim

(d)

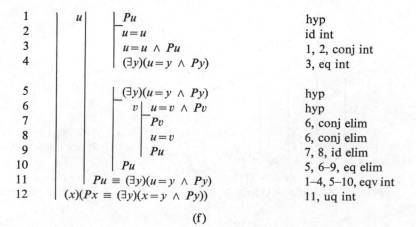

1	u Pu	hyp
2	$u=u$	id int
3	$u=u \wedge Pu$	1, 2, conj int
4	$(\exists y)(u=y \wedge Py)$	3, eq int
5	$(\exists y)(u=y \wedge Py)$	hyp
6	v $u=v \wedge Pv$	hyp
7	Pv	6, conj elim
8	$u=v$	6, conj elim
9	Pu	7, 8, id elim
10	Pu	5, 6–9, eq elim
11	$Pu \equiv (\exists y)(u=y \wedge Py)$	1–4, 5–10, eqv int
12	$(x)(Px \equiv (\exists y)(x=y \wedge Py))$	11, uq int

(f)

1	~(∃x)(y)(~Pay ∨ Pax)	hyp
2	u Pau	hyp
3	v Pau	2, reit
4	~Pav ∨ Pau	3, dis int
5	(y)(~Pay ∨ Pau)	4, uq int
6	(∃x)(y)(~Pay ∨ Pau)	5, eq int
7	~(∃x)(y)(~Pay ∨ Pax)	1, reit
8	~Pau	2–7, neg int
9	~Pau ∨ Pav	8, dis int
10	(y)(~Pay ∨ Pav)	9, uq int
11	(∃x)(y)(~Pay ∨ Pax)	10, eq int
12	~~(∃x)(y)(~Pay ∨ Pax)	2–11, neg int
13	(∃x)(y)(~Pay ∨ Pax)	12, neg elim

(j)

1	u (z)Puuz	hyp
2	(z)Puuz ⊃ (z)Puuz	1, imp int
3	(∃x)((z)Puuz ⊃ (z)Puxz)	2, eq int
4	(y)(∃x)((z)Pyyz ⊃ (z)Pyxz)	3, uq int

(k)

4. (c) From $(x)(Px \supset Qx)$ to derive $(y)(x)((Ry \land Syx \land Px) \supset (\exists z)(Qz \land Syz))$, where *Pu* stands for '... is a car', *Qu* for '... is useful', *Ru* for '... is a person', and *Suv* for '... has ___'. Domain: all physical objects.

1	(x)(Px ⊃ Qx)	hyp
2	u v Ru ∧ Suv ∧ Pv	hyp
3	Pv	2, conj elim
4	(x)(Px ⊃ Qx)	1, reit
5	Pv ⊃ Qv	4, uq elim
6	Qv	3, 5, m p
7	Ru ∧ Suv	2, conj elim
8	Suv	7, conj elim
9	Qv ∧ Suv	6, 8, conj int
10	(∃z)(Qz ∧ Suz)	9, eq int
11	(Ru ∧ Suv ∧ Pv) ⊃ (∃z)(Qz ∧ Suz)	2–10, imp int
12	(x)((Ru ∧ Sux ∧ Px) ⊃ (∃z)(Qz ∧ Suz))	11, uq int
13	(y)(x)((Ry ∧ Syx ∧ Px) ⊃ (∃z)(Qz ∧ Syz))	12, uq int

(f) From $a=a$ to derive $(\exists x)x=a$, where *a* stands for 'Pegasus'. Domain: all mythical animals.

1	a=a	hyp
2	(∃x)x=a	1, eq int

(j) From $Pa \lor Pb$ to derive $(\exists x)Px$, where Pu stands for '... is the capital of the Netherlands', a for 'Amsterdam', and b for 'the Hague'. Domain: all cities.

1	$Pa \lor Pb$	hyp
2	Pa	hyp
3	$(\exists x)Px$	2, eq int
4	Pb	hyp
5	$(\exists x)Px$	4, eq int
6	$(\exists x)Px$	1, 2–3, 4–5, dis elim

(m) From $(x)(Pxx \supset (y)(\sim x=y \supset Pxy))$ to derive $(x)(Pxx \supset (y)Pxy)$, where Puv stands for '... causes ___'. Domain: all things.

1	$(x)(Pxx \supset (y)(\sim x=y \supset Pxy))$	hyp
2	$u \quad Puu$	hyp
3	$v \quad Puu$	2, reit
4	$(x)(Pxx \supset (y)(\sim x=y \supset Pxy))$	1, reit
5	$Puu \supset (y)(\sim u=y \supset Puy)$	4, uq elim
6	$(y)(\sim u=y \supset Puy)$	3, 5, m p
7	$\sim u=v \supset Puv$	6, uq elim
8	$\sim Puv$	hyp
9	$u=v$	hyp
10	Puu	2, reit
11	Puv	9, 10, id elim
12	$\sim Puv$	8, reit
13	$\sim u=v$	9–12, neg int
14	$\sim u=v \supset Puv$	7, reit
15	Puv	13, 14, m p
16	$\sim \sim Puv$	8–15, neg int
17	Puv	16, neg elim
18	$(y)Puy$	17, uq int
19	$Puu \supset (y)Puy$	2–18, imp int
20	$(x)(Pxx \supset (y)Pxy)$	19, uq int

Chapter X

1. (a)

1	$(x)(y)(Qx \supset . y=x \supset Qx)$	AS1
2	$(x)((y)(Qx \supset . y=x \supset Qx) \supset . Qx \supset (y)(y=x \supset Qx))$	AS4
3	$(x)((y)(Qx \supset . y=x \supset Qx) \supset . Qx \supset (y)(y=x \supset Qx))$ $\supset . (x)(y)(Qx \supset . y=x \supset Qx)$ $\supset (x)(Qx \supset (y)(y=x \supset Qx))$	AS5
4	$(x)(y)(Qx \supset . y=x \supset Qx) \supset (x)(Qx \supset (y)(y=x \supset Qx))$	2, 3, m p
5	$(x)(Qx \supset (y)(y=x \supset Qx))$	1, 4, m p

(d) 1 $(x)((P \supset . P \supset P \supset P) \supset . (P \supset . P \supset P) \supset . P \supset P)$ AS2

    2   $(x)((P \supset . P \supset P \supset P) \supset . (P \supset . P \supset P) \supset . P \supset P)$
       $\supset . (x)(P \supset . P \supset P \supset P)$
       $\supset (x)((P \supset . P \supset P) \supset . P \supset P)$ AS5

    3   $(x)(P \supset . P \supset P \supset P) \supset (x)((P \supset . P \supset P) \supset . P \supset P)$ 1, 2, m p

    4   $(x)(P \supset . P \supset P \supset P)$ AS1

    5   $(x)((P \supset . P \supset P) \supset . P \supset P)$ 3, 4, m p

    6   $(x)((P \supset . P \supset P) \supset . P \supset P) \supset . (x)(P \supset . P \supset P)$
       $\supset (x)(P \supset P)$ AS5

    7   $(x)(P \supset . P \supset P)$ AS1

    8   $(x)(P \supset . P \supset P) \supset (x)(P \supset P)$ 5, 6, m p

    9   $(x)(P \supset P)$ 7, 8, m p

   10   $(x)(P \supset P) \supset . P \supset (x)P$ AS4

   11   $P \supset (x)P$ 9, 10, m p

(f) 1 $(x)(y)(x = y \supset . y = y \supset y = x)$ AS8

    2   $(x)(y)((x = y \supset . y = y \supset y = x) \supset . x = y \supset y = y$
       $\supset . x = y \supset y = x)$ AS2

    3   $(x)((y)((x = y \supset . y = y \supset y = x) \supset . x = y \supset y = y$
       $\supset . x = y \supset y = x) \supset . (y)(x = y \supset . y = y \supset y = x)$
       $\supset (y)(x = y \supset y = y \supset . x = y \supset y = x))$ AS5

    4   $(x)((y)((x = y \supset . y = y \supset y = x) \supset . x = y \supset y = y$
       $\supset . x = y \supset y = x) \supset . (y)(x = y \supset . y = y \supset y = x)$
       $\supset (y)(x = y \supset y = y \supset . x = y \supset y = x)) \supset . (x)(y)((x = y$
       $\supset . y = y \supset y = x) \supset . x = y \supset y = y \supset . x = y \supset y = x)$
       $\supset (x)((y)(x = y \supset . y = y \supset y = x) \supset (y)(x = y \supset y = y$
       $\supset . x = y \supset y = x))$ AS5

    5   $(x)(y)((x = y \supset . y = y \supset y = x) \supset . x = y \supset y = y \supset . x = y$
       $\supset y = x) \supset (x)((y)(x = y \supset . y = y \supset y = x)$
       $\supset (y)(x = y \supset y = y \supset . x = y \supset y = x))$ 3, 4, m p

    6   $(x)((y)(x = y \supset . y = y \supset y = x) \supset (y)(x = y \supset y = y$
       $\supset . x = y \supset y = x))$ 2, 5, m p

    7   $(x)((y)(x = y \supset . y = y \supset y = x) \supset (y)(x = y \supset y = y$
       $\supset . x = y \supset y = x)) \supset . (x)(y)(x = y \supset . y = y \supset y = x)$
       $\supset . (x)(y)(x = y \supset y = y \supset . x = y \supset y = x)$ AS5

    8   $(x)(y)(x = y \supset . y = y \supset y = x) \supset (x)(y)(x = y \supset y = y$
       $\supset . x = y \supset y = x)$ 6, 7, m p

    9   $(x)(y)(x = y \supset y = y \supset . x = y \supset y = x)$ 1, 8, m p

   10   $(x)((y)(x = y \supset y = y \supset . x = y \supset y = x) \supset . (y)(x = y$
       $\supset y = y) \supset (y)(x = y \supset y = x))$ AS5

   11   $(x)((y)(x = y \supset y = y \supset . x = y \supset y = x) \supset .(y)(x = y$
       $\supset y = y) \supset (y)(x = y \supset y = x)) \supset . (x)(y)(x = y$
       $\supset y = y \supset . x = y \supset y = x) \supset (x)((y)(x = y \supset y = y)$
       $\supset (y)(x = y \supset y = x))$ AS5

   12   $(x)(y)(x = y \supset y = y \supset . x = y \supset y = x) \supset (x)((y)(x = y$
       $y = y) \supset (y)(x = y \supset y = x))$ 10, 11, m p

   13   $(x)((y)(x = y \supset y = y) \supset (y)(x = y \supset y = x))$ 9, 12, m p

14    $(x)((y)(x=y \supset y=y) \supset (y)(x=y \supset y=x))$

     $\supset . (x)(y)(x=y \supset y=y) \supset . (x)(y)(x=y \supset y=x)$ AS5

15    $(x)(y)(x=y \supset y=y) \supset (x)(y)(x=y \supset y=x)$ 13, 14, m p

16    $(x)(y)(y=y . x=y \supset y=y)$ AS1

17    $(x)((y)(y=y . x=y \supset y=y) \supset . (y)y=y$

     $\supset (y)(x=y \supset y=y))$ AS5

18    $(x)((y)(y=y . x=y \supset y=y) \supset . (y)y=y \supset (y)(x=y$

     $\supset y=y)) \supset . (x)(y)(y=y . x=y \supset y=y)$

     $\supset (x)((y)y=y \supset (y)(x=y \supset y=y))$ AS5

19    $(x)(y)(y=y . x=y \supset y=y) \supset (x)((y)y=y$

     $\supset (y)(x=y \supset y=y))$ 17, 18, m p

20    $(x)((y)y=y \supset (y)(x=y \supset y=y))$ 16, 19, m p

21    $(x)((y)y=y \supset (y)(x=y \supset y=y)) \supset . (x)(y)y=y$

     $\supset (x)(y)(x=y \supset y=y)$ AS5

22    $(x)(y)y=y \supset (x)(y)(x=y \supset y=y)$ 20, 21, m p

23    $(x)(y)y=y$ AS7

24    $(x)(y)(x=y \supset y=y)$ 22, 23, m p

25    $(x)(y)(x=y \supset y=x)$ 15, 24, m p

2. (b)   1 $(y)((y)Ryya \supset Ryya)$ AS6

     2    $(y)((y)Ryya \supset Ryya . (\exists x)Qx \supset . (y)Ryya \supset Ryya)$ AS1

     3    $(y)((y)Ryya \supset Ryya . (\exists x)Qx \supset . (y)Ryya \supset Ryya)$

         $\supset . (y)((y)Ryya \supset Ryya) \supset . (y)((\exists x)Qx$

         $\supset . (y)Ryya \supset Ryya)$ AS5

     4    $(y)((y)Ryya \supset Ryya) \supset . (y)((\exists x)Qx \supset . (y)Ryya \supset Ryya)$ 2, 3, m p

     5    $(y)((\exists x)Qx \supset . (y)Ryya \supset Ryya)$ 1, 4, m p

     6    $(y)(((\exists x)Qx \supset . (y)Ryya \supset Ryya) \supset . (\exists x)Qx \supset (y)Ryya$

         $\supset . (\exists x)Qx \supset Ryya)$ AS2

     7    $(y)(((\exists x)Qx \supset . (y)Ryya \supset Ryya) \supset . (\exists x)Qx \supset (y)Ryya$

         $\supset . (\exists x)Qx \supset Ryya) \supset . (y)((\exists x)Qx \supset . (y)Ryya$

         $\supset Ryya) \supset (y)((\exists x)Qx \supset (y)Ryya \supset . (\exists x)Qx \supset Ryya)$ AS5

     8    $(y)((\exists x)Qx \supset . (y)Ryya \supset Ryya) \supset (y)((\exists x)Qx$

         $\supset (y)Ryya \supset . (\exists x)Qx \supset Ryya)$ 6, 7, m p

     9    $(y)((\exists x)Qx \supset (y)Ryya \supset . (\exists x)Qx \supset Ryya)$ 5, 8, m p

    10    $(y)((\exists x)Qx \supset (y)Ryya \supset . (\exists x)Qx \supset Ryya)$

         $\supset . (\exists x)Qx \supset (y)Ryya \supset . (y)((\exists x)Qx \supset Ryya)$ AS4

    11    $(\exists x)Qx \supset (y)Ryya \supset . (y)((\exists x)Qx \supset Ryya)$ 9, 10, m p

    12    $(\exists x)Qx \supset (y)Ryya$ hyp

    13    $(y)((\exists x)Qx \supset Ryya)$ 11, 12, m p

   (d)   1 $(x)(P \supset . x=x \supset Qx)$ hyp

        2    $(x)(P \supset . x=x \supset Qx) \supset . P \supset (x)(x=x \supset Qx)$ AS4

        3    $P \supset (x)(x=x \supset Qx)$ 1, 2, m p

        4   P hyp

        5    $(x)(x=x \supset Qx)$ 3, 4, m p

        6    $(x)(x=x \supset Qx) \supset . (x)x=x \supset (x)Qx$ AS5

        7    $(x)x=x \supset (x)Qx$ 5, 6, m p

	8	$(x)x=x$	AS7
	9	$(x)Qx$	7, 8, m p

3. (a)

	1	$Qa, u=a \vdash Qa$	H_s
	2	$Qa, u=a \vdash Qu$	1, M41
	3	$Qa \vdash \sim Qu \supset \sim u=a$	2, H_s
	4	$Qa \vdash (x)(\sim Qx \supset \sim x=a)$	3, M40

(c)

	1	$(y)(z)Ruyz \vdash (y)(z)Ruyz$	H_s
	2	$(y)(z)Ruyz \vdash (z)Ruvz$	1, M29
	3	$(y)(z)Ruyz \vdash Ruvw$	2, M29
	4	$(y)(z)Ruyz \vdash (\exists x)Rxvw$	3, M48
	5	$(y)(z)Ruyz \vdash (z)(\exists x)Rxvz$	4, M40
	6	$(y)(z)Ruyz \vdash (y)(z)(\exists x)Rxyz$	5, M40
	7	$(\exists x)(y)(z)Rxyz \vdash (y)(z)(\exists x)Rxyz$	6, M50

(e)

	1	$a=b, (\exists x)Rabx \vdash (\exists x)Rbbx$	M42
	2	$a=b, (\exists x)Rabx \vdash (\exists y)(\exists x)Ryxy$	1, M48

4. (a)

	1	$\sim\sim(x)\sim\sim A^{\,x}/u \vdash (x)\sim\sim A^{\,x}/u$	H_s
	2	$\sim\sim(x)\sim\sim A^{\,x}/u \vdash \sim\sim A$	1, M29
	3	$\sim\sim(x)\sim\sim A^{\,x}/u \vdash A$	2, H_s
	4	$\sim\sim(x)\sim\sim A^{\,x}/u \vdash (x)A^{\,x}/u$	3, M40
	5	$\sim(\exists x)\sim A^{\,x}/u \vdash (x)A^{\,x}/u$	4, D16

(d)

	1	$A \vdash B$	assumption
	2	$\sim B \vdash \sim A$	1, H_s
	3	$(x)\sim B^{\,x}/u \vdash (x)\sim B^{\,x}/u$	H_s
	4	$(x)\sim B^{\,x}/u \vdash \sim B$	3, M29
	5	$(x)\sim B^{\,x}/u \vdash \sim A$	2, 4, H_s
	6	$(x)\sim B^{\,x}/u \vdash (x)\sim A^{\,x}/u$	5, M40
	7	$\sim(x)\sim A^{\,x}/u \vdash \sim(x)\sim B^{\,x}/u$	6, H_s
	8	$(\exists x)A^{\,x}/u \vdash (\exists x)B^{\,x}/u$	7, D16

(i) Let v be an individual parameter not occurring in A or in B, and proceed
as follows:

	1	$A \supset B^{\,v}/u, A \vdash B^{\,v}/u$	H_s
	2	$A \supset B^{\,v}/u, A \vdash (\exists x)B^{\,v}/u^{\,x}/v$	1, M48
	3	$(\exists x)(A \supset B^{\,v}/u^{\,x}/v), A \vdash (\exists x)B^{\,v}/u^{\,x}/v$	2, M50

But $B^{\,v}/u^{\,x}/v$ is the same expression as $B^{\,x}/u$; therefore $(\exists x)(A \supset B^{\,x}/u)$,
$A \vdash (\exists x)B^{\,x}/u$.

(n)

	1	$A \vdash A$	H_s
	2	$A \vdash (x)A$	1, M40

Chapter XI

1. (a) F   (b) T   (c) T
   (d) F   (e) T   (f) T

2. (a) T   (b) T   (c) F
  (d) F   (e) T   (f) F

3. (a) T   (b) F   (c) F   (d) T
  (e) T   (f) T   (g) F   (h) F

4. In all the following examples except (b), let $D = \{1, 2, 3, \ldots\}$ and V be a valuation on D.

  (a) To satisfy this formula let $V(P) = \{\langle m, n \rangle \mid m = n\}$. To invalidate it, let $V(P) = \{\langle m, n \rangle \mid m < n\}$.

  (b) To satisfy this formula let $D' = \{1\}$ and V be any valuation on D'. To invalidate it let $D' = \{1, 2, 3\}$ and V be any valuation on D'.

  (c) To satisfy this formula let $V(P) = \{1\}$ and $V(u) = 2$. To invalidate it let $V(P) = \{1\}$ and $V(u) = 1$.

  (d) To satisfy this formula let $V(P) = \varnothing$. To invalidate it let $V(P) = \{1\}$.

  (e) To satisfy this formula let $V(P) = \varnothing$ and $V(Q) = \varnothing$. To invalidate it let $V(P) = \{1\}$ and $V(Q) = \{2\}$.

  (f) To satisfy this formula let $V(P) = \{\langle m, n \rangle \mid m = n\}$. To invalidate it let $V(P) = \{\langle m, n \rangle \mid m < n\}$.

  (g) To satisfy this formula let $V(P) = \varnothing$ and $V(Q) = F$. To invalidate it let $V(P) = \{1\}$ and $V(Q) = T$.

  (h) To satisfy this formula let $V(P) = \varnothing$ and $V(Q) = \varnothing$. To invalidate it let $V(P) = \{1\}$ and $V(Q) = \varnothing$.

  (i) To satisfy this formula let $V(P) = \varnothing$. To invalidate it let $V(P) = \{\langle m, n \rangle \mid m < n\}$.

5. (a) Let D be any nonempty domain and V be any valuation on D. Suppose that $V((x)(Px \supset Qx)) = T$ and $V((x)Px) = T$. Let d be a member of D; $V^d/u(Pu) = T$ and $V^d/u(Pu \supset Qu) = T$, and thus $V^d/u(Qu) = T$. Therefore $V^d/u(Qu) = T$ for all $d \in D$, so that $V((x)Qx) = T$. Then in any case $V((x)(Px \supset Qx) \supset . (x)Px \supset (x)Qx) = T$. It follows that for any valuation V on any domain D, $V((x)(Px \supset Qx) \supset . (x)Px \supset (x)Qx) = T$; i.e. $(x)(Px \supset Qx) \supset . (x)Px \supset (x)Qx$ is valid.

  (c) Let D be any nonempty domain and V any valuation on D. Let $V(a) = d$, and let e be an arbitrary member of D. Assume that $V^e/u(a = u) = T$ and that $V^e/u(Pu) = T$. Then $e = d$, and therefore $V^e/u(Pa) = T$. Then in any case $V^e/u(a = u \supset . Pu \supset Pa) = T$ for all $e \in D$, so that $V((x)(a = x \supset . Px \supset Pa)) = T$. It follows that $(x)(a = x \supset . Px \supset Pa)$ is valid.

  (f) Let D be any nonempty domain and V any valuation on D. If $V(P) = D$, then $V((x)Px) = T$, and therefore $V^d/u(Pu \supset (x)Px) = T$ for all $d \in D$, so that $V((\exists x)(Px \supset (x)Px)) = T$. On the other hand, if $V(P) \neq D$, then there is a member d of D such that $V^d/u(Pu) = F$, and therefore $V^d/u(Pu \supset (x)Px) = T$, so that again $V((\exists x)(Px \supset (x)Px)) = T$. In any case, then, $V((\exists x)(Px \supset (x)Px)) = T$; this formula is therefore valid.

6. (a) Suppose that $(\exists x)(y)(z)Pxyz \wedge \sim Pyxz)$ were satisfiable; then for some nonempty domain D and valuation V on D, it would be the

case that $V((\exists x)(y)(z)(Pxyz \wedge \sim Pyxz)) = T$. Then for some $d \in D$, $V \, d/u \, e_1/v \, e_2/w(Puvw \wedge \sim Puvw) = T$ for all $e_1, e_2 \in D$, and therefore $V \, d/u \, d/v \, d/w(Puvw \wedge \sim Puvw) = T$ so that $V \, d/u(Puuu) = T$ and $V \, d/u(\sim Puuu) = T$, which would be impossible. Therefore

$$(\exists x)(y)(z)(Pxyz \wedge \sim Pyxz)$$

is not satisfiable.

7. (a) Let D be any nonempty domain and V any valuation on D. Suppose that $V(A) = T$; then $V(B \supset A) = T$. In any case, then, $V(A \supset. B \supset A) = T$. It follows that $A \supset. B \supset A$ is valid.

8. (c) Let D be any nonempty domain and V be any valuation on D. Suppose that $V((x)(A \supset B^x/u)) = T$. Let v be an individual parameter not occurring in A or B, and d be an arbitrary member of D. Since $(x)(A \supset B^x/u)$ is the same formula as $(x)(A \supset B^v/u^x/v)$, $V((x)(A \supset B^v/u^x/v)) = T$ and so $V \, d/v(A \supset B^v/u) = T$. Now, if $V(A) = T$ then $V \, d/v(A) = T$ by M7, since V and $V \, d/v$ agree on A, and therefore $V \, d/v(B^v/u) = T$. Since this holds for any $d \in D$, $V((x)(B^v/u^x/v)) - T$ if $V(A) - T$, and so $V(A \supset (x)B^v/u^x/v) = T$ if $V((x)(A \supset B^x/u)) = T$. Therefore

$$V((x)(A \supset B^x/u) \supset. A \supset (x)B^x/u) = T$$

in any case. Thus, this formula is valid.

9. The argument used to prove M32 shows equally well that $V(A^s/t) = V \, V(s)/t(A)$. Suppose $V(s) = V(t)$; then it follows that $V(A^s/t) = V(A)$. Now, A^s/t is the same formula as $A^s//t^s/t$; but if $V(s) = V(t)$ then $V(A) = V(A^s/t)$ and $V(A^s//t^s/t) = V(A^s//t)$. Therefore $V(A) = V(A^s//t)$. We will use this fact to show $s = t \supset. A \supset A^s//t$ valid. Let D be any nonempty domain and V be any valuation on D. Suppose that $V(s = t) = T$; then $V(s) = V(t)$ and therefore $V(A) = V(A^s//t)$ so that $V(A \supset A^s//t) = T$. In any case, then, $V(s = t \supset. A \supset A^s//t) = T$. This formula is therefore valid.

13. Let D be a finite, nonempty domain and V be any valuation on D. Let $V(P) = R$, i.e. for all $d, e \in D$ let dRe iff $\langle d, e \rangle \in V(P)$. Suppose that $V((x)(y)((\exists z)Pxz \wedge (z)(Pxy \supset. Pyz \supset Pxz)) \supset (\exists x)Pxx) = T$. Then for all $d \in D$ there is an $e \in D$ such that dRe, and R is transitive: for all $c, d, e \in D$ if cRd and dRe then cRe. Now, let d_1 be any member of D, and define a sequence $d_1, d_2, d_3, \ldots$ by letting d_{i+1} be any member of D such that d_iRd_{i+1}. Since R is transitive, d_jRd_k if $j < k$. But since D is finite there must be some j and k such that $j < k$ and $d_j = d_k$. Then d_jRd_k, so that d_jRd_j. There is thus a $d \in D$ such that $V \, d/u(Puu) = T$, and therefore $V((\exists x)Pxx) = T$. It follows that $(x)(y)((\exists z)Pxz \wedge (z)(Pxy \supset. Pyz \supset Pxz)) \supset (\exists x)Pxx$ is valid in all finite domains.

On the other hand, if we let $D = \{1, 2, 3, \ldots\}$ and let $V(P) = \{\langle m, n \rangle \mid m < n\}$, then $V((x)(y)((\exists z)Pxz \wedge (z)(Pxy \supset. Pyz \supset Pxz)) \supset (\exists x)Pxx) = F$. Therefore this formula is not valid. Since it is invalid but is valid in all finite domains, its negation is satisfiable, but is satisfiable only in infinite domains.

Chapter XII

1. (a) Let $D = \{1\}$, and define a valuation V on D by letting $V(P) = \{1\}$. V does not satisfy $(\exists x)Px \supset (\exists x)\sim Px$, so that this formula is invalid. By M3, not $\vdash (\exists x)Px \supset (\exists x)\sim Px$.

(b) Let $D = \{1, 2\}$ and define a valuation V on D by letting $V(P) = \{1\}$. Since V does not satisfy $(x)(Px \equiv (\exists y)Py)$, this formula is invalid. By M3, not $\vdash (x)(Px \equiv (\exists y)Py)$.

(c) Let $D = \{1, 2, 3, \ldots\}$ and define a valuation V on D by letting $V(P) = \{\langle k, m, n \rangle \mid k + m = n\}$. There is no $n \in D$ such that for all $m \in D$, $1 + m = n$, so that $V((x)(\exists z)(y)Pxyz) = F$; but $V((x)(y)(\exists z)Pxyz) = T$. Therefore V does not satisfy $(x)(y)(z)Pxyz \supset (x)(\exists z)(y)Pxyz$, and this formula is invalid. By M3, not $\vdash (x)(y)(z)Pxyz \supset (x)(\exists z)(y)Pxyz$.

(d) Let $D = \{1\}$ and define a valuation V on D by letting $V(P) = \varnothing$. Since V does not satisfy $(x)(y)(Pxy \supset x=y) \supset (x)Pxx$, this formula is invalid. By M3, not $\vdash (x)(y)(Pxy \supset x=y) \supset (x)Pxx$.

(e) Let $D = \{1, 2\}$ and define a valuation V on D by letting $V(P) = \{\langle m, n \rangle \mid m \in D$ and $n \in D\}$. Since V does not satisfy $(x)Pxx \supset (x)(y)(Pxy \supset x=y)$, this formula is invalid. By M3, not $\vdash (x)Pxx \supset (x)(y)(Pxy \supset x=y)$.

2. (a) $\vdash Q \equiv (x)Q$, as is shown by the following argument:

1	$Q \vdash Q$	H_s
2	$Q \vdash (x)Q$	1, X.M40
3	$(x)Q \vdash (x)Q$	H_s
4	$(x)Q \vdash Q$	3, X.M29
5	$\vdash Q \equiv (x)Q$	2, 4, H_s

(b) $\vdash (x)(Px \supset (\exists y)Py)$, as is shown by the following argument:

1	$Pu \vdash Pu$	H_s
2	$Pu \vdash (\exists y)Py$	1, X.M48
3	$\vdash Pu \supset (\exists y)Py$	2, H_s
4	$\vdash (x)(Px \supset (\exists y)Py)$	3, M40

(c) $\vdash (x)Px \equiv (Pa \wedge ((x)Px \vee (x)\sim Px))$, as is shown by the following argument:

1	$(x)Px \vdash (x)Px$	H_s
2	$(x)Px \vdash Pa$	1, X.M29
3	$(x)Px \vdash (Pa \wedge ((x)Px \vee (x)\sim Px))$	2, H_s
4	$Pa, (x)\sim Px \vdash (x)\sim Px$	H_s
5	$Pa, (x)\sim Px \vdash \sim Pa$	4, X.M29
6	$Pa, (x)\sim Px \vdash (x)Px$	5, H_s
7	$(Pa \wedge ((x)Px \vee (x)\sim Px)) \vdash (x)Px$	6, H_s
8	$\vdash (x)Px \equiv (Pa \wedge ((x)Px \vee (x)\sim Px))$	3, 7, H_s

(d) Not $\vdash ((x)(y)(z)((Pxy \wedge Pyz) \supset Pxz) \wedge (x)(\exists y)Pxy) \supset (\exists x)(y)Pxy$ since this formula is invalid, being falsified by the valuation V on $\{1, 2\}$ such that $V(P) = \{\langle 1, 2 \rangle, \langle 2, 2 \rangle\}$.

(e) $\vdash Pa \equiv (\exists x)(x=a \wedge Pa)$, as is shown by the following argument.

1	$u=a \wedge Pa \vdash Pa$	H_s
2	$(\exists x)(x=a \wedge Pa) \vdash Pa$	1, X.M50

3	$Pa \vdash a=a$	X.M45
4	$Pa \vdash a=a \wedge Pa$	3, H_s
5	$Pa \vdash (\exists x)(x=a \wedge Pa)$	4, X.M48
6	$\vdash Pa \equiv (\exists x)(x=a \wedge Pa)$	2, 5, H_s

(f) Not $\vdash (x)Px \supset Q \supset (x)(Px \supset Q)$ since this formula is invalid, being falsified by the valuation V on $\{1, 2\}$ such that $V(P) = \{1\}$ and $V(Q) = F$.

(g) Not $\vdash (x)(y)((\exists z)Pxzz \supset (\exists z)Pxyz)$, since this formula is invalid, being falsified by the valuation V on $\{1, 2\}$ such that $V(P) = \{\langle 1, 1, 1 \rangle\}$.

(h) $\vdash \sim(x)(Px \supset Qx) \supset . \sim(x)Px \supset \sim(x)Qx$, as is shown by the following argument.

1	$\sim(x)Px, (x)Qx, Pu \vdash (x)Qx$	H_s
2	$\sim(x)Px, (x)Qx, Pu \vdash Qu$	1, X.M29
3	$\sim(x)Px, (x)Qx \vdash Pu \supset Qu$	2, H_s
4	$\sim(x)Px, (x)Qx \vdash (x)(Px \supset Qx)$	3, X.M40
5	$\sim(x)(Px \supset Qx), \sim(x)Px \vdash \sim(x)Qx$	4, H_s
6	$\vdash \sim(x)(Px \supset Qx) \supset . \sim(x)Px \supset \sim(x)Qx$	5, H_s

3. (a) Every member of Γ is satisfied by the valuation V on the domain $\{\ldots, -3, -2, -1, 0, 1, 2, 3, \ldots\}$ of all integers such that $V(P) = \{\langle x, y \rangle \mid x < y\}$. By M5, then, Γ is consistent.

4. Suppose there were no term t of M such that $A\,^t/u \in \Gamma$. Then for all terms t of M, $\sim A\,^t/u$ would be in Γ and hence we would have $(x) \sim A\,^x/u \in \Gamma$. But this is impossible, since by assumption Γ is consistent and $(\exists x)A\,^x/u \in \Gamma$. Therefore there must be some term t of M such that $A\,^t/u \in \Gamma$.

5. Consider the formula $(\exists x)((\exists x)Px \supset Px)$. This formula is provable, in view of X.M51. However, there is no term t such that $\vdash (\exists x)Px \supset Pt$ since this formula is invalid, as is shown by choosing V on $\{1, 2\}$ such that $V(P) = \{1\}$ and $V(t) = 2$.

Chapter XIII

1. (a) Suppose that $u \in X \cap Y$; then $u \in X$ and $u \in Y$, and hence $u \in Y \cap X$. Similarly, if $u \in Y \cap X$ then $u \in X \cap Y$. Hence $X \cap Y = Y \cap X$.

2. Suppose that $X \subseteq Y$. Then if $u \in X$ then $u \in Y$, so that $u \in X \cap Y$. Also, if $u \in X \cap Y$ then $u \in X$. Hence $X \cap Y = X$. On the other hand, suppose that $X \cap Y = X$. Then if $u \in X$ then $u \in X \cap Y$, so that $u \in Y$. Therefore, $u \in X \cap Y$. Thus, $X \subseteq Y$ if and only if $X \cap Y = X$.

3. (a) Let $X = \{1, 2\}$ and $Y = \{1\}$. Then $X - Y = \{2\}$, but $Y - X = \varnothing$.

   (b) Suppose that $X - Y = Y - X$, and assume that there is some u such that $u \in X - Y$. Then $u \in Y - X$, so that $u \in X$ and $u \notin X$, which is impossible. Thus, there is no u such that $u \in X - Y$, and therefore if $u \in X$ then $u \in Y$. Similarly, there is no u such that $u \in Y - X$, so that if $u \in Y$ then $u \in X$. Therefore $X = Y$.

(d) Suppose that $u \in (X - Y) - Z$. Then $u \in X - Y$ and $u \notin Z$, and so $u \in X$ and $u \notin Y$ and $u \notin Z$. But then $u \notin Y \cup Z$, and therefore $u \in X - (Y \cup Z)$. On the other hand, if $u \in X - (Y \cup Z)$ then $u \in X$ and $u \notin Y \cup Z$, so that $u \notin Y$ and $u \notin Z$. Then $u \in (X - Y)$, so that $u \in (X - Y) - Z$. Therefore $(X - Y) - Z = X - (Y \cup Z)$.

(e) Suppose that $X \subset Y$ and $U \subseteq X$, and let $u \in X - U$. Then $u \in X$, so that $u \in Y$. Also, $u \notin U$, so that $X - U \subseteq Y - U$. Since $X \subset Y$, there is a y such that $y \in Y$ and $y \notin X$. Since $U \subseteq X$, $y \notin U$, so that $y \in Y - U$. Therefore $X - U \subset Y - U$.

5. (a) Suppose that $X \cup \{X\} = \varnothing$; then $X \subseteq \varnothing$ and therefore X has no members, so that $X = \varnothing$. But then $\{\varnothing\} \subseteq \varnothing$, so that $\varnothing \in \varnothing$, which is impossible since $\varnothing$ has no members. Therefore for all sets X, $X \cup \{X\} \neq \varnothing$.

(b) If $X \cup \{X\} = \{\{\varnothing\}\}$, then $\{X\} \subseteq \{\{\varnothing\}\}$ and therefore $X \in \{\{\varnothing\}\}$ so that $X = \{\varnothing\}$. But also $X \subseteq \{\{\varnothing\}\}$, so that $\{\varnothing\} \subseteq \{\{\varnothing\}\}$ and therefore $\varnothing \in \{\{\varnothing\}\}$ so that $\varnothing = \{\varnothing\}$. But then $\varnothing \in \varnothing$, which is impossible. Therefore for all sets X, $X \cup \{X\} \neq \{\{\varnothing\}\}$.

(c) Suppose that $X \cup \{Y\} = X \cup Y$. Then $\{Y\} \subseteq X \cup Y$, so that $Y \in X$ or $Y \in Y$. Suppose that $Y \in X$. Now, $Y \subseteq X \cup \{Y\}$, so that $Y \subseteq X$ or $u \in \{Y\}$ for some $u \in Y$. In the latter case, $Y \in Y$, so suppose $Y \subseteq X$. Then, since $Y \in X$ and $Y \subseteq X$, $Y \cup \{Y\} \subseteq X$.

Chapter XIV

1. If $n = 0$, then $X = \varnothing$ and there is only one subset of X, namely $\varnothing$. Since $2^0 = 1$, this furnishes the basis step of the induction. For the inductive step, assume that there are exactly 2^n subsets of any set X having exactly n members, and let Y be a set having exactly $n + 1$ members. Let u be a member of Y, and let X be $Y - \{u\}$; X has exactly n members. Now, there are as many subsets of Y containing u as there are subsets of X, since for each subset V of X, $V \cup \{u\}$ is a subset of Y containing u, and for each subset U of Y which contains u, $U - \{u\}$ is a subset of X. The number of subsets of Y is therefore twice the number of subsets of X. But by the hypothesis of induction there are exactly 2^n subsets of X; therefore there are $2 \cdot 2^n$, i.e. 2^{n+1}, subsets of Y. This completes the induction.

2. (a) $t(n) = 2^{(2^n)}$. To establish this by induction, notice first that there are exactly 4 truth-tables for one parameter. Since $2^{(2^1)} = 4$, this furnishes the basis step of the induction. For the inductive step, assume as hypothesis of induction that there are exactly $2^{(2^n)}$ truth-tables for n parameters. Now we can regard each truth-table T for $n + 1$ parameters as a result of putting two truth-tables T_1 and T_2 for n parameters end to end. (The table T_1 gives the truth-values of T when the additional parameter is true, while T_2 gives the truth-values of T when the additional parameter is false.) There are

therefore as many truth-tables for $n + 1$ parameters as there are ordered pairs of truth-tables for n parameters, so that $t(n + 1) = (2^{(2^n)})^2$. But this is $2^{2(2^n)}$, which is $2^{2^{n+1}}$. This completes the inductive step, and proves the correctness of the formula.

(b) $c(m, n) = m \cdot n$. To show this by induction on m, consider first the case in which $X = \varnothing$. Here, since $X \times Y = \{\langle u, v \rangle \mid u \in X \text{ and } v \in Y\}$, $X \times Y$ must be empty; $X \times Y = \varnothing$. Therefore $c(0, n) = 0 = 0 \cdot n$, and the basis step is established. For the inductive step, assume as hypothesis of induction that $c(m, n) = m \cdot n$, and let X be a set having exactly $m + 1$ members, and Y be a set having exactly n members. Let u be a member of X, and let W be $X - \{u\}$; then $X \times Y = (W \times Y) \cup (\{u\} \times Y)$. Furthermore, the number of members of $X \times Y$ is the sum of the numbers of members of $W \times Y$ and $\{u\} \times Y$ since $(W \times Y) \cap (\{u\} \times Y) = \varnothing$. But by the hypothesis of induction $W \times Y$ has exactly $m \cdot n$ members, and $\{u\} \times Y$ clearly has exactly n members. Therefore $c(m + 1, n) = (m \cdot n) + n = (m + 1) \cdot n$. This completes the inductive step, and proves the correctness of the formula.

(c) $p(m, n) = m^n$. To establish this by induction on n, first suppose that $n = 2$; then, since $X^2 = X \times X$, E2(b) shows that X^2 has exactly $m \cdot m$, i.e. m^2, members. Thus $p(m, 2) = m^2$, and the basis step is complete. For the inductive step, assume as hypothesis of induction that $p(m, n) = m^n$, and let X be a set having exactly m members. By the hypothesis of induction, X^n has exactly m^n members; but $X^{n+1} = X \times X^n$ and so by E2(c) X^{n+1} has exactly $m \cdot (m^n)$, i.e. m^{n+1}, members. Therefore $p(m + 1, n) = m^{n+1}$. This completes the inductive step and proves the correctness of the formula.

(d) $r(m, n) = 2^{(m^n)}$. To establish this, let D have exactly m members. Now, the set of n-ary relations on D is $\mathscr{P}(D^n)$. By E2(c), D^n has exactly m^n members, and so by E1, $\mathscr{P}(D^n)$ has exactly $2^{(m^n)}$ members.

3. We will induce on n. If $n = 0$ then $Y = \varnothing$ and $\varnothing$ is the only function from Y to X: $X^Y = \{\varnothing\}$. (The set $\varnothing$ counts as a function from Y to X because it is a subset of $Y \times X$, i.e. of $\varnothing$, and it is vacuously true that for all $y \in Y$ there is an $x \in X$ such that $\langle y, x \rangle \in \varnothing$.) Then X^Y has exactly $1 = m^0$ members. (We assume here that $0^k = 1$ if $k = 0$ and $0^k = 0$ if $k > 0$.) In the inductive step, assume as hypothesis of induction that X^Z has exactly m^n members for all sets Z having exactly n members, and let Y have exactly $n + 1$ members. Let $y \in Y$, and let $W = Y - \{y\}$. By the hypothesis of induction there are exactly m^n functions from W to X. For each of these functions, there are exactly m functions from Y to X, corresponding to the m possible values in X that can be given to y. The number of functions from Y to X is therefore $m \cdot m^n = m^{n+1}$, as desired.

4. The trouble is with the inductive step of the argument, where it is assumed without justification that for some u and v, $u \in U$ and $v \in V$. For instance, let $n = 0$, $U = \varnothing$, and $V = \{v\}$. Then there is no $u \in U$ and we cannot use the hypothesis of induction to show that $\varnothing \simeq \{v\}$.

8. (a) $f(0) = 0; f(n + 1) = f(n) + 3$.
   (b) $f(0) = 1; f(n + 1) = 2 \cdot f(n)$.
   (c) $f(0) = 1; f(n + 1) = f(n)$.
   (d) $f(0) = 1; f(n + 1) = (f(n) - 1)^2$. Or $f(n) = 1; f(n + 1) = 0$ if n is even
       and $f(n \cdot 1) = 1$ if n is odd.
   (e) $f(0) = 2; f(n + 1) = 2 + (n \cdot (f(n) - 1))$.

Index